PRAISE FOR AVENGERS, WILDCATS, AND CRICKETS

"*Avengers, Wildcats, and Crickets* is a thrill and truly connects the reader with authentic experiences. Russell Low is a gifted writer and chronicler. I felt as if I was in the plane as he creatively described the different missions. His verbiage is certainly magical. As a Lt. Colonel in the Airforce, I could relate to the very real smells, sounds and G-Forces even though some of my experience has been in a simulator."

"The book draws you into scenes that capture your full imagination. True Heroism and Americanism are displayed throughout the book. I honestly believe that with all that is going on around the world, there has never been a better time for such books as Low's masterpieces, *The All-American Crew and Avengers, Wildcats, and Crickets.*

— **Douglas M. Smith**, *Lt Colonel, USAF*

"Avengers, Wildcats, and Crickets" is a treasure, in every sense of the word. A young Avenger crewman aboard a World War II aircraft carrier keeps handwritten journals and first-hand accounts of combat hidden in a fighter plane starter cartridge box for eighty years. Through research, creativity, and good fortune, Author Russ Low establishes a connection with this veteran, now 97 years old, and the box is opened. Here you have the stories- unvarnished, timeless, and true.

— **Phil Scearce**, *author of Finish Forty and Home: The Untold World War II Story of B-24s in the Pacific*

Avengers, Wildcats and Crickets

A Story of the Men Who Fought in the Skies Over the Pacific in WWII

Russell N. Low

As Told by Andrew J. Winnegar

To Seth
Honor, Valor, and Patriotism Filled the Hearts of These Young Airmen who 80 years Ago Fought To Preserve our Freedom.
Russell Low
7/9/22

Gum Saan Journeys Press
La Jolla, California, USA

Figure 1 Stinson OY-1 "Cricket"

Library of Congress Control Number 2022904188

ISBN:978-1-7344937-2-6

Cover artwork modified from Colorized WWII photograph by Royston Leonard of the USS Kitkun Bay.

For more information about this book contact threecoins1@yahoo.com

DEDICATION

This novel is dedicated to the men of Composite Squadron Four (VC-4) also known as Deacon's Demons, who flew and fought in the skies over the Pacific in WWII and to the men of the USS White Plains, who, against incredible odds, fought valiantly to protect our nation's freedoms in the Battle off Samar on October 25, 1944.

Figure 2 The Commanding Officer of Composite Squadron Four was LCDR. Edward "The Deacon" Fickenscher. The Deacon's Demons cartoon 1945 VC-4 Scrapbook depicts VC-4 Demons attacking Japanese Emperor Hirohito on the USS White Plains flight deck. VC-4 Scrapbook. US Navy Publication 1945. Courtesy of Andy Winnegar

TABLE OF CONTENTS

FOREWORD

In World War II, I was an 18-year-old Aviation Radioman flying in a TBM Avenger with a Marine Observer during the invasions of Saipan and Tinian. War is unpredictable and dangerous by its very nature, but these Observations Missions required our flying low and slow over an armed enemy. Consequently, these assignments were far more hazardous than our normal duty. So, when they asked for volunteers, we jumped at the opportunity.

Figure 3 Andrew J. Winnegar 1942. Courtesy of Andy Winnegar.

Eight decades later, Russell N. Low, the author of "Three Coins" and "The All-American Crew," contacted me in the spring of 2021, looking for firsthand information on VC-4 and the invasion of Saipan. I was already maintaining the website and Facebook Page for Composite Squadron Four (VC-4) and the USS White Plains. In fact, that is how he found me after leaving a message on the White Plains' Facebook Page.

Reviewing his manuscript of "The All-American Crew" confirmed his expertise with battle scenes and knack for capturing the essence of men in combat. I eagerly made my daily journal and memories of the Saipan invasion available to lend detail and authenticity to his writing.

We recorded several Zoom interviews, then when moving into less formal life experiences, Russell suggested another book based on the VC-4 and USS White Plains war experiences told from the eyes of teenage airmen.

To have a writer with his talent, experience, and reputation turn a nineteen-year-old's journal into an actual book was beyond my imagination. It was also an opportunity to preserve these stories of heroism and sacrifice for future generations.

Now, Russell N. Low's book "Avengers, Wildcats, and Crickets" is a reality. The work uses my recollections reinforced by my daily journal entries and the hundreds of photographs of the men and the war in the Pacific. We spent countless hours discussing life aboard the White Plains, flight operations and flying and fighting from a TBM Avenger and FM-2 Wildcat.

Our collaboration in researching the stories and combining them with realistic dialogue and photographs has created a remarkable work that brings back the lives of my nine hundred shipmates.

This novel is rare in its ability to convey the details of the war in the Pacific by showing rather than talking about the comradery, bravery, humor, and sacrifice of men at war. Russell Low uses realistic and entertaining dialogue to let my squadron's pilots, gunners, and radiomen tell their story.

"Avengers, Wildcats, and Crickets" allows the reader to experience the Pacific War from the sea aboard an escort carrier and from the air onboard a TBM Avenger or FM-2 Wildcat. It captures the essence of the. War. Of course, it's not the same as being there, but it's pretty darn close.

All generations will benefit from learning the discipline, responsibility, humility, and loyalty of their World War II ancestors. The inspirational writing of Russell Low could ignite a spark in the inherited genes of one of the descendants and motivate them to change the world into a better place.

Andrew J. Winnegar - *ARM2/C VC-4 USS White Plains*

PROLOGUE

"Avengers, Wildcats, and Crickets" is a rare personal glimpse of the War in the Pacific seen through the eyes and journals of five young American men who served on the USS White Plains from 1943 to 1944. Their secret writings from eight decades ago tell a fresh and unfiltered dramatic story of heroic patriotism, loyalty, humor, tragedy, loss, and triumph. Four of these men were only teenagers when their country called on them to go to war on small Pacific Islands halfway around the world. To understand the heart of an American warrior, one must gain access to their inner psyche; to understand what makes them tick. Perhaps they are motivated by a belief in the ideals of freedom, or maybe it's much more straightforward.

Andy Winnegar   *Donald Crounse*   *Russell Wood*   *Maurice Hie*   *Bill Lemon*

When asked why he received seven Air Medals, a Distinguished Flying Cross and a personal citation from Admiral Chester Nimitz, Andy Winnegar, a TBM Avenger radio operator and gunner, paused before replying, "I just liked shooting back!" The thrill of battle kept men like Winnegar coming back for more. "I would have hated to miss a mission that had a lot of action."

Explaining more fully, Winnegar continued, "According to a White Plains' shipmate, Jimmy "Bull" Durham, it was my 30 Caliber Gun Camera. The 16mm gun cameras were removed after every mission by the Photographer's Mate, processed, and viewed by the

Intelligence Officer to evaluate the mission and targets."

"He said they argued about who got my film when it came down from the Photo Shop because there was always so much action. I carried two canisters of 300 rounds each and frequently ran out of ammo, whereas other ARMs never fired a round but moved to the center cockpit on bomb and strafing runs to avoid the more dangerous tunnel location. They avoided carrying empty shell casings in and belts of ammo out to their planes and probably didn't clean their guns. It never occurred to me that my recommendations for medals were coming from being aggressive; I just liked shooting back."

"I already knew that I had a reputation in the Ordinance Department for replacing more gun parts than all other ARMs combined, but I wasn't admired for that. They thought I was burning up barrels by firing long bursts, and that was true."

It is fitting that a metal box that once stored the FM-2 Wildcat starter cartridges from World War II has for almost eight decades protected and preserved the hand-written journals of a teenage Andy Winnegar. Winnegar's stories form the basis for this novel, "Avengers, Wildcats, and Crickets – The Story of the Men Who Fought in the Skies Over the Pacific in WWII.

In addition, the journals of TBM Avenger gunners Maurice Hie and Bill Lemon, the Memoirs of War of FM2-Wildcat fighter pilot Russell Wood, and the typed journal of USS White Plains' CIC Radarman, Donald Crounse provide a broad, and personal view of the war in the Pacific fought from the flight deck of the USS White Plains and in the planes of Composite Squadron Four (VC-4) and Marine Observer Squadron VMO-4.

War does not create heroes; it simply creates situations where those with the grit and a spark of gallantry can remain in the fight, running towards the danger to become leaders of men and the defenders of freedom. Now, almost 80 years later, we can thank the men of VC-4 and VMO-4 and the USS White Plains for having the grit and the spark that helped win the war and preserve our nation. Andy

Winnegar had been flying with Pat Owens and Maurice Hie since September 1943, when they were in training for the Pacific War of WWII. Owens and Winnegar flew 66 combat missions in their TBM Avenger off the flight deck of the USS White Plains in the VC-4 squadron composed of Avenger torpedo bombers and Wildcat fighters.

Three of the White Plains' TBM Avengers piloted by Lts. Pat Owens, Rocky Carson, and Coll McLean volunteered for observation missions with VMO-4 Marine observers onboard, men who also flew the tiny unarmed Stinson OY-1 "Crickets." Flying low and slow observation flights over the enemy resulted in TBM Avengers and Stinson Crickets riddled with bullet holes, mounting casualties, a chest full of medals, and stories that are as vivid and heroic today, almost 80 years since these young warriors took to the skies over Pacific in 1944.

Figure 5 Distinguished Flying Cross and Seven Air Medals Awarded to Andrew J. Winnegar for his Service in World War II.

Chapter 1

FROM THE OZARKS TO THE PACIFIC – 1920s

This story begins in the Ozarks of Southern Missouri, 7,000 miles removed from the battlefields of the Central Pacific, where the saga will unfold two decades later. The chirping of birds, a burbling brook, and the soft whispering rush of wind through virgin forests of towering oak, hickory, and shortleaf pine trees filled the pastoral serenity of the Irish Wilderness. These tranquil woodland scenes and melodic rural sounds hadn't changed much in a thousand years until now.

"Boom! Boom!" The percussive blast ripped through the tree-covered landscape. The initial explosion was followed by reverberating echoes that rang through the forest. The birds silenced for a moment, then took flight en masse to escape the danger.

In the 1920s and 1930s, the Winnegar family lived in the Ozarks of Southern Missouri in the Mark Twain National Forest, in a 16,000-acre section the locals referred to as the "Irish Wilderness." Their home was in an area called Spring Creek, which is a tributary of the 138-mile long Eleven Point River, flowing north to south from the

Figure 6 Two-room cabin with bark siding in the Irish Wilderness. Courtesy of Andy Winnegar.

Ozark Mountains through southern Missouri and Northern Arkansas.

Living in the Ozarks of Missouri, Jim and Ellen Winnegar and their children, Andrew and Wanda, never went hungry and always had more than most people around them. Andy's father received a 100% disability for his service in World War I. Somehow, the family not only survived but flourished on the $40-$50 per month the disability check brought in. His father even had several different automobiles during the Great Depression when most people couldn't dream of having one car. If others had an automobile, they couldn't afford to drive it even with ten-cent gasoline.

Since he was on disability, Jim Winnegar had to work at jobs that paid him cash under the table. He was a timber detective, protecting the timber from local thieves who cut down trees and cut them into stave bolt logs that they illegally sold to the local sawmills. Winnegar stamped the ends of the stave bolt with the *Moss Tie Company* logo, and if that weren't enough, he drove a spike into the bark. If a sawmill got one of these stave bolts and was dumb enough to try to mill it, the

Figure 7 Andy's maternal grandparents, John Evans Jr. 1868-1963 and Lavina "Vina" Dotson 1870-1967. Courtesy of Andy Winnegar

spike would tear up their saw. Winnegar also ran trap lines, spending days in the wilderness trapping for furs.

When Andy was two to three years old, the family lived in a two-room cabin about 100 yards down a lane from his maternal grandparents' farm. Little Andy was allowed to go to visit his grandmother by himself. He loved these trips because Grandma made great potato soup and sweet, savory cornbread.

"I liked the thin and crispy cornbread she made. My mother's cornbread was a little thicker."

Andrew's grandparents, John and Vina Evans worked the land owned by Dr. Davis, an old-fashioned horse and buggy physician who had trouble with the new-fangled Model T. Davis delivered most of the babies in these parts, including Andrew and Wanda Winnegar. John Evans grew grain and hay crops to feed the livestock, which was the money crop. Cattle and hogs grazed the pastures and leased Mark Twain National Forrest land during the spring and summer when Jim Winnegar rounded them up and sent them to market in the fall.

The stock kept for breeding was fed during the winter months. The Evans family owned the chickens and the eggs which brought in Vina's

Figure 8 Jim Winnegar and his dog. Courtesy of Andy Winnegar.

spending money. Large vegetable gardens and a butchered steer and hog kept the family fed. In addition, they received a monthly salary and an annual bonus from Dr. Davis. [1]

His grandparents always called Andrew by his middle name, Jack or Jackson, but the nickname never stuck.

"When my grandfather John came in from the fields, he sat down by the fireplace in his rocking chair to smoke his pipe. Sometimes he smelled of the moonshine he kept hidden in the barn."

"Jack, come over here by the fireplace so I can tell you a story," John

---

[1] Recollections of Andy Winnegar November 6, 2021. The land where the farm buildings and cabin stood is now overgrown with trees and is part of the Mark Twain National Forrest. The Evans family originated in Wales while Vina's Dotson family was from Scotland.

Evans absently said as he lit his pipe with a glowing ember from the fire.

Grandpa told Jack stories of his past, including tales about the Civil War events that occurred not far from where they were living. Missouri was technically a neutral state, but most of the area in Southern Missouri was Confederate.

John Evans was hard of hearing, especially when it came to his wife, Vina. He could never hear her, instead retreating into his feigned deafness, puffing away on his pipe."

Figure 9 Jim Winnegar. Courtesy of Andy Winnegar

When Andy's father came home to the cabin after working the trap lines, he usually had a surprise for Andrew in his coat pocket. His pockets were stuffed with Paw Paws in the late summer and fall. Kids loved the round Paw Paws, which tasted sweet like a banana. One day, he reached into his pocket. Andy expecting his favorite Paw Paw, was even more delighted when his father pulled out a little brown puppy.

"Oh, he's so cute. I love him," Andy gushed, laughing as the puppy licked his face.

Andy and Brownie were inseparable. There were no other children in the area, so Brownie was Andrew's constant companion.

Figure 10 Cave behind the Bockman Place that supplied spring water to the Winnegar family in Spring Creek, Missouri. Courtesy of Andy Winnegar.

One morning, Andrew's mother and grandmother went to gather fresh wild greens down in the valley. Andy was playing in the backyard with a steel trap and his little hound dog, Brownie.

"You keep a close watch on Andrew, Jim We'll be gone for a spell."

"Sure, sure," he replied absently.

Later, Jim Winnegar could hear Andy and Brownie playing in the backyard, so he closed his eyes and drifted off. When his mother returned, Brownie was in the back, but Andy was missing.

"Where is Andrew?"

"He's in the backyard playing."

"No, he isn't! You were supposed to watch out for him. Instead, you're sleeping!" Ellen shouted, dropping her basket loaded with watercress and Polk greens to the floor.

They started searching for Andrew in a panic, first in the backyard and then in the surrounding dense "Irish Wilderness."

"How could you let him get lost out here in the wilderness, Jim? He's so small. Some wild animal could have carried him away!" Ellen sobbed.

John and Vina joined the search frantically, combing the hills and woods around both homes.

Ellen's face turned white, and her hands were shaking as she gasped and whispered the one place they hadn't searched, "The pig pen! Please, God. No! Don't let..." She couldn't finish the sentence, but her mind had raced ahead to the horrible conclusion as she pictured Andy's half-eaten remains. Ellen sobbed uncontrollably. "No!"

Jim finally noticed that Brownie was running back and forth between the house and a pathway leading deeper into the woods. "What are you trying to tell us, Brownie?"

After a few yards, Brownie took off down the path.

"Brownie! Come back!" Jim Winnegar called out. "Where is that dang dog?"

"We're wasting time here, Jim!" Ellen sobbed.

As they came around the next bend, they found Andrew sound asleep on a pile of leaves with Brownie licking his face and pawing at his friend to wake up.

Ellen Winnegar rushed over to her son, picking him up, sobbing and clutching Andrew while glaring daggers at her husband.

"I'm OK, Mom. Not so tight. I can't breathe!"

"Brownie saved me, but more than that, he saved my father from my mother's wrath! At 4 foot 11, she was not someone to be trifled with."

With the birth of his sister, Wanda, in October 1928, the Winnegars were crowded in the cabin, so they moved to a two-story home in Spring Creek called the Bockman Place. His grandfather's farm and the little cabin were not too far away, just a mile and a half over a ridge called the "Devil's Backbone."

The unique feature of the property was the spring flowing from a cave about 200 feet behind the house. The spring provided cool drinking water year-round.

"Mother also used the cave as a refrigerator to store butter and other perishables."

The Winnegars lived in the Bockman Place from 1929 until 1931. They enjoyed the solitude that came with living in the Irish Wilderness. Not having any neighbors was just fine with Jim and Ellen, who, like most Missourians, were self-reliant, butchering hogs and canning fruits and vegetables. At the Bockman Place that Grandma Huldah Winnegar came for a visit and never left.

Figure 11 Andy Winnegar and his sister Wanda 1929. Courtesy of Andy Winnegar.

The spring flowing out of the cave formed a pretty creek just wide enough to require a footbridge. So, when grandma Winnegar came to stay, she brought her fishing pole and spent hours fishing from the footbridge, usually catching herself a "mess of fish."

"You can't eat your grandma's 'rot gut' fish, Andrew," his father warned. "They're not good for you. Probably stunt your growth. I'll go catch you bass or a trout, you know, real fish."

"Andrew, I'll cook you some of these fish with cornmeal mush and fresh-baked bread," Grandma Winnegar smiled at her four-year-old grandson.

"Sure, grandma. I'm walking to visit Grandma and Grandpa Evans tomorrow!" Andy proclaimed although his mother forbid Andrew from venturing out onto the Devil's Backbone on his own.

Then, of course, there was always the danger of the "pigpen" to consider. To make the trip to visit his grandparents required walking right past the dreaded pigpen. The local legend was that some foolish kid had wandered in there and never come out.

"Stay away from the pigpen, Andrew," his mother warned, pulling her four-year-old son down the footpath over the Devil's Backbone.

Figure 12 Andy Winnegar six years old with a "stick horse" in Thomasville, MO. Courtesy of Andy Winnegar.

"Ah, Ma! Those pigs don't scare me."

"You listen to me, young man! Those squealing pigs outweigh you and have sharp teeth. They'd love to dine on a four-year-old for dinner," she replied, trying to scare some sense into her all-too-brave son.

Andy looked back towards the pigpen, picked up a rock, and chucked it at the pigs for good measure. *I'm not afraid of you, mister pig!*

Running ahead on the path towards his grandparents' house, Andy imagined the taste and smell of his grandma's warm cornbread.

"Look at the way Andrew's butt wiggles," Aunt Jenny shouted gleefully.

"My butt doesn't wiggle," Andy protested.

"Whatever you say, Andrew. But it's pretty cute."

Andy spent the rest of the one-and-a-half-mile walk trying to look over his shoulder at his four-year-old rear end.

The Winnegars lived in the Bockman Place until Andy was almost six years old when he needed to attend school in Thomasville. Some neighborhood girls took Andy to their one-room schoolhouse in Spring Creek. Andy recalled that the students used slate on slate to write. Similarly, the blackboard was also made of slate. Andy attended as a guest for a few days. This early experience made quite an impression, helping to shape his natural curiosity.

Uncle Lanty was his father's older brother and Andrew's favorite. Andy could always count on Uncle Lanty for a bit of excitement and a raucous display of his independent spirit.

Once, when needing some liquor to make Andrew's measles break out, Uncle Lanty took matters into his own hand, leaving five dollars on Moonshiner Croper's tree stump. Sam Croper was a local bootlegger who maintained a brisk business selling moonshine out of a stump on his property. The next day Uncle Lanty returned to the tree stump to pick up his pint of moonshine. While the cure didn't do much for Andrew's measles, Uncle Lanty didn't let the moonshine go to waste, drinking the pint for Andrew.

Uncle Lanty was six foot two and red-headed. William Alonson, aka "Lanty," was quite a character. Ugly as sin, he looked and dressed like a hobo. As a teenager, he had lost an eye when he filled a tree stump with black powder, making a trail of black powder serving as the fuse. But when he lit the "fuse," the black powder burned a lot faster than he expected. The stump and black powder blew up in his face, burning his skin and destroying his eye. Not to be deterred, one-eyed Lanty continued to experiment with explosives. Those early experiences led Lanty to a career as the local "powder money" or an explosives expert.

On one occasion, Lanty showed up at the Bockman Place in his brand-new Model T. When tasked with babysitting his nephew, Andrew, while the parents went into town, Lanty decided the stumps in the front of the property needed his attention. It would take his brother months to dig them out by hand. So, cutting some dynamite sticks into quarter lengths, he proceeded to ply his craft as a "Powder Monkey." Taking the explosive blasting cap, he crimped the metal around the fuse by biting it with his teeth. To Lanty's way of thinking, it was no more dangerous than using pliers. If she blows up, it'll kill you either way![2]

Figure 13 William Alonson "Lanty" Winnegar. Courtesy of Andy Winnegar.

"Come on, Andrew, let's go and have some fun," Uncle Lanty said, taking his nephew's hand.

"OK. You sit over here while I blow up these stumps for your father."

"Well, I got to watch, and it was really exciting!" Winnegar recalled with a smile over nine decades later.

---

[2] Blasting caps are used to detonate an explosive charge. Blasting caps contain a small explosive charge that in turn sets off a larger attached explosive (such as dynamite). As a result, blasting caps are considered explosives and are dangerous, as they could potentially detonate and injure and/or kill someone handling them.

BOOM! BOOM!

The explosions echoed across the woods. Lanty blew the stumps clean out of the ground with dirt, debris, and wood chips flying through the air. With the first dynamite explosion one stubborn stump near the road wouldn't budge.

"Looks like we'll need a double charge on this monster stump, Andrew. So, you'd better back up for this one," Lanty instructed. "And whatever happens, don't ever tell your mother!"

Andy covered his ears as Uncle Lanty lit the fuse on the double dose dynamite charge.

KABOOM!

The explosion was massive, blowing the stump 20 feet into the air, landing in the middle of the road..

"Woah! That was fun, Uncle Lanty. Can I try!"

Lanty looked at his nephew and considered the request for a brief moment. "Well, tell you what, Andrew. When you're a little older, I'll give you some lessons. But for now, just remember, don't ever be afraid of explosions, danger, or bullies!"

"Sure thing, Uncle Lanty. I won't be afraid of explosions, danger, or bullets!"

"I said bullies, not bullets!"

But Andy was already off running through the woods with Brownie.

Chapter 2

REED-STEMMED PIPES, BILLY GOATS, & GRANDMA WINNEGAR – 1930s

Lanty may have inherited his colorful personality from his mother. Huldah Winnegar's most distinctive feature was her ever-present reed-stemmed clay pipe. Andy had never seen his grandmother without the pipe or the pocketful of special home-grown tobacco supplied by her nephew Pleasant Coble, or "Ples" as the family called him. Ples' mother was Huldah's niece "Mec," short for her very patriotic name, "America." The Blackburns grew up in the rolling hill country of Northern Kentucky in unincorporated Pendleton. Huldah remarkably would eventually outlive all of her siblings in a family of eleven children with five girls and six boys. Huldah would likely attribute her 94 years of good health to her habitual pipe smoking.

The original Blackburn,

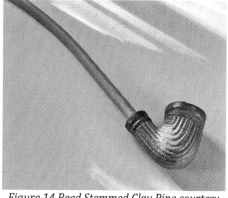

Figure 14 Reed Stemmed Clay Pipe courtesy of Pat.

Benjamin or Zachariah Benjamin immigrated from Scotland to Virginia in 1772 when he was 14 years old. Four years later, he was part of an expedition exploring the Kentucky Territory with James Gay, William Elliott, and Major Samuel Stevenson. Blackburn later settled in Northern Kentucky just south of the Ohio River. He married Sarah Kennedy in 1786 and raised their family of four children in Augusta and Pendleton, Kentucky.[3]

When Jim and Ellen Winnegar moved from the Bockman place into Thomasville in 1931, Grandma Huldah Winnegar came along with them. In seven-year-old Andy's eyes, Grandma Winnegar, born in 1853, had always looked old, and having her around full time made him acutely aware of the dangers of her pipe smoking.

"Andrew, come over here and keep your granny company," Huldah called out from her rocking chair throne on the front porch.

Her long dark gingham dress loosely covered every inch of her body from her feet to her neck. With its long sleeves, only Huldah's wrinkled white hands were left exposed. Huldah kept her ever-present black and white checkered apron tied neatly around her waist, and a pair of wire-rimmed glasses offset her weathered features and short wavy grey hair. But for Andy, it was grandma's pipe that held his full attention. Held loosely on her lips, the reed stem and glowing clay pipe bowl bobbed and weaved as Huldah turned her head to and fro as she spoke and gestured with her hands.

"Come on up here, Andrew. Come sit on my lap." Grandma ordered.

Andrew obeyed but never once took his eye off the bobbing pipe. In his mind's eye, he imagined the burning tobacco heating up the pipe bowl to a red-hot glowing one thousand degrees. It was hot enough to burn the flesh off an unsuspecting boy. He would not be caught off guard again. As Andy looked up, Huldah inhaled and then puffed away with a cloud of smoke encircling her face.

---

[3] Oren Frederic Morton. A History of Rockbridge County, Virginia. Andesite Press 2017

Andy's father appeared from around the side of the home. Huldah turned her head to the right, and Andy deftly ducked as the red-hot clay pipe sailed over his head.

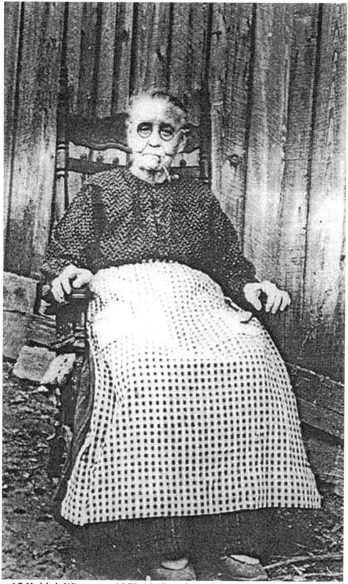

Figure 15 Huldah Winnegar 1853-1947 and Reed Stem Pipe. Courtesy of Andy Winnegar.

"Stop squirming, Andrew! Sit still. James, did you get me a new pipe?" Huldah asked, turning her attention to her son.

"No, Ma, but I bought you these new reeds for your pipe," he replied, presenting Huldah with seven new reeds.

Figure 16 Reed Pipe Stems.

Frowning, Huldah inspected the reeds, turning one over and holding it up to the light while peering down its length with one eye closed.

"Won't do, Jim. The ends are too big to fit in my pipe bowl. Besides, my pipe's cracked. I told you to fetch me a new pipe, not these stems," Huldah said.

Meanwhile, Andy had been dodging his grandma's glowing pipe, which was wildly flying over his head as she weaved and boobed her head, inspecting the stems, speaking, and intermittently puffing on the pipe. Andrew's dexterity and reflexes were a sight to behold.

"Sit still, Andrew!"

"Andrew, come over here. I have a surprise for you," Jim Winnegar called out, rescuing his son from the hazards of his mother's glowing pipe.

Andy quickly hopped down and breathed a sigh of relief. "Did you bring me some Paw Paws or another puppy?"

"Better. Look!" Jim exclaimed, handing Andy the end of a rope with its other end trailing around the house. "Go ahead, Andrew. Pull on it."

Andy took the free end of the rope and tugged on it, pulling out the slack.

Andy looked at his dad, "It's stuck, Pa."

"Pull gently, Andrew."

Andy tugged on the rope and felt something pulling back. He tugged harder.

"Maa! Maa!"

Andy's eyes grew wide when a baby Billy goat came bounding around the corner of the house.

"Is it for me, Pa?" Andy asked as he bent down and picked up the fluffy white and grey baby goat with tiny horns.

"She sure is, Andrew," Jim replied, beaming. "It's called a kid, but you can give him a name."

"Billy, of course!" Andrew announced.

Huldah, watching from her rocking chair, called out, "You spent money on a goat, but you didn't get my new pipe?"

"Relax, Ma. I traded for the goat. It didn't cost a penny."

Meanwhile, Andy ran around the yard with Billy chasing him and butting him with his tiny horns. Brownie watched the interloper with interest from inside the house.

By two months, Billy weighed 50 pounds and had good-sized horns, perfect handholds for Andy in their twice-daily wrestling match. Much to Brownie's displeasure, Billy and Andy became constant playmates, wrestling and butting heads, or just paling around. Whenever Andy came outside, Billy came charging over, ready for their next tussle or adventure. They just had to watch out for Grandma Winnegar,

Figure 17 Red Radio Flyer Wagon.

17

who for some reason took to rapping Billy on his horns with her cane. She likely blamed Billy for her dwindling supply of pipes.

Billy charged up to Andy, jumping up with his front hooves on his favorite seven-year-old. Andy grabbed Billy by the horns and wrestled him to the ground, with the two of them rolling around in the dirt and grass. It was the kind of fun a boy can only have with his goat.

"Gotcha good that time, Billy!" Andy laughed when the wrestling finally calmed down.

"Maa! Maa!" Billy bleated, pushing on Andy with his growing horns as the two lay on the ground. Finally, Billy placed his hoof on Andy's leg and put his head on the ground.

"Come on, Billy, I have an idea," Andy said, running around the side of the house with Billy following right behind.

Their path took them in front of Huldah, who showed incredible speed and agility as she rapped Billy twice on his horns. "Bad Billy Goat!"

Andy hated it when grandma struck Billy, but what was he supposed to do? Telling her off would only get him a scolding or worse.

Andy ran up to his red Radio Flyer Wagon, jumped in, and ordered, "OK, Billy! Push me!"

Billy stood there, looking first at Andy and then at the red wagon. Then, finally, he butted Andy's leg, trying to get his boy out of the red contraption so they could play.

"No, Billy. Not like that! Here let me show you," Andy said, climbing out of the wagon, leading Billy behind the wagon, and placing his head against the back of the red Flyer. "Now push!"

Billy put his front legs in the wagon and began to walk forward, pushing the wagon in front of him.

"Hey! That's great, Billy!" Andy exclaimed, jumping into the wagon as it rolled into the front yard.

"Grandma, look!" Andy called out.

Huldah puffed away on her pipe and smiled at the goat-powered wagon. "Don't go too far, Andrew."

After a while, Andy jumped out of the wagon, got behind it, and pushed his head against the back. Billy finally got the idea and began pushing the red wagon with his horns.

"Yippee! You got it, Billy! Let's go!"

Billy pushed the Red Radio Flyer with Andy onboard around the yard. Unfortunately, on the fifth pass, Andy steered a little too close to Huldah, who reached out and rapped Billy on his horns.

"Grandma, stop that!" Andy protested, but Huldah had her cane raised, ready for the next pass.

After that, Andy steered clear. Billy was tireless as the two of them and the red wagon went around and around the yard. Soon the neighbors were stopping by to observe the spectacle as word of Andy, Billy, and the red Radio Flyer spread around Thomasville.

Two days later, Andy and Billy were horsing around in the front yard. Andy was trying to teach Billy to play hide-n-seek, but the lesson was not going well. Billy simply followed Andy everywhere he went and refused to close his eyes.

Exasperated, Andy sat down on the grass next to Billy. Grandma Winnegar came out onto the porch, enjoying the sunshine and cool Missouri air. As she stepped down off the porch, her pipe fell to the ground. Andy and Billy watched with interest as Huldah, facing away, bent over to pick up her pipe. The view of Grandma's backside made Andy laugh, but Billy had other ideas.

Billy took off in a flash, picked up speed, put his head down, and butted Huldah Winnegar in the rear end, knocking her flat on her face! "Maa! Maa!" Billy bleated as he placed his front hooves on Huldah's backside.

Andy couldn't help himself and roared with laughter.

Huldah sat up sputtering with her dress covered in dirt, her hair disheveled, and her wire-rimmed glasses askew. "Andrew Winnegar! Get that goat away from me!" she yelled, swinging the cane wildly in Billy's direction.

Unfortunately, the sweet justice was short-lived. Billy disappeared the next day and was never seen again around the Winnegar home. There were, however, rumors of a goat-powered wagon in the next town over.

.

Chapter 3

FROM BOXING TO TBM AVENGERS –
1930s – 1940s

Winnegar always remembered that afternoon blowing up tree stumps with Uncle Lanty. Andy kept Uncle Lanty's fearless spirit and his words of advice in his "back pocket," guiding him past bullies and bullets. Learning to "bob and weave" to avoid Grandma Winnegar's clay pipe also prepared him for the next phase of his life in unexpected ways.

Growing up in the Ozarks of Missouri and later in Albuquerque, New Mexico, Winnegar learned to be

Figure 18 Andy J Winnegar 13 years old - Albuquerque, NM

Figure 19 Henry Armstrong 1937. Public Domain. Wikimedia Commons. Carl Van Vechten Photographs collection at the Library of Congress.

a scrapper at an early age.[4] When he was 11 years old, Andy's family moved 1,000 miles due west to New Mexico, in a transition that shook up his White Ozark world. Nothing would ever again be the same. In Albuquerque, Winnegar was the one White face in a sea of Brown-skinned kids.

Because of this, the 15-block walk to Junior High School in Albuquerque was a gauntlet of street fights courtesy of the local Mexican American kids. Except for Winnegar, every kid was Mexican American, which may have shaped his thinking about being a minority. Street fights made him tough and led him to Golden Gloves boxing by the time he was 14 years old, where he developed his skills under the watchful guidance of his coach Tony Wilson. However, Wilson saw something in the young Winnegar that may have had more to do with his heart than his developing boxing skills.

Learning to fight on the vacant lots of Albuquerque shaped Winnegar's fighting spirit

"I wasn't good, but I was ferocious!"

On the other hand, Golden Gloves, and his coach Tony Wilson, gave Andy some direction and got him off the streets and away from the vacant lot brawling with the Mexican-American kids. Andy found a new "home" in Golden Gloves boxing.

---

[4] Family moved from Thomasville MO to Albuquerque NM in the Fall of 1936 when Andy was 11 years old. He turned 12 years old in November that year.

Winnegar recalls, "In Golden Gloves, they were three-round fights, one and a half minutes per round. So, my strategy was to come out as strong as I could the first round, to kind of lay on the guy the second round, and hope that I had worn him down enough so I could beat him up the third round!"

Ultimately, Andy learned as much about human nature and race relations as he did about boxing techniques. Boxing exposed Andy to different races, all of whom had wanted to beat him to a pulp. Yet, somehow, he came through these early years with his head on straight and a rare openness to ideas and people with a skin color distinctly darker than his pale Swiss European heritage.

In New Mexico's Golden Gloves, fighting black boxers exposed Andy to the people whose discrimination he had never witnessed in Thomasville, Missouri, because Blacks were not allowed in Oregon County, MO. Later, Andy would witness in Arkansas the colored-only outhouses, colored drinking faucets, and the back seats in the bus that were outward expressions of deep-seated racial discrimination in the South. Even as a young boy, Andy knew, "It just wasn't right!"

In the ring, Winnegar, for the first time, came face to face with his Black opponents. They fought tough but clean, and he soon realized that, "We were just two people in the ring. Reading Ring Magazine, I admired fighters like Henry Armstrong and Joe Louis. They were all Black and were more my heroes than Jack Dempsey and Gene Tunney." The racism of the real world somehow did not carry over to the boxing world.

When he was 16 years old, Winnegar's family moved the 1000 miles back to Thomasville, Missouri. Small-town Thomasville in the Ozarks did not offer any more formal boxing, but Andy kept the lessons he had learned in Golden Gloves about race and prejudice close to his heart.

Andy Winnegar was seventeen years old when he joined the Navy in July 1942. He embarked on a whirlwind tour of America courtesy of the US Navy. Andy went to Boot Camp at Great Lakes Naval Training School Camp Dewey, Ship Board Radio School at Northwestern University in Chicago, Illinois, Aviation Radio School at NATTC Millington [5] in Memphis, Tennessee, and Aerial Gunnery School and Operations School in Jacksonville, Florida.

Aviation Radio School NATTC Millington, Tennessee

At Aviation Radio School in Millington, Tennessee, Andy was on the NATTC Boxing Team, fighting two matches at the Louisville Kentucky Derby against Black boxers. Andy won both fights on a decision.

"Looking back on it, I would almost question the decisions," Winnegar confided, indicating that the deck was stacked against the Black boxers. "I always felt that the young Black boxers did not get the opportunities that I got."

"I got a chance to talk to these Black boxers. It wasn't a good feeling at all."

Figure 20 Seventeen-year-old Andy Winnegar, kneeling, at Navy Boot Camp in 1942. Courtesy of Andy Winnegar.

"Coming home on leave, I rode the train from Memphis, Tennessee, to Thomasville in southern Missouri. On the Oregon County line, where Thomasville is located, a sign proclaimed that you couldn't be in that county after sunset if you were Black. All along that route at the

---

[5] NATTC – Naval Air Technical Training Command – at Millington Tennessee, near Memphis

Figure 21 Navy boxing match on the flight deck of the USS Monterey. Navy Photograph. Public Domain.

train depots in Arkansas, there were outhouses painted orangish-yellow for "Coloreds" only. I never knew a Black family, but it just didn't seem right at all."

Andy's years in New Mexico had sensitized him to racial bullying and made him identify with the plight of the Black boxers.

"In Albuquerque, I experienced what it was like to be a minority. I was the only White face in a sea of Mexican American kids. They called me names that I quickly learned were not nice, and they picked fights with me every day in those vacant lots. They just didn't like the color of my skin."

Looking back on his experiences with Black boxers, Winnegar observed, "In the ring, we understood that we were just two people.

We found that if we had the chance, we could communicate. If my Black Boxer and I had had the opportunity, we could have changed the world in a minute. But the world wouldn't allow it."

These experiences shaped and colored Winnegar's impressions of

Figure 22 Boxing champions of Great Lake, Illinois. 1943. NARA. Public Domain. Wikimedia Commons.

race and fairness, which would soon lead to some unexpected interactions on the USS White Plains.

Andy was at NATTC Millington when he received news about his father. Jim Winnegar had always been frail as a consequence of a devastating World War I injury in San Diego in which a truck's steering column fell on him, penetrating his chest. Multiple surgeries resulted in the removal of one of his lungs. His condition was made worse by pulmonary tuberculosis with its unrelenting cough that turned bloody over time. Jim Winnegar's "spells" and bad temper from his constant pain had always frightened Andy as a boy.

"Winnegar, we received this from your mother," the commanding officer said glumly, handing Andy the yellow, folded Western Union telegram.

The message was brief and to the point. "Come home quick. Your father is ill. Heart attack."

The Navy made all the arrangements for Andy's emergency leave and transportation back to West Plains, Missouri. The 12-hour train ride felt like a lifetime of worry. The 20-mile cab ride from West Plains to Thomasville was a blur as Andy had a million and one thoughts.

The VA Hospital in Memphis was the closest to Thomasville, and the train, though not the fastest, was still the mode of transportation of choice to get his father medical attention. The troop-train ride back to Memphis would have been uncomfortable for a healthy person. For Jim Winnegar, with crushing chest pain, the train ride was pure agony. Dressed in his usual khaki pants, Scotch-plaid shirt, and 7-7/8" Stetson hat, Winnegar sprawled out on the train car seat. Dressed in his Navy Blues, Andy sat opposite his moaning father.

"Dad, are you OK? Can I do anything for you?"

"Hurts. Can't talk. Damn it." Jim Winnegar grimaced. There were no more attempts at conversation, just endless miles of track and groans as Winnegar felt a bump or lurch and then drifted off, half delirious with pain.

When the train finally arrived at Grand Central Station in Memphis, an ambulance was waiting to take them the three miles to the VA Hospital. Andy climbed into the back of the ambulance with his father as they took off up the beltway with the siren wailing.

Winnegar was rushed to the emergency room at the VA Hospital where a nurse hooked up an EKG machine. The attending physician took over, quickly glancing at the EKG and only briefly examining Jim Winnegar before proclaiming to Andy, "There's nothing we can do for your father. He's not going to survive."

The doctor's lack of bedside manner and blunt assessment stunned and angered Andy, but ultimately, he was correct. Jim Winnegar lived for three days before dying at 11:45 pm on March 28, 1943, with his wife Ellen at his side. [6]

The personnel office at Millington NATTC took care of everything. The body was sent back to Thomasville for the funeral and burial. First, a spare bedroom at Huldah and Lanty's home was requisitioned for viewing so friends and family could pay their last respects. One never knows who will show up for such things, probably more than one deserves and fewer than one expects. On the other hand, the wake had a guest list of one. Andy spent two sleepless nights sitting in a chair in that bedroom, alone, watching over his father's body. Not surprisingly, there were no other volunteers.

Andy did have one visitor during the second, long night. The soft shuffling sound in the dark announced the unexpected visitor. Andy opened his eyes and looked up, startled by the noise, half expecting to see his father rise up out of the bed. In the darkened room, a shiver coursed through his body as a warm breeze from the half-opened window ruffled the curtains.

"Who's there? Is that you, Dad?"

The silence was followed by the sound of pouring, a clink, and the unmistakable grainy, peaty, woody, and fruity smell that brought back memories of Grandpa Evans. He waited in silence.

Andy felt the nudge and the cool smooth glass in his hand, but it was the smell of Sam Croper's moonshine that announced his midnight guest.

"Hello, Uncle Lanty. You know, Prohibition ended in 1933. You can buy your whiskey legally now."

"Yes, but it's not half as much fun. Jim and I always enjoyed a nip of Croper's moonshine, so this is perfect."

"You and all the other men in these parts kept Sam Croper's tree stump business humming," Andy laughed.

"You want to make a toast to your old man?"

"Well, I appreciate the company and the thought, but it's your

---

[6] Andy called his mother relaying the doctor's grim prognosis. Ellen Winnegar came to the VA Hospital and refused to leave her husband's side until he passed away.

whiskey, so go ahead."

Lanty raised his glass which glistened in the moonlight. "To my kid brother, Jim. Here's a good stiff drink of Croper's moonshine so we can all howl at the moon and remember the good times with a good man."

The clink of the glasses and the savory burning taste of the moonshine was the best tribute a son and brother could pay to the man, Jim Winnegar.

"Thanks, Uncle Lanty," Andy whispered. "There are things I wish I had told him, and now it's too late."

"He knew, Andy. He always knew," Lanty said softly as his shuffling steps receded into the next room.

In the darkness, Andy's thoughts turned to Brownie and Billie, and his dad's pockets stuffed full of pawpaws as a single tear trickled down his cheek.

After the funeral, Andy sold his dad's pickup truck and equipment on the small family farm. He also relocated his mother and sister, who moved in with Andy's Evans grandparents.

The two-week absence from his training at Aviation Radio School had little effect on Andy's studies as he had already finished Ship-Board Radio School at Northwestern. Fortunately, radios and Morse Code are the same on a boat or in a plane.

Winnegar first met Steve Walley in February 1943 at NATTC Radio School in Memphis, Tennessee. From that time forward, their training and assignments were identical. In the Navy, many assignments were alphabetical. So, when it was time for their next assignment, Walley and Winnegar invariably headed in the same direction. Walley and Winnegar were joined at the hip, and their subsequent assignments to the TBM torpedo bomber and the VC-4 Squadron were predicted and determined by the "W" in their last names. However, their life-long friendship had more to do with the quality of their relationship.

Yellow Water Aerial Gunnery School

The friendship between Andy, the self-described Ozark Hillbilly, and Steve Walley, the New Yorker, was not immediate, and the two came to blows at Yellow Water Gunnery School out in the Florida swamps. By Andy's recollections, Steve took the first swing, but the reason for the altercation has been long since forgotten. Regional accents were still prominent in the 1940s in the days before television, making the difference between these two even more pronounced.

Figure 23 Steve Walley VC-4 Squadron. Courtesy of Andy Winnegar

Two hundred aerial gunnery students were at Yellow Water outside of Jacksonville including Winnegar and Walley. Training at Gunnery School in 1943 started with shotguns on a mount shooting at clay pigeons and then semi-automatic shotguns shooting at moving targets, leaning to lead and lag the target. The most advanced part of the training involved turrets mounted on a truck with the truck and target moving in opposite directions.

Figure 24 Andrew J. Winnegar VC-4 Squadron. Courtesy of Andy Winnegar

Operational Training Jacksonville, Florida

The Operational Training at Jacksonville NAS is where Naval Aviators, air, and ground crew received their final instruction before assignment to squadrons. But first, the new trainees spent their initial two weeks on the "Crash Squad," riding around in low boy trailers, picking up wrecked airplanes and body parts of cadets who ended their training in a fiery crash. Unfortunately, accidents and fatalities were very common for the new pilots right out of flight school. Following this rude introduction to Navy flying, Winnegar finally got to fly in a TBM Avenger with a pilot and turret gunner.

Andy and Steve were assigned to TBF Avengers, operating as part of a torpedo bomber crew. They learned to fire the .50 caliber machine gun in flight shooting at tow targets. They set up and operated the VHF and HF radios in flight in the Avenger tunnel. They had to send and receive Morse Code with a crude-type key from the air. "Kind of like

Figure 25 Main Gate Jacksonville NAS. Official Navy Photograph. Public Domain.
Post Card. Low Family Collection

sending code with a door knob," Andy recalled laughing.[7]

"They were also used as trainers for some of the new Annapolis graduates. "I wound up on that detail, and I hated it because I think I only had one or two of them who didn't throw up on my gun! The pilots took us up, and I would throw out a yellow dye marker that made a big yellow spot where it hit the ocean. Easy, right? Well, after three years of Annapolis, very few of them could fire the gun and hit the spot. Invariably they would fire 15 or 20 rounds at the marker, miss badly, and throw up. Growing impatient or desperate, Andy offered, "If you want, I'll do this for you. No one will know who fired the gun. Just use the intercom to tell the pilot to go around again," Winnegar instructed, pointing at the "relief tube" with a sly smile.

By the time he was 18 years old, Winnegar was in the Navy onboard the USS White Plains, steaming for parts unknown in the Central Pacific. A radio operator and bombardier/gunner on a TBM Avenger of the Composite Squadron VC-4, Winnegar flew with pilot Lt. Pat Owens and gunner Maurice Hie on strike missions armed with torpedoes, rockets, bombs, machine guns, and Uncle Lanty's fearless advice in his "back pocket." But first, Winnegar was headed across the country on a troop train to the West Coast.

---

[7] In spite of all of the focus on learning to send and receive messages in Morse Code in training, Winnegar never once used Morse Code in battle.

Chapter 4

COMPOSITE SQUADRON VC-4
STATESIDE – 1943 – 1944

In September 1943, the men who would eventually form
Composite Squadron VC-4 converged upon San Diego from every
region of the country. However, any thoughts of heading for the
beach were rudely interrupted as the men immediately received
orders to head to the Pacific Northwest.

NAS Sand Point – 5 September 1943

Their destination was Sand Point Naval Air station, overlooking the
northwest shore of Lake Washington. Established in 1929 on Puget
Sound, NAS Seattle at San Point is located a stone's throw (10 km)
from downtown Seattle. NAS Sand Point was widely considered the
"country club" of naval air stations, described as luxurious, offsetting
the terrible weather and limited flying time.

The camaraderie was high, time logged in the air was low, bull
sessions were many, and the cuisine and liquor at the BOQ[8] were the
best on the coast. The idea of forming a combat squadron from this

---

[8] BOQ – Bachelor Officers' Quarters

Figure 26 NAS Sand Point Seattle, WA. 1953. Public Domain. US National Archives.

group of men with limited flying time in old planes was novel and challenging.

On 2 September 1943, Lieutenant John Mayer of Omaha, Nebraska, Lieutenant Kurz, Lieutenant Palmer, Lieutenant Ferko, Lieutenant JG McLean, Lieutenant Atkinson, five chiefs, and 175 men arrived at Sand Point NAS. Lieutenant Flateboe, a Seattleite, also joined the squadron as executive officer. Flateboe's introduction to the squadron found him trying to tear the wings off his TBF Avenger in a neatly accomplished slow roll, but heaven help the wings.

Lieutenant CMDR George assumed command of the squadron with the unofficial order that no pilot

Figure 27 Coll "Red" McLean TBM Avenger Pilot

should fly with a hangover. The first weeks in October found the squadron growing rapidly with the arrival of Lieutenants Huser, Eli, Maloney, Wood, Laudenslager, Shields, Carson, Osborne, and Wooden.

Andy Winnegar arrived at Sand Point NAS after a miserable trip across the United States from Jacksonville, Florida. He spent the 1800-mile trip from Kansas City to Portland, Oregon, without a seat, standing day and night for over one week. During the second week, Andy met up with his pilot Pat Owens and

Figure 28 Fred E. Kurz FM-2 Wildcat Pilot

gunner Maurice Hie, men with whom he would soon go to war in the Pacific. Each of them had finished Operations training, and now they began the process of forming a TBM Avenger crew. Unfortunately, the rains set in by September, limiting flying out of NAS Sandpoint.

NAS Arlington – 23 September 1943

The squadron picked up and moved 40 miles up the Puget Sound to Arlington Naval auxiliary air station. Arlington, Washington, set amidst the fir trees and White Pines of the Evergreen Peninsula, was a scenic tour of duty. The rugged snow-covered Cascade mountains loomed in the background. Winnegar recalls that NAS Arlington was like "living off the grid." "We had to chase the deer off the runway to take off."

At Arlington, the squadron adopted a dog they named "Rover,"

*Figure 29 Whitehorse Mountain Cascade Mountain Range. Washington.
Jake-T3. CCA SA 3.0. Wikimedia Commons*

whose favorite pastime was to chase the milk truck that was the guys' transportation between the barracks and the airstrip. Rover quickly became a favorite of the squadron. Although otherwise lazy, Rover repeated this mad dash after the milk truck twenty to thirty times per day to the delight of the guys. This was the only time Rover would move, but boy did he run around trees, through the brush, and across the fields using secret shortcuts to meet the milk wagon as it pulled up to the field or barracks!

The peaceful countryside and community of 850 people contrasted with the raucous thundering F4F- 3 Wildcats and TBF Avengers that were constantly flat heading along its riverbeds, flying low over the treetops.

On their first familiarization flight, Pat, took Andy and Hie 300 miles east to see his hometown, Spokane, from the air. Unable to resist the temptation, they buzzed some dams and sawmills flying ten feet above the treetops.

Figure 30 Aerial view of downtown Arlington and the Stillaguamish River floodplain. Wikimedia Commons. Public Domain.

"Let's go buzz Main Street!" Pat suggested diving towards Downtown Spokane.

"Pat, what's that line of cars going down Mainstreet?" Andy asked. "Must be a parade."

"Oh my God! I forgot my father's friend's funeral is today," Pat exclaimed as he pulled the plane out of the dive and banked the TBM, making a climbing turn to the right away from the funeral procession.

The squadron's personnel roster was continually growing larger. Lieutenants Bear, Budget, JG McGaha, Strong, Wiley, and Koran supplemented the officer personnel.

Daily practice in aerial gunnery tactics, bombing and torpedo runs, and navigation kept the squadron busy as they learned the skills they needed to become a combat fighting unit. The importance of this training was not lost on the pilots and aircrew who would need these skills to stay alive. Simulating carrier take-offs and landings necessitated flying over, around, and between the outcroppings of the evergreen forest that surrounded every runway. Lieutenant Schroeder worked hard with the pilots alternating between being encouraging at times and screaming at others. When TBF Avenger pilot Carson found the trees a bit too close to the runway, he proceeded to clip eight feet off the top of the fir trees with his TBF Avenger. When Schroeder approached him, Rocky Carson explained in his Louisiana drawl, "It marks where to start my cross-wind leg."

Lt. Huser was flying the F4F Wildcat when he lost control of the plane while landing, resulting in a "ground loop." The plane dug a long furrow into the airstrip totaling the aircraft. Huser voluntarily kicked himself out of the fighter squadron, and they accepted him as a torpedo bomber pilot.

The rivalry between VC-4 and VC-3 squadrons was natural. With eighteen to twenty-four-year-old guys flying fast planes, shooting guns, and dropping bombs, there was a lot of testosterone in the air and in the officers' club. Russ Wood, a VC-4 Wildcat pilot, recalls, "We were nosier, drank more at the old club and were also shooting and bombing better and liked to think we had the edge on tactics and formation flying."

Simulated strafing and bombing runs on the neighboring Everett High School football stadium, and the local dairy farms were a favorite pastime of the VC-4 pilots. Flying 10,000 feet above Western Washington, the scenery below was endless green forests interrupted by farms as they headed back towards the base.

"Let's go and say good morning to "Bessie and her friends," Wood suggested.

"I'm in," Bear and Ferko replied.

They waited to hear from Carson. "Rocky, are you up for a little cow strafing fun?"

"Mooo! Too!" Rocky replied from his TBM Avenger.

"OK! Now that the Rock's on board, let's go, Wood laughed as he

Figure 31 Holstein Cows. Wikimedia Commons. CC-BY-2.0

put his plane into a steep dive aimed at the nearest Washington state dairy farm.

The three Wildcats and a single Avenger came screaming out of the clouds, headed for farmer John's herd of black and white Holstein cows.

The stampede was short-lived, the cows unharmed, and the guys were entertained until tomorrow when they would do it all over again.

"You know one of these days, Farmer John will be waiting for us with his shotgun," Ferko worried.

"That's why we use stealth tactics and never hit the same dairy twice in the same week."

"Personally, I think the cows enjoy a little stimulation," Bear laughed.

"They probably stand around all day chewing cud, wondering when their flyboys are coming for a visit," Wood laughed.

Not everything was fun and games for the navy aviators. The

deadly serious night flying took place over Seattle and Everett to avoid the trees and clouds enshrouding NAS Arlington. Flying at night was a whole different experience and a skill they would have to master to survive flying over enemy territory at night.

As the milder Fall weather gave way to the approaching winter, flying conditions worsened with frosty cold mornings and overcast skies.

Winnegar remembers Arlington as a "bitter cold and miserable" place. "They offered us coffee with a scoop of ice cream in it. It looked interesting, but it was too cold for geedunks." [9]

It was time to leave the Pacific Northwest to seek a warmer climate and better flying at their next station 1,400 miles to the south.

Russ Wood recalled, "The Arlington command was not in the least sorry to see us go. They helped us pack and load on the train. The dairy ranchers of that vicinity would once again get milk and cream instead of curds and whey." Rover was either smuggled on board or a stowaway. Either way, he made the trip south.

Holtville NAS – 24 November 1943

Located 125 miles east of San Diego, Holtville is in Imperial County, a stone's throw north of the US-Mexico border. The hot and arid climate was a welcome change from winter's cold and rainy weather in the Pacific Northwest. There were few people and absolutely no cows for the VC-4 squadron to pester.

When asked to describe Holtville, Winnegar replied smiling, "If they were going to

Figure 32 NAS Holtville, California Patch.
Low Family Collection.

---

[9] Geedunks is Navy slang for ice cream.

Figure 33 Holtville NAS. Public Domain. Wikipedia.

give the earth an enema. There was absolutely nothing to do. It was the opposite of Arlington. It never rained so you could fly every day. The sun was hot and there was cactus everywhere. We lived in Quonset huts with no air conditioning. On days off, our transportation into El Centro was sixteen-wheeler low boys pulled by a tractor. El Centro had one decent bar called "The Adobe" that the Marine SPs hit every hour on the hour, so you didn't want to drink too much, or you'd end up in the Marine brig.

The auxiliary naval air station was makeshift and spartan at best, but the concrete runway built into the prevailing wind was a pilot's dream. The long runway was certainly a far cry from the short carrier decks they would be landing on in a few short months.

"We started flying at 1600 and flew until almost daybreak," Andy recalled 80 years later. "We were bombing the Salton Sea with tons of 100-pound water-filled bombs at night. Sometimes we used parachute flares so we could see and colored water bombs when we bombed targets in the desert."

The goal of the squadron's training at Holtville was to master night flying. Flying at night in Holtville was unlike anything they had experienced so far. With no surrounding cities, it was a hell of a lot darker. Night formation flying, tactical bombing, and strafing were now second nature during the day. But, in the darkness of night, it was a totally different animal and kept the pilots and crew straining to the limits of their capabilities.

"It was crazy and hairy, flying in pitch-black conditions."

"On one of the blackest of nights, "Square Deal" McLean, out on a routine navigation flight, found himself alone and disoriented.

Figure 34 Curtis McGaha FM2 Wildcat Pilot VC-4. Courtesy of Andy Winnegar

Suddenly out of the dark sky came a voice, screaming as only a wounded eagle could or would, 'Dunlap Tower—Turn on your lights.' The squadron gave McLean very little opportunity to pass it off lightly. Nor did McLean much give a damn, once he was home," Russ Wood recalled.

Night bombing with the aid of parachute flares was a novel experience that the men came to enjoy. Other stories from VC-4's time at Holtville illustrate the dangers of "dropping in" or joining up with another plane and following them blindly.

One night, Fred "The Hot" Kurz, who always wanted to join up, dropped in on "Slim" McGaha.

Figure 35 Fred E Kurz FM-2 Wildcat Pilot VC-4 Courtesy of Andy Winnegar

Minutes later, Fred found to his horror that while flying wing on "Mac," his wing light was reflecting on the ripples of the Mojave sand dunes! In the darkness, he had followed Mac down to a few feet above the deck. Later, Fred's Face was practically as red as his port wing light in the ready room. His face puffed up, his eyes flashed sparks, he stuttered, stammered, and squirmed, then he really exploded. "I know I shouldn't have followed you; my light was f-f-flashing on the sand, flashing on the sand, right in my face! Holy Christ, Mac! Right in my face, my wing light, sand, shouldn't have done sand! Sand! In my face!" Quietly, Fred shut down, shaking his head as the gang in the ready room wiped away tears of laughter. – Russ Wood

On their days off, Palm Springs was the favorite destination for the pilots. They flew a TBM to Palm Springs with six pilots in the back. After a day and night of drinking and carousing in Palm Springs, seven hungover pilots tried the pure oxygen method of combating acute alcoholism, sucking on a face mask in the aft-end of a TBM. Each pilot, in turn, remarked on the extraordinary recuperative power of pure oxygen. But unfortunately, someone later discovered that the oxygen canister hadn't been activated.

In Holtville, the squadron met its new executive officer. Lt. E. R. Fickenscher. His first duty in the squadron was to discipline Bear and Ferko, placing them in "hack" for ten days. Both pilots considered this a small price to pay for 14 hours extra leave in Palm Springs

As their night training in Holtville came to an end, the men of squadron VC-4 bonded more closely and prepared to get the job done the US Navy way. As they prepared for the move to Los Alamitos, their number increased by one with the addition of Ens. Pool.

LOS ALAMITOS NAS - 9 December 1943

Winnegar recalled that the move from Holtville to Los Alamitos was "like going from Hell to Heaven! Los Alamitos was a beautiful place." Located in Los Angeles, Los Alamitos NAS was overflowing with naval aviators. Three other composite squadrons shared the

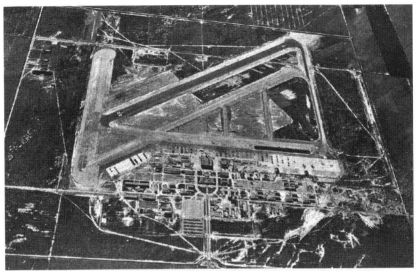

Figure 36 Los Alamitos NAS. 1940. Public Domain. Wikimedia Commons

airbase with VC-4. Although the air station was a bit crowded, the advantages of built-in competition became obvious as squadrons vied for the top spot in gunnery, bombing, and formation flying. Immediately the squadron's gunnery scores showed improvement, and all the crews felt pride when comparing their hits with the other air groups

The order of the day was flying, gunnery, bombing, tactics, coordinated attacks, and then more bombing, gunnery, and tactics. The Navy believed in the old adage that repetition breeds perfection. The weather at Los Alamitos was as

Figure 37 WWII F8F bearcat fighter at Los Alamitos Air Station. US Navy photograph.

44

Figure 38 Cyclone Racer roller coaster at the Pike in Long Beach, Post Card. Low Family Collection.

predictable, as was the lack of rain. Mornings were foggy until 1000 and afternoons hazy after 1600, leaving a four-hour window for the best flying.

At Los Alamitos, "Dunk" Maloney experienced the first of his air-sea rescues with an unplanned water landing. On a routine gunnery training flight between Catalina Island and the Mainland, 'Dunk's" engine quit on him, necessitating a sea rescue. Unfortunately, this experience would not be the last time "Dunk" ditched in the water while in training.

The squadron found the social life around Los Alamitos to their liking. Long Beach, with a reputation as a great Liberty Town, was just up the road. One of Andy's favorite destinations was the Cyclone Racer roller coaster at the Pike along the Long Beach Boardwalk, a short bus ride from the base. Los Angeles and the glamour and glitz of Hollywood were also easily reached on a day off.

Christmas holidays were spent at Los Alamitos. Although a few of the squadron was able to go home for the holidays, most men of VC-4 spent their Christmas holidays in Palm Springs, Lake Arrowhead, Hollywood, and the Biltmore Hotel.

On New Year's Eve day, Andy Winnegar, and three other radiomen of VC-4, Howard Davis, Bob Egan,[10] and Steve Walley, had big plans, including dinner and New Year's Eve Party at the Hollywood Canteen. To get there from Los Alamitos just required a hitchhiker's thumb and four of America's finest in uniform. The thirty-four-mile trip north into Hollywood was a short drive, especially for the first car that stopped for the four sailors.

Figure 39 Andrew J. Winnegar Thomasville, Missouri Hight School Yearbook. Courtesy of Andy Winnegar

A black Lincoln four-passenger sedan with jump seats pulled up, the window rolled down, and the driver asked, "You boys need a lift? Where are you headed?"

"The Hollywood Canteen," Andy replied.

"Well, hop on in. Mr. Grant gave me instructions to never pass up a soldier in need of a ride."

"Do you mean Cary Grant, the actor," Egan asked in disbelief.

"Of course. I am Mr. Grant's driver," he replied as the car sped up, heading for Hollywood.

Figure 40 Steve Walley. High School Yearbook photo. Albany New York.

---

[10] Bob Egan of Plattsburg New York was injured on 21 October 1944 when Lt Rox's TBM was struck by shrapnel. Bob's brother Thomas, also a Radio operator, was killed 8 months later in the Philippines on 16 June 1945.

Figure 41 The Hollywood Canteen founded by John Garfield, Bette Davis, and Jules C. Stein operated at 1451 Cahuenga Boulevard in the Los Angeles, California, neighborhood of Hollywood between October 3, 1942, and November 22, 1945, as a club offering free food, dancing and entertainment for servicemen on their way overseas.

"Enjoy yourselves, boys. You'll love the entertainment and the price of admission."

"Thank you, and say hello to Mr. Grant," the guys waved, now standing in front of the famous Hollywood Canteen on Cahuenga Boulevard.

A smiling hostess greeted Winnegar, Davis, Egan, and Walley in dress whites.

"Right this way, men."

"How much is admission?" Walley asked.

"With your nicely pressed uniforms, admission and the food and drinks are free," she beamed.

The place was packed with soldiers, sailors, and leathernecks in dress uniforms. But it was the sea of movie stars and starlets that grabbed the boys' attention. It was Hollywood at its finest. They were all volunteers out in full force to serve and entertain their men in uniform

Figure 42 Marlene Dietrich and Rita Hayworth serve food to soldiers at the Hollywood Canteen in 1942. Library of Congress. Wikipedia. Public Domain

"Can you see who's serving at the counter?" Egan asked. "It's Marlene Dietrich and Rita Hayworth!" he gushed.

The hostess showed the four to their table near the stage. Their waitress was none other than Lena Horne, the singer and actress.

"How are you boys today?" she smiled.

"Ms. Horne, I'm a huge fan," Davis gushed.

"We all love your movies, and the way you sing "Stormy Weather, is the best," Egan added.

"Well, the orchestra is starting up. How are you boys at dancing?"

The four sailors hesitated.

"Don't be shy. I won't bite."

"I would love to dance with you, Ms. Horne," Andy replied, standing and taking her hand.

Lena Horne graciously danced with all four men, asking them about their families back home."

"Where are you from, Andy?"

"I'm originally from Thomasville, Missouri, and have also lived in

Albuquerque, New Mexico."

"You're a good dancer, Andy. You seem very athletic."

"Well, I did some Golden Glove boxing, but that's more bobbing and weaving than waltzing."

"Well, you are graceful, Andy. Any girl would be lucky to have you as her dance partner."

All the guys were captivated by Lena Horne, who autographed whatever napkin or menu they could produce.

"Enjoy your meal, boys, and make sure you stay for the New Year's Eve Party. It will be a special celebration for some very special soldiers and sailors."

Figure 43 Lena Horne Lena Mary Calhoun Horne was an American dancer, actress, Grammy-winning singer, and civil rights activist. Horne's career spanned over 70 years, appearing in film, television, and theater. Wikipedia. Public Domain.

The next day the six sailors were among the 68,000 persons to attend the Rose Bowl Game in Pasadena between the USC Trojans and the Washington State Huskies. Unfortunately, USC won in a lopsided contest 29-0. The seats weren't the best, but the guys enjoyed the afternoon immensely and even ran into Rocky Carson taking in the game, eating a hot dog while munching on pink popcorn, and downing it all with a coke. Somehow, even in a crowd of 68,000, it was hard to miss Rocky.

In Los Alamitos, the squadron was introduced to the brand-new

Figure 44 Hollywood Canteen
New Year's 1944. Public
Domain

FM-2 Wildcat but had little chance to see what she could do in flight.

That would come later. For now, VC-4 was off to their next destination, Santa Rosa NAS and the Valley of the Moon.[11]

NALF Santa Rosa 14 January 1944[12]

Heading north to the Bay Area and Marin County, VC-4 arrived with brand new planes without identifying modex numbers. [13] The skipper advised, "If you are going to buzz anything, now is the time to do it." Well, the pilots and aircrew did not have to be invited to the party twice.

They proceeded to buzz the entire Santa Rosa Valley, Marin

[11] Sonoma or the "Valley of the Moon" is the valley where the early settlers had seen multiple moons appearing in one night, it is also known as the birthplace of the California wine industry.
[12] (Naval Auxiliary Landing) NALF
[13] A modex is a number that is part of the Aircraft Visual Identification System

Figure 45 Golden Gate Bridge from the Golden Gate National Recreation Area. National Park Service. Public Domain

County, and every landmark in San Francisco, including the iconic Golden Gate Bridge.

Lt "Pierre" Ferko led a party flight over his mom's house in South San Francisco after calling her so she would be expecting the fly-over. Recognizing the family home on Grand Ave from the air was difficult. Finally, Ferko spotted the cross street and his home.

"There they are!" Ferko shouted. "See! That's my mom, Katie, and my kid brother, Stephen, waving!"

The Wildcats circled, buzzing the neighborhood, and then rocked their wings over Grand Ave as they pulled up into a steep climb, saluting "Lucky Pierre" Ferko's family. To the guys' delight, the local newspaper blamed the squadron of P-39s stationed at the nearby San Francisco airport.

Some buzzing misadventures had

Figure 46 Leo M. Ferko FM-2 Wildcat pilot, VC-4. Courtesy of Andy Winnegar.

Figure 47 Aerial View of Monterey Bay and Santa Cruz. Public Creative Commons Attribution-Share Alike 3.0 Unported license. Wikipedia.

untoward consequences. While over the Monterey Bay, Owens and his crew were admiring the scenery.

"Hey, that's where Steinbeck wrote "Tortilla Flat," Andy shouted.

"I'm more interested in those tourist sailboats," Pat replied as he put the TBM into a dive intent upon buzzing boats in the bay. After doing a close fly-by of a tourist boat, he flew past a small sailboat.

As they roared past the sailboat, Andy looked back, and the little boat's sail was in the water.

"Oh no! We capsized that guy's boat," Andy yelled.

"Oh crap! We didn't want to do that!" Pat said. "We just wanted to give the guy a thrill, not capsize him."

They circled and saw other boats coming to his aid.

"Well, he'll be OK, but he's going to have some story to tell!"

Serious flying also occurred at Santa Rosa in the form of carrier qualifications. Landing on a carrier is universally regarded as the most challenging part of Navy flight training that can strike fear into the heart of the most stoic aviator.

For the VC-4 squadron, carrier qualification occurred aboard the USS Copahee. Unfortunately, what would have been a challenging experience was turned into a nail-biting drama by the adverse weather conditions off the California coast.

Wood recalls, "The pitching and tossing deck was responsible for a few carrier crashes and landings in the catwalk. However, it was a good experience and as a result found everyone working that much harder."

For many of the aircrew and pilots, dinner that night was off base in Santa Rosa at "Lena's" or the "Twin Dragon." Andy, Hie, and Fuller opted for Chinese at the "Twin Dragon" restaurant, where the guys feasted on the

Figure 48 Lena's Restaurant Santa Rosa, California. Post Card Public Domain. Low Family Collection.

house specialty dish Mango Chicken with Sweet and Sour Pork, Egg Foo Young, and Lo Mein Noodles.

The pilots dined at Lena's Buon Gusto, the finest nightclub restaurant in Northern California. Owned the Battaglia family, Lena's specialized in Italian food prepared in a unique manner.

Trips into The City by the Bay were a highlight of the men's stay in Santa Rosa. The 60-mile drive south on US 101 was almost as gorgeous as the view from the air. Crossing over the spectacular Golden Gate Bridge added to the excitement of leave in one of the most beautiful cities in the world.

The bus heading from Santa Rosa NALF to San Francisco transported the entire VC-4 aircrew. Their destination was the Grant Hotel in downtown San Francisco where they had rented out an entire floor of the hotel. The anticipation of four days' leave in the "City by the Bay" had been building for days. For some, this would be four days of smoking cigars, drinking, shows, and women!

Located two minutes from Union Square at 753

Figure 49 Grant Hotel 753 Bush Street. San Francisco, CA.

Bush Street, the Grant Hotel is one of San Francisco's historic hotels built-in 1910. The bar downstairs off the lobby was a popular meeting place. Most of the guys wanted to get out and experience The City.

Come on. Andy, put your book down. Let's look for some action," Hie encouraged his friend.

"OK! My guide book says to head towards Union Square."

"Where's that?" Walley asked.

"Follow me, boys. It's this way, and then we go south on Powell for one block," Andy instructed, heading up Bush Street.

At Union Square, Andy paused. "That tall thing is the Dewey Monument. Union Square is the heartbeat of San Francisco."

"Sheesh, Winnegar! We don't want to look at some old monument. We want strippers!" Hie sputtered.

"I want to see a cabaret show. You know, with a little culture."

*Figure 50 Persian Room Sir Francis Drake Hotel San Francisco. Post Card.
Low Family Collection*

Walley added, sounding a bit more refined.

"Yeah. With scantily clad women!" Hie interjected.

"OK. How's this? The 'Persian Room' marque says 'Strippers and Belly Dancers.' Is that enough culture for you two?" Andy laughed.

The guys paid the cover charge, found a table, and ordered drinks all around.

"Wow! Will you look at the dame? Walley gushed. "I have never seen a woman that flexible."

A female contortionist was lying on her stomach, extending her back and placing her head between her two feet, looking backward at the audience.

Wally whistled and smiled at the performer, who returned his smile.

Later that evening, the performer came up to their table and began chatting with Steve.

"Hello, sailor. My name is Grace. You're cute!"

Walley who was not known as a ladies' man, really hit it off with Grace, who spent the rest of the day with the trio.

"Let's go back to the bar and get drinks with Grace," Walley suggested.

After a few rounds, Andy made a crack about her flexibility

"Hey, Grace. Can you stick your head up where the sun doesn't shine?"

Well, petite Grace was much feistier than they guys expected.

"Drop dead, you curly-headed SOB!"

Changing the subject to defuse the tension, Steve suggested, "Let's go down to Fisherman's Wharf for seafood.

Eating was a favorite pastime, so it did not require twisting anyone's arm.

The Powell and Hyde Street Cable Car got them close to the Fisherman's Wharf, and then they walked the rest of the way in the late afternoon.

As they strolled along Fisherman's Wharf, the squawking sea gulls looking for a handout greeted the sailors and their dates.

"Look at those big tanks full of lobsters and crabs," Hie exclaimed.

"Let's get a crab and some sourdough bread and a bottle of wine," Walley suggested.

Figure 51 Crab vendor San Francisco Fisherman's Wharf 1940s. Post Card. Low Family Collection.

"Perfect!"

Andy picked out two crabs. The vendor reached in, grabbed the crabs, and plunked them into a huge metal vat of boiling water.

"Ouch! That's gotta hurt," Hie squirmed.

"We check the color to see when the crabs are cooked to perfection," the vendor explained for the hundredth time that day.

"OK! They're ready!" The vendor pulled out the crabs and proceeded to crack and partially shell them. He then wrapped the crabs in white paper, taped it up, and handed the packages to Winnegar.

"That will be two dollars! You can get the sour sourdough bread at the next stall and a bottle of wine and some cheese in that shop. Get the Boudin sourdough."[14]

They sat on the dock, enjoying the savory crab, the wonderful Boudin sourdough bread, cheddar cheese, and cheap chianti wine, surrounded by dozens of fishing boats.

Figure 52 Fisherman's Wharf San Francisco. Post Card.
Low Family Collection

---

[14] Boudin Bakery is based in San Francisco, California, famous for its sourdough bread. Founded in 1849, the bakery is recognized as the "oldest continually operating business in San Francisco.

The sounds of the foghorn in the distance set the mood with the Golden Gate Bridge partially covered by billowing clouds rolling in from the ocean. The last glimmering rays of sunshine reflected off the bridge's orange stanchions. The evening was perfect for the three friends plus one.

"Man! Let's never leave this place," Andy murmured, enjoying the last of the wine and cheese.

"Amen to that," Hie agreed as the sun set over the bay.

"Let's go bowling," Walley suggested.

A few days later, back at the base, Andy was working on the cockpit radio when Lt Russ Wood, the Personnel Officer, stopped by.

"Hey, Winnegar. How are you doing? Are you fixing to fly that TBM?" Wood laughed

"You know, I did apply to flight school, and I still want to fly," Andy replied.

"Are you old enough?"

"Sure. I'm 17 years old. They're taking 17-year-old pilot trainees."

"Well, what happened when you applied before?"

"I flunked the eye exam."

"Who gave you that exam? A doctor?"

"No. It was just some 3rd class Pharmacist's Mate."

"That's bullshit, Winnegar. He probably just took one look at you and decided you weren't pilot material."

"Well, I still want to fly."

"Come by my office, and let's have you make an application for Pilot Training. If your application is accepted, Dr. Donelson can give you a physical and the battery of tests they'll require." [15]

---

[15] Dr. Donelson gave Andy Winnegar his physical exam after D-Day on Saipan 15 June 1944. The battery of tests was sent to Donelson who administered the almost weekly tests while on board the USS White Plains in July-September. The tests included Federal Air Regulations, physics, mathematics, psychological tests.

"Thanks, Lieutenant."

"You'd make a good pilot, Winnegar. Pat says you're smart as a whip and fearless. That would put you ahead of half the pilots in the squadron."

Andy smiled and got back to work on the radio. Lt. Wood had, in that moment, rekindled his dream of being a Navy pilot. Things were looking up.

Alameda NAS – 27 February 1944

The one-week stop at Alameda NAS involved sailing beneath both the Golden Gate Bridge and the Bay Bridge to reach Alameda, an island in San Francisco Bay. Trips through the Posey Tunnel took the men under the San Antonio Creek to Oakland just north of Alameda and dumped them off in the middle of Oakland's Chinatown.

Figure 53 US Aircraft Carrier passing beneath the Golden Gate Bridge

"Let's go get some dim sum for lunch," Andy suggested.

"Dim what?" Walley asked

"Dim sum. You know pork buns or cha siu bow and shrimp rolls or *ha gow*, and *siu mai* or pork balls. It's delicious!

Figure 54 Chinese Dim Sum

"When did you learn to speak Chinese?"

"It's Cantonese, and I speak lots of languages, especially when we're talking about food," Andy laughed.

"Let's try this dim sum joint," Andy suggested.

"Ok, but you have to order," Hie said.

"No problem."

The dim sum lunch was tasty and exotic for the VC-4 crewmen.

"Man, we gotta do this again soon. That food was delicious, and it only cost a couple of dollars," Walley said, licking his fingers while scrounging through the pink box, looking for more hidden treats.

"My guidebook hasn't let us down yet," Andy added.

The VC-4 squadron continued to grow with the arrival of Ens. Byrd, Dennis, and Billinghurst.

NAS San Diego North Island – 5 March 1944

On North Island, the aircrew lived in two Quonset huts positioned on the beach on San Diego Bay with 20 men per hut. When you went out the front door, there was just nothing but sand all the way down to the water.

"On Easter, we went swimming in that bay. It was really cold!" Andy recalled. "A lot of guys turned back, but growing up in Missouri, I was used to the cold."

On 8 March 1944, Composite Squadron VC-4 came aboard the USS White Plains for the first time. For the free-flying aircrew, life onboard the CVE carrier was stifling.

"It was crowded, hot, and I hated the smell when they burned out the stacks with sulfur."

The squadron practiced carrier landings on different CVE carriers during the next two months, always returning to North Island NAS. The White Plains was in dry dock during this time, having the barnacles scraped off her hull.

"My number one goal was to avoid barnacle duty!" Winnegar confided. "That looked like miserable work."

Figure 55 Andy Winnegar and Cody in doorway of Quonset Hut at North Island NAS San Diego 1944.

While at North Island, the command of the squadron changed hands. With the loss of their skipper, Lieut. Comdr. Speake, who was promoted to Air Officer of the U.S.S. MAKIN ISLAND, Lieut. Evins assumed command of the Squadron, previously he had been executive officer of VF 21.

The VC-4 squadron performed the shake-down of the U.S.S. SAGINAW BAY on its maiden flight operations. Leading from the front, the new Skipper, Lieutenant Evins was the first to land aboard the Saginaw Bay. It was also his first landing aboard a carrier and was perfectly executed.

The VC-4 pilots watched their new Skipper closely and agreed that

Figure 56 Maurice "Hie" Hie, Bill "Smiley" Lemon, Dewey "Web" Weber, HR "Hos" Ross, RW "Dick" Borcher at the VC-4 Party held at The Little Club in the Grant Hotel, San Diego, California. 1944. Courtesy of Chrissy Hie and Christopher Dean.

Lt Evins was a pilot's pilot and a leader of men. Flying with him was going to be alright!

VC-4 came aboard the USS White Plains on 22 April 1944 for the last time before she shipped out two days later. The VC-4 squadron included 33 officers, 38 enlisted men, and a maintenance crew of 160 men, who were transferred to the ship's company. Their next stop was Pearl Harbor. The war in the Pacific was calling, and things were heating up as the ship's crew, and Composite Squadron VC-4 prepared to go to war.

Chapter 5

USS WHITE PLAINS STATESIDE & SHAKEDOWN CRUISE – 1944

T he USS White Plains was a Casablanca class escort carrier. These small aircraft carriers were by far the most numerous United States carrier built during World War II, with escort carriers accounting for an astounding 122 out of a total of 151 American carriers. These small escort carriers were variously referred to as "baby flat tops," "jeep carriers," and "Woolworth carriers." The CVE designation officially stood for "carrier vessel escorts," although some preferred the "tongue-in-cheek" name "combustible, vulnerable, and expendable."[16]

The USS White Plains was laid down at the Kaiser shipyards in Vancouver, Washington, on 11 February 1943 and was launched into the Columbia River just six months later on 27 November 1943, the 12th aircraft carrier completed by Kaiser. Although their fates were not yet bound, at that moment, the men and planes of VC-4 were training at Arlington NAS, only 200 miles to the north. The ship's

---

[16] Fifty Casablanca Class escort carriers were laid down, launched, and commissioned in less than two years during 1942-1944.

Figure 57 5-cylinder Uniflow steam engine. Thinktank Birmingham Science Center. Public Domain CC BY-SA 4.0 Wiki

connection to the Washington state area was evident in her ship's crew and aircrew, many of whom were from Washington state. Displacing 10,400 tons with a 512-foot length, she was a fraction of the size of the later Midway Class carriers, which had a displacement of 45,000 tons and 968-foot length.

Two five-cylinder reciprocating Skinner Uniflow engines, powered by four oil-burning × 285 psi boilers, drove two shafts and two propellers with 9,000 hp. With a maximum speed of 19.3 knots (35.7 km/h), the White Plains had a range of 10,240 nm (18,960 km) @ 15 km (28 km/h). The White Plains was lightly armored with a single 5" L/38 gun, sixteen 40mm guns, and twenty 20-mm antiaircraft guns. She carried 28 planes and a crew of 860 men.

Despite her small size, the White Plains earned five battle stars during World War II and the Presidential Unit Citation for her part in the Battle off Samar. This is her story and the story of the men of Composite Squadron VC-4 who flew off her flight deck during World War II.

Figure 58 USS White Plains ship's crew on the flight deck. US Navy Photograph.

The USS White Plains was delivered to the Navy on 15 November 1943 at Astoria, Oregon, and commissioned that same day, with Captain Oscar A. Weller in command. She began shakedown training on 8 December 1943. After her initial cruise, the warship entered San Diego on 21 December.

On 29 December, the White Plains returned to sea on her first cruise, in which she ferried fresh planes and soldiers to the front and returned with damaged aircraft and wounded soldiers. She was bound for Oahu carrying forty planes and 333 Marines bound for Kiribati in the Gilbert Islands. The White Plains stopped at Pearl Harbor, where she picked up 39 more Corsair planes and 385 Marines. The White Plains arrived at Tarawa Atoll[17] early on 14 January 1944. The situation on the flight deck was tense as neither the Marine pilots nor the White Plains' crew had previously performed a catapult launch.

Nevertheless, the first of 36 Corsairs to fly off the White Plains soared aloft at 0829 on the 14th, marking the ship's first

---

[17] Tarawa is in the Gilbert Islands.

catapult launches. Some 22 more planes flew from the ship in the following 40 minutes, and thirteen more shortly afterward. On 16 January, the White Plains used its arresting gear for the first time as 34 F6F Hellcats of the VF-1 Fighting Squadron from the Tarawa Garrison landed on the flight deck. The White Plains headed back to Pearl Harbor with the planes and 500 battle-weary and wounded soldiers, arriving six days later. They passed 100 ships headed for the impending Marshall Islands campaign on that trip. Following a six-day turnaround in Oahu, on 28 January 1943, the White Plains next headed for the Central Pacific to provide aircraft logistics support for the Marshall Islands Operation Flintlock. The United States carriers in this campaign needed replacement planes. So, the deck crew crammed 70 replacement aircraft onto the White Plains, along with pilots and the mail, arriving at the Majuro Atoll on 4 February and Kwajalein the next day. The White Plains transferred the aircraft by

Figure 59 USS White Plains transporting aircraft.US Navy Photograph.

flight and barge to the carriers USS Intrepid, Corregidor, Coral Sea, Manila Bay, Belleau Wood, Enterprise, and Nassau.

However, the action in the Marshall Islands was essentially over before they arrived. The Americans occupied the undefended Majuro Atoll in the Marshall Islands, and the Japanese garrison at Kwajalein Atoll had been all but subdued.

There was some excitement on the White Plains while in the Marshall Islands. Radarman Don Crounse recalls, "At 2130 on 7 February, we were anchored off Roi Island,[18] and we had an alert and manned general quarters. Planes came within 20 miles and then went out. We lost contact at 38 miles. They were believed to be torpedo planes."

Figure 60 Warrant Officers on the deck of the USS White Plains (CVE 66), 1943. Front Row: Meske- Bosin; Story- Electrician; De Franco- Machinist; Young-Carpenter; Risley- Chief Pay Clerk. Back Row: Brisson- Chief Gunner; Riggs-Ship's Clerk; Echant- Radio Electr

---

[18] Roi-Namur Island is in the north part of Kwajalein Atoll in the Marshall Islands.

On 13 February, accompanied by two Destroyer Escorts, the White Plains passed into the lagoon at Makin Island in the Gilberts, where they picked up 260 army aviation engineers. These men had taken part in the invasion of Makin Island 20-23 November 1943 and since then had built Starmann Field out of the dense coconut-tree-covered jungle. Loren Low and Fred Kossow of the 804th Aviation Engineers boarded the White Plains, glad to be headed back to Pearl Harbor and Schofield Barracks after months of jungle living.[19] The threat of attack by Japanese submarines was ever-present. On 14 February, the DE USS Reynolds made a sound contact at 600 yards and dropped six ash cans.[20] At about the same time, the White Plains also made contact with a surfaced submarine without incident. The White Plains

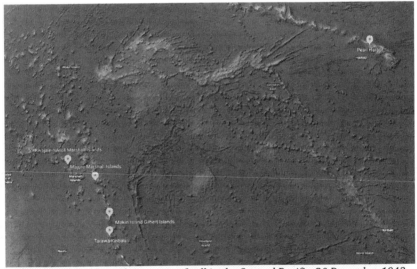

Figure 61 USS White Plains ports of call in the Central Pacific. 30 December 1943 through 23 February 1944. Google Earth

---

[19] The White Plains also picked up 30 USAAF Bell P-39 *Aircobras* for delivery to Tarawa on the way back to Pearl Harbor.
[20] Ash Can is common term for the 300-pound KM 6 depth charge.

stopped briefly at Oahu, arriving a day late on 23 February due to engine trouble. She picked up 199 more passengers and an assortment of planes with poetic names like Hellcats, PB-Y Catalinas, a J2F Duck, and a Piper Grasshopper before continuing toward the West Coast on 26 February. She passed under the Golden Gate Bridge on 3 March, arriving at Alameda NAS on San Francisco Bay. The USS White Plains sailed over 26,000 km or 16,000 miles (14,000 nm) in this initial two-month cruise. The White Plains did not see any action on this deployment, but that was about to change

While off the West Coast, the White Plains conducted operational training for her own ship's company and carrier qualifications for three air squadrons between 19 March and 26 March.[21] For the most

Figure 62 USS White Plains' first carrier landings included this off-center landing on the flight deck 16 January 1944. Sailors standing of the starboard wing are attempting to shift the weight of the plane in a precarious position. Public Doman

---

[21] Air operations with qualification training for VC-68, VD-11, and VB-20.

part, the new pilots accomplished the carrier landings without incident, but there were some mishaps and close calls as expected. Overall, the White Plains conducted 182 successful launchings and landings, with four minor accidents.

Finally, on 8 March, the White Plains' permanently assigned air unit, Composite Squadron 4 (VC-4), composed of 16 FM-2 Wildcat fighters and 12 TBM Avenger torpedo planes, came aboard for the first time. FM-2 Wildcat pilot, Russ Wood, recalls mutual satisfaction when the squadron and ships' officers met for the first time at a party in San Diego at the U.S. Grant Hotel on 19 April 1944. "From the outset, the VC-4 Squadron was looked upon as the ship's main batteries, while the CVE would be home to the pilots for at least six months. " [22]

Figure 63 USS White Plains (CVE-66) at San Diego, 8 March 1944, with Wildcat fighters and Avenger torpedo bombers on her deck. She is followed by a Fletcher-class destroyer in the pattern camouflage widely used in the Pacific during 1944.

---

[22] Russ Wood. Memoir of Battle – VC-4. Scrapbook. US Navy 1945.

Chapter 6

WHITE PLAINS AND VC-4 SET SAIL FOR THE PACIFIC WAR – APRIL 1944

I n April 1944, the sailors and aviators of the USS White Plains set sail for their first active engagement. The White Plains departed the West Coast from the San Diego North Island NAS on 24 April, pulling up the gangplank at 0900. On board were VC-4's 33 officers and 38 enlisted aircrew men as the USS White Plains sailed past Point Loma.

Figure 64 USS White Plains CVE-66.US Navy Photograph.

The aviators and ground crew had prepared the Composite Squadron's Four (VC-4) twelve Grumman FM-2 Wildcat Fighters and eight TBM Avenger Torpedo Bombers for the voyage.[23] The pilots and crew, including Pat Owens, Andrew J. Winnegar, and Maurice Hie, were preparing for their first war-time action.

Also, on board the USS White Plains was the Marine's VMO-4 observation squadron, under the command of Captain Nathan D. Blaha. In preparation, they boxed and placed their eight Stinson OY-1 observation planes into wooden crates. The Marine observers of VMO-4, including Leonard Wollman, Grady Gatlin, Thomas Rozga, George Hooper, and James Motley, loaded their small crated planes onboard the USS White Plains. While the Navy called them the "Cricket Circuit," a reference to their tiny OY-1 Stinsons, their job was deadly serious. These small fabric-covered planes and their pilots and observers would soon become the eyes and ears of the US Marine Corps' commanding officer during invasions of multiple Pacific islands. Their Marine brothers landing on Saipan, Tinian, and Iwo Jima would depend on their spotting and neutralizing the enemy.

Figure 65 Henry Grady Gatlin 1942 Yearbook Photo.

Marine OY-1 pilot, Thomas Rozga, recalled, "I have to admit that the first time I saw this airplane, I scratched my head and wondered out loud, 'We're flying these in combat?' ...the OY-1 looked like a toy model. I was disappointed, to say the least until I actually flew it. I quickly learned why the OY-1 was the obvious choice for battlefield missions. You could stall it, spin it, loop it, and land it in a few hundred

---

[23] Initially, twelve FM-2 Wildcat and eight TBM Avengers were loaded. At Eniwetok the squadron aircraft was increased to 16 FM-2 Wildcats, three TBF and nine TBM Avengers.

feet. It wasn't going to set any speed records, but boy oh boy, was that little Stinson maneuverable."[24]

The excitement in the air was palpable. Winnegar entered in his journal, "We are on our way to Pearl Harbor with 422 Marines and a load of SB2Cs, SBDs, TBMs, F6Fs, and FM2s. [25] We will let the Marines and all except our squadron planes off at Pearl Harbor. Most of us are green, with from six months to two years in the Navy. Flight crewmen all have at least 18 months of service, but only two of us have seen action."[26]

The next morning, Andy Winnegar, Maurice Hie, and Steve Walley of VC-4 were on the flight deck getting some air after a rough first night at sea. The small CVE carrier with excess topweight pitched and rolled mercilessly in a storm.

Figure 66 In April 1944, the sailors and aviators of the USS White Plains set sail for their first active engagement, departing the West Coast from the San Diego North Island NAS on 24 April, pulling up the gangplank at 0900. On board were VC-4's FM-2 Wildcats and TBM Avengers.

---

[24] Thomas P. Busha Wings of War. Zenith Press 2015.
[25] SB2C Helldiver dive bomber, SBD Dauntless scout plane, TBM Avenger, F6F- Hellcat fighter, FM2-Wildcat.
[26] Andrew J Winnegar journal of WWII experiences in the Pacific.

Figure 67 CVE 57 rolling heavy seas. The small escort carriers with excess.

"I think the helmsman was steering us into every storm he could find," Hie complained. "it was like trying to sleep on the Cyclone Racer roller coaster!"

Andy noted, looking at the ship's edge, "I think some of our Marine brothers are a little green this morning."

"They'd better puke over the side of the ship and not mess up the flight deck and our planes," Hie said.

"No green eggs for those leathernecks this morning," Steve laughed.

A few minutes later, the anti-aircraft guns saluted the crisp morning air with gunnery practice on the five-inch gun and the Oerlikon 20-mm and Bofors 40-mm guns. Gunnery Officer, Lt. JB. Roper was in charge. The noise was deafening as the five-inch gun shook the White Plains when she fired her shells.

Steve observed, "Well, I'll give them this. Those gunners are enthusiastic, but they're not very good."

"Give them time. We're all pretty green out here," Andy replied.

Figure 68 Ship's steward's mates man a 20-mm gun. 1941-45 Public Domain. NARA Wikimedia Commons.

"Hey, the mess cooks look pretty good on the 20-mm guns," Maurice yelled.

"Well, let them practice all they want because when the Zeros and Jap Dive Bombers start coming at us, I want those guys locked, loaded, and ready to fight!" Andy said.

The next day, the aircrew cleaned all of the aircraft machine guns, a task that was second nature to the Navy aircrew. The TBM Avenger had two wing-mounted .50 caliber guns, a turret-mounted .50 caliber gun, and a .30 caliber stinger in the tunnel. Andy's pride and joy was the stinger. He spent hours cleaning, disassembling, and reassembling his .30 caliber machine gun.

Today, the aircrews were to be issued their Smith and Wesson .38 caliber sidearms. Instead, Captain Weller made an announcement over the ship's PA system.

"Attention. Someone has stolen nine .38 caliber revolvers that were to be issued to the aircrew. Until that person steps forward and returns these weapons, all shore leave is indefinitely canceled. Do I make myself clear?"

The groans amongst the crew were heard and felt throughout the White Plains.

The next day, two of the missing revolvers showed up in the ammunition belting room. Seven were still outstanding, and shore leave was still canceled.

At mess that afternoon, Bob Fuller asked, "Where do you think we're headed, Andy?"

"Your guess is as good as mine. I've heard a dozen rumors. One is that we will remain in Pearl Harbor for a few months; another is that we're going to be stationed on an island. Most of this is wishful thinking or bullshit."

"I like the tropical island rumor," Fuller replied.

"I just want to fire my .30 caliber gun at some bad guys!" Andy confessed.

The aircrews were not too good at responding to the ship's readiness drills. They all slept through the first Battle Stations drill and didn't see what all the fuss was about when they finally made it up on deck. The next day they were supposed to muster on the flight deck for general quarters and on the fantail for abandon ship drill. Instead, three of them mustered on the flight deck for both.

"Winnegar! Where's the rest of your squadron!"

"Don't know, sir, but we're here."

"You flyboys had better learn to follow directions and participate in drills. This is a United States Navy ship, and you will abide by our rules, or we will throw you overboard!"

That night Andy had his first four-hour watch from 20:00 until 00:00 on the White Plains' flight deck.

I have just enough time to review my ship recognition before reporting for my watch. I don't want to call a GQ over one of our ships.

The weather was good, and there were no enemy ship sightings that night.

At 21:30, two Marines approached Winnegar. "How's your watch going, sailor?"

"Just fine, sir!" Andy replied smartly, noticing the stripes and bars on the Marines' uniforms.

"Relax, sailor. I'm Grady Gatlin, and this is Thomas Rozga. We're Marine aviators.

"Me too," Andy exclaimed. "I mean, I'm an aircrewman on a TBM Avenger, a radioman."

"Well, Andy, our Stinson planes are in crates, so we may be riding on anti-sub patrols with you guys in your torpedo bombers," Thomas added.

"What's a Stinson? We have TBM's and FM-2 wildcats in VC-4."

"We're in VMO-4 Marine Observation Squadron. The OY-1 or L5 is our aircraft."

"Oh, you mean those little boxed-up "Crickets!"

"Yes, but we prefer the name 'Warbug' or 'Maytag Messerschmitt.' I just know that before this thing is over, we'll have a lot more bullet holes in our Stinsons than you'll have in your Avengers," Grady smiled.

"Scuttlebutt is that we may be flying missions together in the TBM Avenger, so we may be counting the same bullet holes," Andy laughed.

"See you around, Andy. Don't shoot down any good guys tonight!" Thomas smiled.

Everyone was eager to get to Pearl Harbor, although old salts in the know said the place was overrun with sailors and aviators. Hardly worth the trouble, they said. But Andy doubted that anyone would pass up the chance to go ashore if only they could find those seven missing revolvers.

The following day, 30 April, resulted in an unexpected modification of the VC-4 aircraft. The aircrew had to cut holes in the flaps of their planes to permit the loading of rockets with the wings folded.

"You've got to be kidding me!" Andy groaned.

"What yoyo thought up this brilliant solution?"

Later that night, Andy wrote in his letter home, "We will arrive at Pearl Harbor tomorrow. I'm anxious to see Hawaii." [27]

---

[27] The censors deleted Andy's last sentence with a pair of scissors. Ranking officers often did the censoring.

Chapter 7

PEARL HARBOR – RUMORS AND MORE WAITING – MAY 1944

I got my first glimpse of the islands this morning at 0645, fifteen minutes after sunrise. They looked peaceful and quiet in spite of the fact the Japs had been here only three years ago," Andy Winnegar wrote in his secret journal and then stashed it in its hiding place, a metal box that held the starter cartridges for the FM2-Wildcat. *I hope I don't get caught with this journal.*

As the White Plains steamed into Pearl Harbor, the entire ship's crew and the VC-4 aircrew were on the flight deck, taking in the sights.

"This is a pretty swell greeting," Andy exclaimed as he and Steve Walley stood on the flight deck.

"Yeah! The salute from the two carriers was really cool," Steve replied. "But we still haven't seen any hula girls in grass skirts."

At that moment, the White Plains' port-side 20-mm guns fired to announce their arrival. On the dock, the Navy band struck up a Hawaiian greeting playing "Aloha-Oe." Next came a stirring rendition of "Anchors Aweigh" and the "Marine Hymn" for the leatherneck passengers on board the White Plains. They appropriately finished

Figure 69 By the end of the War, Andy Winnegar had five hand-written journals stashed safely in his metal box. Courtesy of Andy Winnegar.

with another stanza of "Anchors Aweigh" to the applause of the 860 Navy sailors and airmen of the USS White Plains. The escort carrier then tied up just ahead of the USS Nassau at Pier Foxtrot 10 at Ford Island, where they discharged the transported planes. But unfortunately, the seven revolvers were still at large, so there was little hope of liberty in Honolulu.

Figure 70 Barbers Point NAS. WWII. US Navy. Public Domain. WWII Database.

The White Plains took the VC-4 squadron off, and they flew on to Barber's Point Naval Air Station, 40 miles west of Pearl Harbor. At Barbers Point, Ens. Stamatis, Schaufler, and Reams came aboard, joining the ranks of the seasoned VC-4 pilots. The pilots later flew back to the White Plains to practice carrier landings and take-offs while the aircrew stayed behind for a week in paradise. Barber's Point was a holiday for Andy and the rest of the VC-4 enlisted crew,

"My biggest problem was trying to find a pair of swim trunks small enough to fit my 28" waist. I discovered that Hawaiian sizes are

Figure 71 Robert B Stamatis FM-2 Wildcat Pilot VC-4 Courtesy of Andy Winnegar

quite a bit larger. Once I got my trunks, everything was great at Barber's point. We had a fantastic beach," Andy recalled.

The following week the aircrew returned to the White Plains and began conducting air operations and amphibious support training out of Pearl Harbor. [28] Finally, on 8 May, the aircrew was issued their 38s and shoulder holsters. That evening the White Plains five-inch gun and 20-mm and 40-mm guns fired practice rounds, continuing throughout the night.

"Man, that five-inch gun really shakes the ship, Bob Fuller groaned from his bottom bunk.

"I'll be glad to get off this ship and get back to Barber's Point. I'm just about out of clean laundry, and I left most of my clothes there," Andy said.

On 10 May, the aircrew returned to Barber's Point for another

---

[28] Now known as "White Plains Beach," it is located one mile southwest of the Barber's Point airstrip.

week of rest and relaxation, and they even got in a bit of baseball practice. Evening movies were so popular that you'd probably be turned away that if you didn't arrive early.

Three days later, the TBM Avengers and Wildcats flew from Barber's Point out to rendezvous with the White Plains about 50 miles offshore. Pat's landing was a rough one. As the plane handlers were pushing the plane back into position, the tire came off a wheel that had broken during the landing.

"Hey, Pat! That was a pretty rough landing," Andy said to his friend.

"Don't give me any grief, Andy. What's that in your box? Some sort of contraband?"

"No! It's just a case of pineapple juice."

"Well, I have some spirits of a different nature," Pat smiled, holding up a paper bag as they left the flight deck and headed for their compartments.

By mid-month, Andy's journal entries expressed his frustrations about not knowing when or where they would be going to fight. Rumors were too numerous to count. "I still don't know where I'm going. I've heard that we would be back in Pearl Harbor by 19 May. I'm beginning to believe that possibly the White Plains will be part of a task force sailing for enemy waters soon. I think I'd like that."

Not everything was drudgery, waiting, and baseless rumors. Flights over the islands were spectacular. Andy wrote, "The second hop we flew over what I believe to be Maui. It was beautiful, waterfalls on the side of the mountain. There were cliffs and rocky reefs almost all the way around it. Coconut trees were set in straight patterns. There were scattered farms and a few cattle roaming the hills. We passed low over some farmhouses. One man came out to look at us. He was olive-skinned. We were almost low enough to see his eyes."

...

Figure 72 Grumman TBF Avengers flying in echelon formation. Public Domain. Wikimedia Commons

Liberty finally came on 21 May. Fortunately, the missing revolvers were forgotten. Andy went into Honolulu with Steve Walley and Maurice Hie in dress whites. The old salts on the White Plains were correct; the place was overrun with sailors, leathernecks, and Army grunts.

After standing in lines all day, Steve suggested, "Let's have dinner on Waikiki Beach."

"I hope you brought enough dough."

"No sweat. We just got paid," Steve replied.

"Let's go for a walk on Waikiki Beach first. It'll be something to write home about. Maybe we'll run into some hula girls," Andy added hopefully.

"Man, will you look at that surf, sand, and those glorious clouds,"

*Figure 73 Waikiki Beach, Diamond Head, Oahu by Howard Hitchcock 18861-1943.
Public Domain. Wikimedia Commons.*

Andy marveled at the tropical island paradise.

In the late afternoon, the trio made it to the Wagon Wheel Restaurant at 270 Kalakaua Ave and was surprised to find a table without waiting for an hour.

"What luck!" Maurice said.

Andy looked around the room and was surprised to see his pilot, Pat Owens, at the bar, "Hey, Pat! I never expected to see you here! Come and join us for dinner."

"Hi, Andy. Are you checking up on me?"

"No. Have you been dancing on the bar yet?"

"Not yet, Andy, but the night is young."

"Well, then I guess we're right on time," Andy laughed.

"Here, pull up a seat and put some grub in your stomach."

"You know Steve Walley, Carson's radioman."

"Sure. In fact, I came here with Rocky, but he's not much of a drinker. He's around here somewhere."

Andy looked around the room and spotted Rocky Carson chatting up a waitress in the corner. "Hey, Rocky! Come over and join us for dinner."

Carson looked up and smiled when he saw his friends. "How y'all doin' this fine Hawaiian evening?"

"Just fine, Rocky," Pat replied. "Do these Hawaiians understand your Southern accent?"

"Sure do. We're like brothers. I like these people."

"Aloha!" Rocky waved at the waitress, who smiled as he excused himself to join his shipmates.

"Well, boys, what kind of rations are they serving at this joint?" Rocky asked.

"You name it, Rocky, and they can fix you up with whatever you like," Pat laughed. "Just don't ask for grits!

"OK. I'll eat Hawaiian like a local. How about Spam and grits with pineapples on the side?" Rocky laughed.

Figure 74 US Navy sailors in front of the Wagon Wheel Restaurant, Oahu, Hawaii. 1940s

Grabbing the menu, Andy offered, "I think we better order for you, Rocky."

Rocky signaled for the waitress and smiled, "We'll have a Pupu Platter, Rumaki, Ono Ribs, Shrimp Ono Nui, followed by the main courses of Hawaiian roasted pork, Hawaiian grilled fish, Lomi Lomi Salmon, Aloha sweet potatoes, and yes Mai Tai's for my friends and a coke for me! Mahalo."

The guys looked at Rocky with mouths open.

"Where did all that come from, Rocky?" Pat asked in disbelief.

"There are mysteries about me that you may never understand," Rocky replied, smiling.

Rocky motioned for the waitress to come back. "The handsome pilot over there and I are splitting the check."

"Gee, thanks, Rocky and Pat!"

"Yeah. Thanks. You guys are swell."

As the evening wound down, Andy glanced at his watch. "Oh crap! We gotta go! It's 1845, and liberty is over at 1930. We'll never make it back in time. Our bus took over an hour to get here."

"Don't worry, Andy. We got you covered. Rocky, go out in the street and hail a cab."

Pat was correct. They did make it back to the White Plains in time, but just barely."

Andy looked at his watch and whistled, "We just made it. 1925. Five whole minutes to spare!"

Russ Wood, FM2 Wildcat pilot, recalled, "The stay at Pearl Harbor lasted through the month of May, although the ship made three short trips out for rehearsal of flight operations. All during the time we were at Hawaii, however, there was a feeling of restlessness throughout the ship. Something big was obviously impending, and we were all anxious to get on it."

Over the next week, VC-4 flew practice missions and maintained their aircraft and radio equipment. On 28 May, each aircrewman was issued a steel helmet with a gas mask and a jungle pack to attach to his parachute harness. Things were definitely heating up.

"Rumor is we're leaving tomorrow," Hie told Andy at the mess.

"There's a new rumor every day, Maurice," Andy replied. "I'll believe it when the ship starts moving."

On 30 May, Andy cleaned the 30-caliber tunnel gun. That afternoon Maurice and Andy were working on the airplane when Andy looked up.

"The ship's moving!" he shouted to Maurice. "We're finally on our way!"

That evening, Andy wrote in his journal, "While we were working or the airplane, the ship got underway. We are going to Eniwetok. There are Jap held islands all over the area we'll sail through. When we reach Eniwetok, we will join another convoy and escort them to our final destination. We have 21 transports, 35 ships in all with us now. I wouldn't be surprised to find that Frank McCormick and I are in the same task force. It is still difficult to realize that we are at war. I can't wait to get into this fight!"

Chapter 8

INTO THE DRINK – JUNE 2, 1944

On the way to Eniwetok, the pilots and aircrew practiced takeoffs and landing from the White Plains' deck and flew the tedious antisubmarine patrols. A couple of days out from Pearl Harbor, events on board the USS White Plains took a decidedly deadly turn.

Ensign "Bugs" Clyde F. Reams Jr. hailed from the small town of Hominy, Oklahoma. However, the Reams family traced their roots back to Colonial America, among the original Pennsylvania Dutch settlers. Jonathan Eberhard Ream emigrated from Leimer, Germany, in 1717 and was granted 200 acres in Lancaster County. In 1740, his son, Tobias, divided up the land given to him by his parents and founded the town of Zoar in honor of his father. The locals always called it "Reamstown."

Clyde left Oklahoma for Southern California, where he worked for Vega Aircraft Company in Burbank when he was 18 years old. Vega was a subsidiary of Lockheed Aircraft and was responsible for most of its World War II production.

Eighteen-year-old Ensign Clyde F. Reams Jr. enlisted and entered Naval Flight School, becoming an FM-2 Wildcat pilot. Along with

Ensigns Stamatis and Schaufler, Reams was a late addition to VC-4, coming aboard the White Plains at Barbers Point, Hawaii, in May 1944 just before she shipped out for Eniwetok. As late additions, Ensigns Reams, Stamatis, and Schaufler joined the squadron fresh out of Flight School without benefiting from the eight months of stateside training the older guys in the VC-4 had undergone.

On the morning of 2 June 1944, the White Plains was four days out from Pearl Harbor, steaming towards Eniwetok. A Japanese submarine fired on the convoy, but no ships were hit. Andy Winnegar and Bill Lemon were on the flight deck that morning working on their TBM Avengers. Watching the Wildcats preparing to take off from the White Plains, Andy saw a Wildcat pilot with his engine already running, motioning for him to come over to his plane.

Stepping up onto the Wildcat's wing, Andy leaned into the open cockpit to see what he needed. The pilot was a new Ensign, not much older than he was. He was perspiring with beads of sweat running down his forehead.

"How do you turn on the darn radio?"

Andy poked around the cockpit and found the problem right away. "Your main switch is on. But you also have to flip on this switch to turn on the receiver and transmitter."

"Oh. Ok," Reams replied, visibly nervous, reaching for the auxiliary switch.

Andy noticed that the pilot's hand was shaking, and his voice was quavering.

I hope the Ensign is alright. Maybe I should tell him to make up some problem and ground the plane.

Reams was the third Wildcat in the lineup and was up next for take-off. Andy had to get off the wing quickly. He took one last look at Reams, gave him a thumbs-up, and jumped off the Wildcat's wing onto the flight deck.

All pilots are taught to apply a little right rudder on take-off to compensate for the engine's torque. Otherwise, the torque will pull the airborne plane to the left, but too much right rudder will put the

*Figure 75 F4F Wildcat piloted by Julius Brownstein ditching in the sea upon take-off.
Public Domain. (Photo: NARA RG 80 G 89619 / CVE 13 / # 409)*

aircraft into a stall.

Reams held the Wildcat back, standing on the brakes as he advanced the throttle to rev up the engine.[29]

Andy watched the Ensign's takeoff at 0931. He made his run alright, but he went into a steep climbing right turn when he left the deck.

"Crap! He's overcorrecting for torque! Too much right rudder and back stick!" Winnegar shouted.

The Wildcat went "over the top." The right wing went down. The left wing came up, and the plane dove right into the water off the starboard bow. Everybody ran over to the starboard side of the ship.

"Get back!" the Deck Officer ordered.

Reams didn't appear to move after the crash but could only be seen for a few seconds as the fighter quickly disappeared beneath the

---

[29] Reams was in FM-2 47019

Figure 76 F4F Wildcat piloted by Julius Brownstein in water off CVE 13 (Photo: NARA RG 80 G 89624 / CVE 13 / # 414).

water and sank within two minutes. This was Ensign Reams' first take off from the White Plains. His death was VC-4's first operational casualty. A thorough but futile search was conducted by accompanying destroyer escorts.

At precisely the same time that morning, Ensign Edward Billinghurst's FM2 Wildcat[30] crashed into the water about five miles from the ship and the destroyer USS Callaghan picked up the pilot, who was no worse for wear.

Another man fell overboard without a life belt. He wisely ignored a life raft thrown to him, staying as close as possible to a smoke flare until a destroyer picked him up.

Nerves were on edge for the rest of the afternoon. The last flight on

---

[30] Billinghurst was piloting FM2 Wildcat 16273.

June 2nd was John Hearn's TBM Avenger with Bill Lemon and Edens on board. Bill Lemon's journal entry is telling.

"After what had happened, I was a little nervous. Especially, when it turned out that we were the last plane to land. We made it Okay, though after we got down, we noticed that we caught the last wire and that they had to let a barrier down so we wouldn't hit it. What made it bad was that the flight deck ahead of the barriers was packed with planes. One of the pilots ahead of us made a perfect three-point landing, but he hit so hard that he blew out both front tires and broke the tail wheel clear off. It was quite a day, in fact, too much of a day."

Chow in the mess hall that evening made up for the day's stress. The guys were fed chilled pineapple juice, apricots, and hamburger steak.

On June 4, 1944, Winnegar's journal entry stated, "Today we refueled three destroyers. We gave each of them fresh bread and twenty gallons of ice cream. In turn, one of the destroyers gave us our pilot Billinghurst who they had rescued after his forced water landing."

Water landings were common in training and in battle. For example, in training, VC-4 had four non-fatal landings water, including two by "Dunk" Maloney. Two TBM Avengers also had forced water landings in training due to pilot error. The TBM pilot forgot to switch gas tanks and ran out of fuel in one case. In the second case, the TBM prop pitch dropped.

In the heat of battle, it is not surprising that over-the-side landings and forced water landings occurred. Ensign Ream's stall on take-off and crash into the water off the White Plains was the first of many such incidents in which the plane and pilot ended up in the water. At least eight FM-2 Wildcat and a single TBM Avenger ended up in the water in battle. Four of these resulted in fatalities. Usually, if the pilot could exit the plane in the daytime, he would be rescued by a

Figure 77 FM-2 Wildcat ditching in the water. 1945 Pilot Ed VanHise Jr. VC-68.
Public Domain

destroyer escort. However, at night, the chances of being picked up after a water landing were very poor as visibility was limited, and it is a vast ocean.

That afternoon as Owens, Winnegar, and Hie prepared for yet another ASP, Pat came by and struck up a conversation with Andy. "How are you coming on your second-class rating, Andy? You have to stay on top of it, you know."

"Yeah! I'm all over it, Pat."

There's been a lot of guys going in the water lately," Pat added, changing the subject.

"Well, it's a big ocean, so it's kind of hard to miss," Andy laughed.

"I hear you're a pretty good swimmer."

"Yep. We have hundreds of lakes in Missouri. So, I was swimming since before I could walk!"

Pat, deadly serious, replied, "Well, I don't swim. So, if anything happens, I'm sticking with you."

The convoy arrived at Eniwetok on June 9. The ship's crew was astounded by the sheer immensity of the combined fleet filling the lagoon, more overwhelming than any other in history. The startling news published aboard the ship was that Task Force 52 was the northern attack force for the amphibious landings on Saipan in the Marianas. The White Plains' mission was to support the troops fighting for the beachheads, a relatively new tactic that had only been tried once in the Marshall Islands. The challenges and risks on the heavily fortified Saipan were considerably greater. Yet, the White Plains and the other small escort carriers were tasked with making this plan work.

At Eniwetok, the VC-4 complement of aircraft was increased to thirty with the addition of four FM-2 Wildcats and four TBM Avengers. The number of VC-4 pilots also grew as Ens. Baker, Robinson, Stewart, and Dyer joined the Squadron. Russ Wood, FM2 Wildcat pilot, recalled the view from the air. "At Eniwetok, the anchorage was full of various

Figure 78 "Ships of the Fifth Fleet at a Marshalls Anchorage, shortly before departure for the Marianas, as seen from USS GAMBIER BAY (CVE-73), 10 June 1944." US Navy photo

types of naval craft.[31] It was the gathering of the clan for a big strike somewhere and sometime soon. A few days later, on June 11th, the carrier was underway again, and the crew was informed that we were headed northwest to support the marine occupation of Saipan. The following day contact with an enemy submarine was reported, and we realized that from then on, the game was for keeps."

---

[31] White Plains arrived at Eniwetok on 9 June 1944 and next departed for Saipan on 11 June 1944.

Chapter 9

LT. WILEY'S READY ROOM WIRE RECORDER – JUNE 11, 1944

As the convoy set sail from Eniwetok to Saipan, the men were spending more and more time in the Ready Room. This was their home away from home and a good place to meet up between missions for a friendly card game or to shoot the breeze. It was also Lt. Albert Wiley's private domain.

Lt. Albert Wiley was the Intelligence Officer in charge of planning and coordinating all missions for the VC-4 squadron. At 5'10", overweight, and hairy-chested, Wiley was all business. The weight of the squadron sat squarely on Wiley's shoulders as he daily made life and death decisions about missions and armament. The stress of the job showed in his face and his demeanor. Wiley kept a bunk in a compartment at

Figure 79 Albert Wiley Jr. Intelligence Officer VC-4 Courtesy of Andy Winnegar.

the back of the Ready Room, so he was always on duty and rarely in a good mood. Heaven help the poor enlisted man who had to awaken Lt Wiley because he invariably woke up swinging.[32]

Figure 80 Bob Fuller

On board the White Plains, the thirty-six enlisted aircrewmen in the VC-4 squadron were berthed in two separate compartments located on the same level as the Ready Room and CIC.[33] Andy was in a top bunk in the "Tech" Compartment with the other radio operators and radio technicians. Charles Selig, the squadron radio technician, and Bob Fuller, a radio operator, were in the two bunks directly below Andy. George Fournier, another radio operator of French descent, was in the opposite top bunk.

Space was at a premium aboard the ship. "I could reach out and punch Fournier with my right arm," Andy recalled.

"Hey, Andy! Let's go hang out in the Ready Room," Maurice Hie called out. "Maybe we can find a craps game in Gowan's parachute rigging room."[34]

"No craps for me, but I'll come along to keep you company," Winnegar replied, rolling out of the top bunk in one practiced motion.

Andy and Maurice exited the sleeping compartment, entering a corridor that took them no more than 50 feet to the Ready Room's side entrance. At a leisurely pace, it took all of a minute. But, in an

---

[32] Lt. Albert Wiley, Jr. Intelligence Officer USS White Plains. Public Domain. US Government photograph.
[33] CIC – Command Information Center is a room in a Navy war ship that functions as a tactical center and provides processed information for command and control of nearby battle space and areas of operation.

emergency, Andy could be there in seconds.[35]

"I can't believe how close your bunk is to the Ready Room. You could sleep-walk and end up here!" Maurice laughed.

"Yeah. I always have my head in the game, Maurice. Did you know that my bunk is directly below the flight deck? That red battle lamp over my head starts shaking whenever a plane lands or takes off."

"It must be kind of noisy in your bunk

Figure 81 George F. Fournier

when the Wildcats and Avengers are rolling overhead."

"It's not the noise I'm worried about. But if some Jap Zero decide to strafe the White Plains, their bullets are going right through the wooden flight deck and end up in my bunk!"[36]

"Ouch!

"Enough morbid talk for now, but I do think about it from time to time," Andy commented as they entered the side door of the VC-4 Ready Room.

"Are you sure you aren't up for a game of chance?" Maurice asked, looking towards Gowan's parachute rigging room that often held the promise of a crap game."

"No. Yesterday was payday. I think I'll hold onto my $15 for a while longer." Andy laughed. [37]

"Suit yourself. Lt Owens may give us another lesson. He's quite a

---

[35] Bob Fuller, Radio Operator on a TBM Avenger.

[36] United States aircraft carriers in WWII had wooden flight decks to facilitate ease of repair.

[37] Pay day was on the 1st and 15th of each month. Andry drew $15 and the rest was sent home. Base pay was $96, with 50% additional for flight pay, 20% more for sea duty, 3% more for longevity after 3 years. Pay was close to $200 per pay periol

Figure 82 1st Class Petty Officer Gowan in charge of the parachute rigging room was adjacent to the Ready Room. Courtesy of Andy Winnegar.

Wildman. When we get back to San Diego, he's taking the guys out to the Pirate's Cove."

"Sometime, I'll tell you a story about Lt Owens dancing on the bar at the Pirate's Cove!"

"Hey, Andy! Check this out," Bob Fuller called out from the front of the Ready Room. [38]

Andy and Maurice approached the desk where Bob was inspecting Wiley's wire recorder.

"Will you look at that? Wiley's wire recorder is finally free! Let's play around with it," Maurice encouraged.

"Do you guys know how to operate this thing?" Bob asked.

It's pretty high-tech. You're lucky Seelig has been cross-training me as a radio and electronics technician," Andy commented. "He's also tutoring me in German. Sprechen Sie Deutsch?"

"OK, smart guy. Then how do you operate this thing?"

"Wie machst du das an? "Andy laughed. [39]

Noticing the blank stares, Andy continued in English, "It's easy. You just set this to record and speak into the microphone. Maurice, you got something you want to record?"

"How about some dirty jokes. I know a bunch."

"Some yoyos recorded a dirty story for kicks and then forgot to

---

[38] The squadron Ready Room was the "hang out" location for the enlisted men who rarely socialized in the berthing compartments. The Ready Room was where they met for cards and bull sessions. The games of craps were held in the adjacent parachute rigging room.
[39] "Wie machst du das an? – German with English translation: How do you turn this on?

Figure 83 WWI US Navy Wire Recorder.

erase it. Lt Wiley mistakenly played the recording for the whole squadron at the morning briefing. Man, was he ever pissed off."

"It was a hoot! Wiley turned beet red and had steam coming out of his ears!"

"He's still looking for the jokers."

Andy paused, thinking, and then suggested, "Why don't we sing something together?"

"Like a barbershop quartet?"

"Well, yeah. Kind of, except there's only three of us."

"What you got in mind for our trio, Andy?"

"One of my favorite Andrews Sisters tunes, "Don't Sit Under the Apple Tree."

"You know the words?"

"Sure. Everyone knows the words. Something like this."

Figure 84 Andrews Sisters Public Domain.

"Yeah. We know the words," Maurice interrupted. "Just press record, and let's make our VC-4 Demo Recording." [40]

"OK. Here goes."

"OK! Now play it back. Let's hear our sweet voices," Maurice crooned.

Andy pressed the play-back button as the guys waited expectantly. They were not disappointed.

"Wow! We sound great! We can't erase this!"

"Yeah! We need an agent. This thing is going platinum!"

"You want Wiley after our butts?" Andy warned.

"No, but let's play it again and try another song," Bob encouraged as the guys gathered around admiring their vocal rendition.

"I still want to record some dirty jokes, though. You know, like a stand-up comic."

---

[40] Maurice Hie, gunner on board Walter P Owen's TBM Avenger.

The slamming door at the back of the Ready Room got their attention.

"Who the hell is howling in here? I was sleeping, and now thanks to you bozos, I'm not!"

"Oh crap! It's Wiley. Now we're in for it," Andy groaned as they stood at attention.

"You pieces of donkey shit! Winnegar, Hie, and Fuller. I should have known. You woke me up!"

"Ah. Sorry, sir. We were just horsing around," Fuller said with his hand still on the wire recorder.

"You were horsing around with US Government property! My Wire Recorder is not a toy! What does the sign on the back say, Winnegar?"

Andy bent down and read the printing on the back of the Wire Recorder, "Special Devices Division United States Navy Bureau of Aeronautics, Device Number 13-A-3e, and Serial Number..."

"That's enough!" Wiley stormed. "Does it say anything about the Andrews Sisters or an Apple Tree?"

"No sir!" the three replied in unison.

"Then, unless you want to dress up in drag and perform for the squadron tomorrow, I strongly suggest you get the hell out of here!"

"And I better not find any dirty jokes on that wire!"

"No, sir," Andy said as he quietly erased the recording before they headed out the side door of the Ready Room.

Once in the corridor, Andy, Bob, and Maurice stopped, looked at each other, and burst out laughing.

"I still think we sounded pretty darn good," Maurice commented. "You sing a mean baritone, Andy."

"Yep. A gold record in the making. Hollywood, here we come. We need a name for our trio," Bob encouraged, looking at his two friends.

"How about the 'Three Avengers'?"

"Sounds good to me. So, who's up for a game of Gin Rummy. It's a penny a point," Andy said.

Figure 85 Navy Gin Rummy Game WWII. Public Domain

"And Gowan still owes me seven dollars," Andy added. "The guy's a compulsive gambler, but he's a lot better at craps than Gin Rummy."

At that moment, a general announcement came over the White Plain's PA system. "The Smoking Lamp is ON." [41]

Within moments cigarette smoke was wafting through the corridors of the ship.

---

[41] The term "The Smoking Lamp is Lit" is a throwback to an era before the invention of lighters and modern matches when ships would have communal lamps so sailors/Marines could light their tobacco. The phrase is quite old, twice as old as the United States Navy and Marine Corps, originating from the 1500s when Western sailors started to have regular access to tobacco. With fire being one of the greatest dangers abroad wooden ships back then crewmembers could only smoke in designated areas at certain times, usually toward the end of the day.
They were oil lamps that were lighted by boatswains and hung well away from anything that was highly flammable. Upon lighting them, the boatswains or officers of the deck would say, "The smoking lamp is lighted" and after dousing the flame, "The smoking lamp is out.
- Thomas Lewandowski former Sgt US Marine Corps.

"I hate the smell of cigarettes," Andy complained.

"Yeah, my dad calls those things cancer sticks," Bob agreed.

"Even with the smoking lamp, guys are always cheating and sneaking out on the weather deck for a smoke!"

"Those yoyos may end up in the brig so they can satisfy their nicotine habit. What idiots!"[42]

"You know Andy, you don't smoke, drink much, or gamble except for Gin Rummy, and that hardly counts as gambling," Bob observed.

"That's right. Gin Rummy is a game of skill and brains," Andy proclaimed. "And I've got too much brainpower to waste it on booze, cigarettes, and craps."

"OK, Andy. Lead us to the Gin Rummy match in the compartment. That smoking lamp will be out in a few minutes anyway," Hie added.

Running down the passageway, Bill Lemon stuck his head into the compartment. "No time for Gin Rummy. We have Mail Call!"

The guys dropped their cards, running after Lemon to the Ready Room.

One of the White Plain's yeomen had a sack of hundreds of letters and packages emptied out onto a desk and was sorting them while another crewman called out names for the lucky airman with a letter from home.

"Man! This is our first mail since leaving San Diego! Look for Lemon!"[43] Bill shouted to the Yeoman over the din of the excited men.

The Yeomen looked up from his sorting, "What's your name?"

"Everett Lemon, but they all call me Bill or Smiley," Lemon laughed

"Well, Smiley, here you go," the Yeoman replied handing Bill five letters.

Bill tore into the first envelope and pulled out a letter and a stack of photos from home. "Will you guys look at this!"

The guys gathered around. "What's that picture?"

---

[42] According to Andy Winnegar about half of the flight crew smoked.
[43] On June 11, 1944 they were departing Eniwetok. This was the first mail they had received since leaving San Diego.

"It's my family's hog farm in Hillsboro, Oregon! Look at those pigs! Aren't they a sight for sore eyes?"

"Well, Smiley, I'm glad it's not your girlfriend!" Edens laughed.

"No, my girlfriend, Doris, is a doll, but those pigs are really something too. To tell the truth, I miss 'em both. Any of you guys need a job after the war, you can come work on my hog farm!" Bill laughed.

Figure 86 Bill Lemon. Courtesy Christopher Dean.

"Winnegar! Walley! Hie! Get your butts up here. You've got mail!"

The rest of the hour was a whirlwind of reading letters from loved ones and swapping stories and photographs with friends. These letters sustained the guys and helped lift their spirits as they remembered why they were fighting this war halfway around the world.

Chapter 10

"YOU GUYS SMELL DIFFERENT!" – 1944

The sail from Pearl Harbor to Saipan was over 4,000 miles long, with the stop in the Eniwetok Atoll. Sailors and aviators needed something to take their minds off the long voyage.

The hangar deck of the USS White Plains was crowded with sailors and aviators hooting and waving their money, trying to place bets on the upcoming boxing match. The quickly assembled ring with ropes, poles, and the regulation timer was all the invitation the sailors needed to cluster around, hoping for some welcome entertainment to break the monotony of the endless days at sea.

Avenger pilot Rocky Carson, serving as referee, towered over the two combatants. But at 6'2" and 225 pounds, there wasn't a man on board who would step into the ring with the Gentle Giant from Louisiana.

"All right, you two. Come out swinging, but keep it clean, or you'll have me to answer to," Cason advised the two boxers, who silently nodded in agreement.

"We'll have three two-minute rounds," Carson said as he motioned for them to touch gloves."

"Now go to your corners and wait for the bell."

The two boxers were a navy version of the children's book "Big and Little."

Andy Winnegar was 5'8" and 150 pounds of muscle. He was one of the few men on board with formal boxing training in the Golden Gloves and at NATTC Millington radio school outside of Memphis. At NATTC, Winnegar had two major bouts during the Kentucky Derby that year. He won both bouts by decision against black boxers. Other skilled black boxers at NATTC could have helped Winnegar develop his boxing skills, but the Navy regulations in the 1940s forbid mixing white and black sailors.[44]

Goldberg was 6'1" and 200 pounds of Jewish fury and was clearly in a different weight class than Winnegar. It should have been no contest, but in this kind of David and Goliath scenario, you just never know what's going to happen. For obvious reasons, the betting odds were highly in Goldberg's favor.

The navy chief turned official timer struck the bell, starting the exhibition match. Both boxers came bounding out of their corner with headgear in place and gloves up.

A natural right-handed boxer, Winnegar, led with a left jab to the jaw followed by a right cross. Goldberg easily dodged the right cross.

This oaf is faster than he looks.

Goldberg countered with his own combination of a double left jab and a monstrous right roundhouse, going for an early knockout blow.

Winnegar easily bobbed under the roundhouse, which flew harmlessly into the air. Winnegar countered with a left body blow and a right cross to Goldberg's exposed head, landing a clean blow just above Goldberg's left eye.

Points and more points! There's no way I can knock out this guy. Just

---

[44] Not until July 26, 1948 did Harry Truman sign Executive Order 9981, establishing equality of treatment and opportunity in the US military regardless of race.

*Figure 87 Photograph of a Boxing Match Aboard Ship], February 10, 1945;
University of North Texas Libraries, The Portal to Texas
History, https://texashistory.unt.edu; Texas Parks & Wildlife Department*

gotta stay away from his knockout punch and keep scoring points.

Winnegar kept moving and weaving in the second round, landing the occasional left jab and right cross while Goldberg came thundering back with body blows and left uppercuts.

Points! I need more points before this gorilla knocks me out! Let him keep swinging to tire himself out!

Winnegar bobbed and dodged Goldberg's blows, although enough landed, so the match was dead even.

Andy was still fresh in the third round, while Goldberg was breathing heavily from his missed punches.

Winnegar led with the left jab, a right cross combination that Goldberg was expecting. However, the follow-up left cross to the body surprised him and landed squarely over his liver as Andy kept bobbing and weaving, keeping Goldberg off balance.

Feeling the match slipping away, Goldberg needed a knockdown or a knockout blow to win the match. Faking a left jab that Andy dodged,

Figure 88 Boxing Match USS President Truman. National Archives..

Goldberg quickly followed with a right roundhouse body blow to Andy's ribs.

Ah crap! I let him get to me.

Andy stumbled to his right as the crushing blow to his left lower ribs landed with the full force of Goldberg's 200 pounds.

Sensing his opportunity, Goldberg charged at Winnegar with blows to his head and body. Winnegar covered up to protect himself but was getting pummeled.

The bell sounded, ending the third round. The two boxers touched gloves and nodded with Rocky standing between them, reviewing the scorer's sheet. Then, quickly calculating the score, Rocky looked at the crowd of expectant sailors and aviators, each hoping for a winning bet.

"By my unanimous decision, the USS White Plains boxing federation proclaims that the winner of this match by a points decision is..." Rocky paused for effect, keeping the crowd waiting and hoping.

"The winner of this boxing match is Andy Winnegar!"

A chorus of partisan cheers and boos greeted Rocky Carson's decision as money somewhat reluctantly exchanged hands that afternoon.

In the back of the hangar deck, a group of black mess cooks had been watching the bout with great interest.

"Willie, you can take that guy!"

"Yeah, but keep your mouth shut. The Navy pays us to work in the galley, not box the next Great White Hope."[45]

As the crowd of sailors was clearing, Captain Grady Gatlin approached Winnegar with another Marine, both smiling broadly.

"Andy, what a fight! You were definitely the David in this story!"

"Thanks, Captain Gatlin. Who's your friend?" Winnegar asked, peering at the other man, shorter than Gatlin and could have been Andy's brother.

"Leonard Wollman," the other Marine replied, extending his right hand. "And you just made us both a fistful of hard-earned cash from our navy brothers!"

"You both fly those "Crickets?" Andy asked.

---

[45] Boxer James Jeffries was nicknamed the Great White Hope." In 1910 a black heavyweight champion Jack Johnson beat Jeffries, sparking racial violence.

"Yeah, but we prefer the name Stinson OY-1 Marine Observation Plane or "Flying Jeep."

"Sorry. Around here, the guys call it the Cricket Circuit," Winnegar explained. "No guns. Just a little chirping engine!"

"We'll be riding anti-sub patrols with you in your TBM Avenger for now," Wollman explained, grinning. "I like those big guns and bombs you guys carry. I can't wait to fire the .50 caliber machine gun at some Jap target!"

Andy smiled, "I will have to check you two out on the radio equipment and turret .50 caliber gun."

"Yeah, sure. And we'll give you a tour of the K-20 observation camera since that will be your job when we are aboard the TBM Avenger.

Figure 89 Lt. Leonard Wollman US Marine Corps. Courtesy of Wollman family.

OK. But I still have my air-cooled .30 caliber stinger down in the tunnel. I can't very well shoot at the enemy with your camera," Andy laughed, unlacing his gloves.

The next day Andy was headed for the fantail showers, passing through the crew berthing compartments with bunks stacked three high on either side of the narrow passageway. He was deep in thought and oblivious to the changing composition of the crew as he made his way towards the stern of the White Plains.

"Psst! Hey, you over here!"

Andy paused and looked around, finding himself surrounded by the Black messmen.

"Psst! Yeah, you! Over here. Come on down the aisle."

Winnegar walked forward, squeezing between the bunks stacked to the ceiling, and came face to face with a Black messmen about his size and build.

"You box. Right?"

"Yeah, I try!" Winnegar replied.

"I saw you box that huge Jew. You did alright. Where'd you learn to box?"

"Golden Gloves in Albuquerque."

"I'm Willie. I box too. Maybe we can spar sometime," Willie suggested tentatively.

"My name is...."

"Winnegar," Willie finished for him. "We saw you box, remember. We was in the back."

"You can call me Andy. Where do you bunk?"

Willie proceeded to show Andy his bunk.

Figure 90 Andy Winnegar. Courtesy of Andy Winnegar

"OK, Willie. Next time we're in port, maybe we can go to the hangar deck and do some sparing. We need to be careful that no one spots us."

Willie nodded and smiled as Winnegar stuck out his hand before heading back towards the fantail and his salt-water shower.

At the next port, the crew was given 24-hour liberty. The White Plains was almost deserted within an hour as the men couldn't wait to go ashore. Seeing his opportunity, Andy headed back towards Willie's bunk. Sure enough, Willie was waiting.

"Hey, Willie. You still want to spar with me?"

"Yes, sir. I been waiting for you," Willie replied.

"Let's head down to the hangar deck. It should be really quiet down there. Everyone is ashore or asleep."

As they made their way down to the hangar deck, Andy sized up

Figure 91 USS Bogue (CVE 9). Boxing onboard showing the final heavyweight bout – Willard vs. Beers. The later won, right side. Photograph released: July 2, 1944. Official U.S. Navy photograph, now in the collections of the National Archives. 2016/1

Willie. He was definitely in the same weight class, but Willie was all muscle.

"How much do you weigh, Willie?"

"155 pounds. How about you."

"Same here."

"Let's scrounge up some gear," Andy suggested. "Should be gloves over in the corner."

They located some 16-ounce oversized gloves without laces.

"We won't have time to set up a ring with ropes," Andy lamented.

"Won't need one. Let's just spar over here in the corner," Willie said, putting on the gloves.

Andy looked around the empty hangar deck to make sure they were alone.

"Looks all clear."

"Show me your best combination, Winnegar."

Both men assumed the boxing stance, and Andy led with a left jab followed by a right cross to Willie's head.

Willie deftly blocked the jab and let the right cross through, which landed with a tap to his left cheek.

"Pretty good. You got a quick left jab. Try following up the right cross with a quick left uppercut," Willie suggested. "Like this."

Both men traded combinations and made suggestions for countermoves. It was an informal but good training session.

"You know your stuff, Willie. Where'd you learn to box?"

"I grew up in Chicago and was in Golden Gloves just like you."

"You must have done pretty good. You've got really fast hands."

"Yeah, I done alright. Here, try this move," Willie suggested, showing Andy another rapid-fire combination.

It was the most fun either of them had had on the White Plains since they'd boarded the ship in San Diego.

"We should do this again sometime, Willie," Andy invited. "I wish we could put on a demonstration match, but they'd never let that happen," Andy lamented.

"No, I don't imagine they going to let a White boy and a black mess cook box anytime soon."

"You know, Willie. I have to say I like you, but you guys smell different."

The silence was brief as Willie retorted, "Well, you smell different too, man!"

Both boys laughed as they touched gloves. That afternoon on the hangar deck, Willie and Andy moved a step closer to understanding that they were just two young men who had a lot in common on this floating city.

As they took off and stowed their gloves, both men nodded and smiled, not noticing the dark outline of a figure lurking in the recesses of the hangar deck.

Chapter 11

FROM LOUISIANA TO THE USS WHITE PLAINS

Harold Hugh Carson, the part-time boxing referee on the USS White Plains, was born in Springhill, Louisiana, located in Webster Parish in the extreme northwestern corner of the state. With less than 5,000 people, Springhill had deep ties to the lumber industry dating back to 1896. Springhill took the name "Barefoot, Louisiana" on the notions of a Mrs. Maxwell, who assigned the name based on her observations that many men in the community went to work without shoes.

Figure 92 Harold Carson TBM Avenger Pilot VC-4. Courtesy of Andy Winnegar

The town of Springhill was finally incorporated in 1902.

Hugh's father, Ned Roy Carson, and mother, Emma Dean Davis, had family roots in Arkansas just over the Stateline from Springhill. His only sibling, George, was four years older, born in 1914. Harold Hugh Carson went by his middle name "Hugh" until his fellow Avenger pilots gave him the handle "Rocky" in flight school.

By the time Hugh was 12 years old, his father was no longer in the household. Instead, Hugh was living with his maternal grandmother, Catherine Davis, in Stamps, Arkansas. A town of 2700 people, Stamps is located 29 miles north of Springhill, Louisiana.

Easy-going, affable, and always smiling, Hugh made friends easily. Hugh had the distinction of never saying an unkind word about anyone. He and his brother George were always hungry, making it challenging to keep the pantry stocked. Hugh grew at an alarming pace, reaching 6'1" by his sixteenth birthday. Initially tall and lanky, Hugh soon filled out to 200 pounds, making him a "bear of a man."

Hugh attended the College of Mines in El Paso, Texas, later becoming the University of Texas El Paso (UTEP). He enlisted in the US Naval Reserves on 1 My 1943. Rocky performed well enough in flight school to be assigned to the new TBM Avenger torpedo bomber, which had entered service in 1942.

While Rocky's flying was not always orthodox, he flew with enthusiasm and was an excellent pilot. In one incident during training, it was Carson's turn to tow the aerial gunnery target behind his Avenger. The target was attached to the plane via a long line. The line was coiled up so that as the plane took off, the line uncoiled. At the end of its length, the aircraft should be off the runway. To make a real-hot pilot takeoff in a TBM Avenger, you can put your gear in the up position while you're still on the ground. When the pressure comes off the gear, it will fold up immediately. Carson did this, and when he reached the end of the line, he had just barely gotten off the ground.

When he hit the weight of the tow target, the additional drag brought the plane back down. Well, the gear was coming up, the plane was coming down, and finally, the prop was cutting into the asphalt, and he had to shut the engine down. It was a bad day for Rocky.

Pat Owens was Rocky's flight leader in the VC-4 Composite squadron and felt responsible for his friend. One day in training in the TBM Avenger, the flight was supposed to take off, climb to altitude, join up at the designated spot and then go to the target area.

"We were up in the circle, and two of the planes had joined up with us. Carson comes sailing by and crosses in front of us, going the wrong way. He can't turn. He's going in the wrong direction. Wrong footed, you might say," Winnegar recalled.

Owens was on the mike. "Would you look at that Carson, fat, dumb and happy with his thumb up his ass!"

"Pat!" Winnegar called out.

"Yeah."

"You're on the air!"

"He thought he was on intercom, but he was transmitting it."

In truth, there wasn't an officer or enlisted man aboard the USS White Plains that did not admire and love then big, affable Rocky Carson, the gentle giant from Louisiana. Rocky and Owens, in particular, had a special bond that went far beyond their relationship as flight leader and pilot. They were as different as night and day, but either man would gladly have given his life for the other.

Rocky was outgoing but conservative. He would rather go to a football game than to a bar or a dance. Pat was more on the celebrity side.

Andy Winnegar recalled, "I would see Pat in places that Rocky would never have gone. For example, they had a place in San Diego called the Pirates Cave. Not many officers would go in there, but Pat waltzed right in and was dancing on the bar before the night was over. I only went there on two occasions, and there were three fights."

For obvious reasons, Pat and Rocky did not usually do leave together. But, despite their differences, the bond of brotherhood between Pat Owens and Rocky Carson ran deep and was unbreakable.

Andy Winnegar saw Rocky Carson from across the hangar deck. At 6'2" and 225 pounds, it was hard to miss Rocky.

"Hey, Winnegar. You got a sec?"

"Sure thing Mr. Carson. How can I help you?

"You can start by calling me Rocky."

Uh, sure, Mr. Rocky."

Rocky's smile was infectious. "I saw you boxing that Black mess cook."

"Please don't tell anyone. We were just messing around. You know, sparing and stuff."

"Stop worrying, Andy. It's cool with me if y'all can throw a few punches, but how about an exhibition match between you two here on the hangar deck?"

"Uh. I don't think the ship is ready for that. A Black mess cook and a White radio operator boxing? No, I don't think so."

"Why not? Y'all are evenly matched, and it would be a much better match than you and Goldberg!"

"Plus, you both have formal boxing training, and you look good together in the ring."

"We were both in Golden Gloves. Willie trained with Golden Gloves in Chicago, and I was in Golden Gloves in Albuquerque, New Mexico."

"I knew it! You and Willie are trained boxers. The rest of the guys on the ship are brawlers at best."

"Willie has really fast hands. I can learn a lot from him.

"Don't sell yourself short, Andy. You have plenty of boxing skills and a huge heart."

"Thanks, Rocky. I still don't think the US Navy is ready for the Black and White Tornado boxing match."

"I'll run it by the captain if you're interested. In the meantime, come check out the exhibition boxing match tomorrow. We'll have a California Golden Boy vs. a Bronx Bomber."

Figure 93 WWII 120.B3.F5.7: Snapshot of a boxing match in a makeshift boxing ring on the deck of the U.S. Navy transport ship the USS General J. H. McRae (AP-149) during World War II. Photograph taken by or collected by U.S. Navy storekeeper Elbert C. Jackson.

The next day's boxing match pitted a blond-haired Southern California beach boy named Hasselbach against a New York City brawler named Rotenberg.

"My money's on surfer boy!"

"No way! The Jewish Bronx Bomber is going to eat him for lunch."

"Put your money where your mouth is! Or are you talking out of your ass?"

"Here's twenty on blondie."

"Here's thirty, and a pastrami on rye says that the Bronx bomber knocks out Blondie in two rounds!"

The boxing match was less entertaining than the prefight kibitzing. Neither fighter had any formal boxing training, but they put on a show with lots of wild roundhouse punches and clinching.

"Boo! Boo! The Bronx Bomber is a bum!"

"Send Blondie back to sunny California. I hope he can surf because he sure as hell can't box!"

The spectators had had enough by round three and were ready to throw the two boxers overboard.

"Come on! Do something! Throw a real punch, you Bum!"

Just when Rocky thought he would lose control of the match and the crowd, fate intervened.

Blondie charged Rotenberg, swinging wildly. Rotenberg easily bobbed and weaved, avoiding Hasselbach's wild onslaught. With a final surge of newfound energy, Blondie wound up his right arm and launched a massive roundhouse at Rotenberg's torso. Rotenberg sidestepped the wild roundhouse. Blondie's momentum spun him around as his right arm swung wildly through the air.

Blondie's scream was audible throughout the hangar deck as his right arm dropped to his side, and Hasselbach collapsed to the floor, grabbing at his limp right arm.

"Shit! It hurts!"

Rocky immediately went into action. Placing Hasselbach on his back, Rocky grabbed his right wrist and looked him in the eye.

"This is going to hurt. On the count of three, grit your teeth and hold on. Ready?"

"One, Two and...Rocky applied forward pressure to Hasselbach's wrist and arm, snapping the dislocated shoulder back into its socket.

"Crap! You didn't say 'Three,'" Hasselbach complained.

"Oh well. Guess I forgot. How's it feel?" Rocky asked.

Hasselbach gingerly moved his right arm. "Wow! You cured me, Rocky!"

The crowd of sailors and airmen had been silent but now erupted into applause and cheers, not for the injured boxer but rather for Rocky, the hero of the day.

"Way to go, Rocky!"

"Now we'll have to call your Doc Rocky!"

Chants of "Rocky! Rocky!" echoed across the hangar deck and cemented the crew's adoration of the gentle giant from Louisiana.

Rocky smiled and bowed with a flourish.

Pat Owens jumped up onto the stage and proclaimed, "The winner of today's fight by unanimous decision is.....Doc Rocky!" as he grabbed Rocky's right hand and raised it triumphantly into the air to the cheers of the several hundred sailors and airmen.

The proposed exhibition match between Winnegar and Willie, the Black mess cook, never did happen, but it was clear that Rocky was fine with the Black and White Tornados mixing it up on the Hangar Deck of life.

Chapter 12

TBM AVENGER – THE GREAT TURKEY IN THE SKY – AND ITS CREW

Nicknamed the "Turkey," or the "Pregnant Beast," the TBM Avenger was not pretty nor sleek, but she was a brute who could pack a punch with a torpedo, bombs, 5-inch rockets, three .50 caliber machine guns, and a single .30 caliber gun. A large bomb bay could accommodate a Bliss-Leavitt Mark 13 torpedo, a single 2,000-pound bomb, four 500-pound bombs or depth charges, or twelve 100-pound bombs.

The TBM was the heaviest single-engine aircraft of World War II, with a gross weight of just under 18,000 pounds. TBM pilots joked that the Avenger was so heavy it could fall faster than it could fly. In fact, with a top speed of 275 miles per hour and a range of 905 miles, the Avenger could almost keep up with the more agile fighters. The TBM was usually paired with an FM-2 Wildcat fighter on anti-sub patrols.

The Grumman TBF Avenger and the General Motors TBM Avengers were American torpedo bombers that entered service in 1942, making their less than stellar debut at the Battle of Midway. Subsequently, the Avenger became the most widely used and effective

Figure 94 TBM Avenger with folded wings. A 500-pound bomb and rockets are being loaded. Crewman in the middle is positioning a bomb hoist. US Navy Photograph.

torpedo bomber in World War II. The Avengers were involved in the sinking of 12 carriers, six battleships, 19 cruisers, 25 destroyers, and 30 submarines in the Pacific and Atlantic theaters.

The Avenger was a crucial element in the sinking of the Japanese super battleships Musashi in the Battle of Leyte Gulf on 24 October 1944 and her sister battleship Yamato the following spring on 7 April 1945. The TBM Avenger remained in service for over 20 years until it was retired in the 1960s with 9,839 TBM built for the US Navy and Royal Navy, Royal Canadian Navy, and the Royal New Zealand Air Force.

Designed for use on aircraft carriers with limited space, the TBM Avenger utilized the new Sto-Wing patented "compound angle" wing-folding mechanism to maximize storage space on carriers. The plane's wingspan was reduced from 54 feet to 18 feet, saving precious space on the small escort carriers. Unlike the manually folded wings on the FM-2 Wildcat, wing folding was accomplished with hydraulics.

Figure 95 TBM Avengers over Wake Island November 1943. US Navy Photograph.

Figure 96 U.S. Navy Grumman TBM-3E Avenger aircraft of anti-submarine squadron VS-31 on board the escort carrier USS Siboney (CVE-112), 1949. US Navy Photograph. Public Domain.

The TBM Avenger initially had a crew of three; pilot, radioman bombardier, and turret gunner.

TBM Avenger Cockpit and Pilot

Flying the TBM Avenger feels like driving an overloaded grain truck through a muddy field without power steering. [46] Designed before hydraulic-boosted controls became common, the TBM Avenger required lots of muscle to fly with a flying experience referred to as "Turkey Wrestling." Matthew McDaniel states that "if the TBF/M controls are heavy in pitch and roll, they are positively Herculean in yaw. Staying ahead of yaw trim is probably less critical than anticipating pitch or roll trim needs but is no less important for long-duration control inputs. Simply pushing a rudder pedal at cruise speeds to coordinate the aircraft just isn't possible without asking some leg muscles to wake up."

Figure 97 Lt jg Walter Pat Owens. Courtesy of Andy Winnegar

"Level turns in shallow bank angles were accomplished without adjusting pitch trim, but not without adding a good deal of back pressure on the stick to maintain altitude. Turns near 30° of bank required two arms worth of strength to hold altitude. Steeper turns (30° to 60° of bank) would be nearly impossible, sans retrimming, for

---

[46] Matthew McDaniel. Turkey Wrestling – Flying the TBM Avenger. Warbird Digest. https://warbirdsnews.com/warbirds-news/turkey-wrestling-flying-tbm-avenger.html

the average pilot to muscle through without descending." – Matthew McDaniel

Powered by a 1,700HP Wright R-2600-8 engine, 14-cylinder double-row radial engine, the Avenger was Grumman's first torpedo bomber and was the heaviest single-engine aircraft of World War II, weighing 18,000 pounds.

Lt jg Walter Pat Owens was the pilot of Winnegar and Hie's TBM Avenger. "Pat," born in 1921 in Yakima, Washington, was the third of nine children and was a couple of years older than his crew. The Irish Catholic Owens family originated in County Roscommon, Ireland. Pat's great grandfather, Peter Francis Owens Sr., born in 1816, immigrated to the United States in 1846 and settled in Le Suer, Minnesota.

Pat attended Gonzaga University in Spokane and took flying classes at Felts Field in Spokane Valley. He enlisted in the Navy after Pearl Harbor and was commissioned as a Lieutenant jg. Since Pat had a private pilot's license, his Navy Flight School was abbreviated. Owens

Figure 98 TBM Avenger cockpit. Courtesy of Simon Brown - Platinum Fighter Sales, Warbird and Classic Aircraft Broker

completed the regular two-year course in only nine months, including Primary and Advanced Training followed by Operational Training with a crew in a TBF Avenger. Owens was assigned to Composite Squadron Four in September 1943 when he met his radioman Winnegar and turret gunner, Hie, at NAS Sand Point in Washington. The VC-4 squadron came aboard the carrier USS White Plains in the Spring of 1944.

TBM Avenger Radio Operator and Ventral Gunner/Bombardier

The radio operator on board the TBM Avenger was responsible for a massive amount of sophisticated radio gear placed in the tunnel and the center cockpit immediately behind the pilot. The radio operator's job involved tuning, maintaining, and repairing the vast array of radio equipment, including VHF and HF radios, transmitter, ZB homing beacon radio, the TBM's intercom, IFF "Friend or Foe" system, and the newest technology, radar.

Figure 99 TBM Avenger Radio operator's console and entrance to ball turret. Courtesy of Daniel Berek.

Figure 100 Andrew J. Winnegar TBM Avenger Radioman / Gunner

The radio operator sat in the tunnel along the bottom or ventral side of the TBM, encompassing about half of the total airframe. The tunnel was in the most exposed position on the aircraft. Enemy fire easily penetrated the thin aluminum skin of the TBM, putting holes in the fuselage as bullets and shells ripped through the tunnel within inches of the radio operator. Lack of armor in the belly of the TBM placed the radioman in constant danger from anti-aircraft shells and shrapnel. The TBM's tunnel was lacking in creature comforts. It was noisy and had limited visibility through small windows on either side. The smells of engine oil and transmission fluid soon permeated the space, adding to the claustrophobia for the uninitiated.

The radioman sat on a small hard metal seat facing forward, controlling the radios, radar, and all communications. As a bombardier, he adjusted the setting for bomb drop intervals and altitude.

To fire the ventral .30 caliber "stinger" machine gun, the radio operator turned around and sat or laid facing backward, grasping the spade grip of the weapon. This rear-facing gun protected the back of the plane. It was used against ground targets after the TBM flew past

Figure 101 Interior of TBM Avenger tunnel showing radio operator's console.

the target or in a steep 4-G pullout. A 16-mm camera attached to the .30 caliber gun recorded the action whenever Winnegar fired the weapon. In Andy Winnegar's Avenger, the blazing machine gun quickly littered the deck with spent .30 caliber ammunition and filled the tunnel with smoke.

Seventeen-year-old Andy Winnegar loved the adrenaline rush of firing his .30 caliber in battle, the deafening roar of the gun and the Avenger's motor, the sulfur smell of burnt gun powder, and the clattering of spent cartridges scattered on the tunnel floor. When you add in the gut-wrenching 4-G pullout, the enemy bullets passing through the tunnel, and the yelling of the pilot and Marine spotter over the intercom, you begin to feel the chaos and excitement of a TBM Avenger in the heat of battle. For men like Winnegar, this excitement was intoxicating.

TBM Avenger Ball Turret and Gunner

The TBM Avenger turret gunner sat facing rearward, operating the .50 caliber browning automatic machine gun. The Avenger's

Figure 102 TBF Avenger Ball Turret. Creative Commons Attribution 4.0 International license.

electrically-driven turret was a masterpiece of engineering. Previously, few turrets were used on aircraft. The few in existence were miserably slow and wholly inadequate mechanical or hydraulic systems. An ex-General Electric engineer, Oscar Olsen, tackled the challenge head-on using a series of Amplidyne motors that offered complete control over both speed and torque. This electrically-powered amplidyne motor-driven turret was groundbreaking in design and operation and was used in other aircraft after the TBF Avenger.[47] The designed ball turret was a self-contained unit with a gun, gunner, controls, and 400 rounds of ammunition, all held within the Plexiglas shell.

Maurice Hie, whom Andy simply called "Hie," shared Winnegar's love of the excitement of firing his .50-caliber turret machine gun in battle. He and Andy were the same age, born in 1924. Hie was from Linton, Indiana, but now lived with his mom, Jeanne, and older brother, Lucien, on Grand Avenue in San Diego, just a few blocks north

---

[47] http://aviationtrivia.blogspot.com/2010/10/groundbreaking-gun-turret-of-tbf.html

of Mission Bay. Hie worked as a mechanic for Consolidated Aircraft Corp., where they turned out a new B-24 Liberator bomber every 90 minutes.

Hie's great grandparents were from Germany, although subsequent generations listed Avion, Pas-de-Calais, France, 200 km north of Paris, as their home. This area was the Mining Basin of France, shaped by three centuries of coal mining. Hie's grandfather Adolph Sr. immigrated to the United States in 1903 with his daughter and three sons, including eight-year-old Adolph Jr. The Adolph Hie family found their way to Linton, in

Figure 103 Maurice Hie Gunner TBM Avenger. Courtesy of Andy Winnegar

Greene Country, Indiana, where an enclave of French migrants worked in the local coal mines. Adolph Sr. worked in the Linton coal mines, and his son, Adolph Jr., followed his father's footsteps down the coal mine shafts by the time he was a teenager.

With just over 3,000 people in 1900, the city of Linton in Greene Country quadrupled in population within ten years. Linton, in 1910 could claim sixteen coal mines within a three-mile radius, employing 2500 men and yielding twenty thousand tons of coal a day. Linton in the 1920s boasted 35 houses of worship and at least that many saloons.[48]

The worst mining disaster in Greene County annals occurred at the

---

[48] https://indianapublicmedia.org/momentofindianahistory/golden-age-coal-greene-county/

Little Betty mine, five miles southwest of Linton. A methane gas explosion at 2:57 p.m. on Wednesday, 28 January 1931, was propagated by coal dust. When the dust cleared, 28 men were dead. Many of the dead and injured were friends and a few countrymen of the French coal miners from Pas-de-Calais, France.

Adolph Jr. married Jeanne Hennette, whose father was also an Indiana coal miner. Unfortunately, Adolph Jr. died prematurely at 41 years of age from a heart attack in 1936. Widowed, Jeanne Hie in 1940 was the Chief Cook for the Salvation Army in Detroit, Michigan. Later, Jeanne Hie went west to San Diego to work at Consolidated Aircraft Corporation, while Maurice stayed in Indiana with his aunt and uncle to finish high school.

After graduation, Hie rode a coal-powered steam train across the country from Indiana to San Diego. It was summer, and the weather was unbearably hot. There was no air conditioning, so they kept the windows open, traveling through the arid countryside. At the end of each day, their faces were covered with coal dust and smoke, making

Figure 104 TBM Avenger Ball Turret with .50 caliber machine gun on display at the Intrepid Sea Air Space Museum New York. Rania al-Bahara CC-BY-SA-4.0 Wikimedia Commons.

Hie look a lot like his coal-mining ancestors.

In San Diego, eighteen-year-old Maurice Hie enlisted in the US Navy on 30 October 1942. Hie's working-class roots, combined with a fearless personality, made him the perfect aerial gunner. He excelled at aerial gunnery school and relished every chance to engage in combat. On observation missions over Saipan and Tinian, the Marine observer who sat in the turret displaced Hie. Nevertheless, Hie begged his pilot, Owens, to let him sit in the center cockpit so as not to miss out on a mission. In short, Hie was cut from the same cloth as his friend Andy Winnegar. When given a choice, both young men ran towards the danger seeking the excitement that combat brings forth.

Marine Observer from VMO-4

Henry Grady Gatlin Jr. was the USMC observer who rode in Owen's TBM, occupying the seat in the rear-facing turret. "Grady" was born in Hawaii in 1921. The Gatlins were Southerners with a long string of multiple generations in Mississippi. The family originally migrated from England before the Revolutionary War. Grady's birth in Hawaii was courtesy of his father's occupation. Lt CMDR Henry Grady Gatlin (1891-1972) was a United States Navy

Figure 105 Captain Henry Grady Gatlin Jr. USMC Photograph. Public Domain.

Chaplain posted around the world and served tours on board aircraft carriers. In the early 1920's he was stationed in Honolulu, serving as a chaplain aboard the cruiser USS Brooklyn. In 1935, the Gatlin family arrived at Pensacola NAS, where LCDR. Gatlin assumed the duties of the Base Chaplain. Exactly two years, later in 1937, the now very popular Chaplain Gatlin gave his last sermon before reporting for duty on the aircraft carrier USS Yorktown. Two years later, in 1939, the family moved yet again to Vallejo California, followed by San Diego in 1941. By July of 1942, Lt Comdr. Gatlin again served aboard ship. By November 1944, Gatlin was promoted to US Navy Captain, ultimately spending over 30 years as a US Navy Chaplain.

Grady Jr. attended Vanderbilt in Nashville, Tennessee, in 1942 before his education was interrupted by the war. Grady enlisted in the US Marine Corps in early 1942. By July, PFC Gatlin was in Officer Candidates School in Quantico, Virginia graduating as a 2nd Lt in October. On October 15, 1942, Lt Henry Grady Gatlin USMC married Jane Gilmore in Nashville, Tennessee. In 1943, following additional training, Gatlin was assigned to Camp Pendleton in Oceanside, California, and then to the VMO-4 Marine Corps Observation Squadron of the 4th Marine Division. By the end of April 1943, Captain Grady Gatlin was aboard the USS White Plains, going overseas along with eight crated Stinson OY-1 Sentinel Observation Planes.

Chapter 13

"POGEY BAIT AND GEEDUNKS" – JUNE 1944

As the convoy steamed on from Eniwetok to Saipan, the threat of Japanese submarine attacks was ever-present. The three-hour anti-sub patrol (ASP) in the TBM Avenger was tedium to the max, with endless expanses of empty Pacific Ocean and not a single Japanese sub sighting. Protecting the convoy steaming from Pearl Harbor across the Pacific was Composite Squadron VC-4's primary role until the actual battles began when the Marines and Army landed on Saipan. For now, tedious ASPs were the order of the day. Once again, they hadn't spotted any enemy ships and would be bringing their four 500-pound depth charges and four rockets back to the White Plains.

"Not a damn thing out here but ocean," Andy grumbled, scanning the starboard side with his binoculars while Gatlin searched the port side of the TBM from the turret.

"Time to head home, boys," Owens said from the cockpit. Thanks for operating the autopilot, Andy. It gave a nice break."

"No problem, Pat. Now you can get us back home to the White Plains."

Figure 106 Radio operator /
Bombardier's console located in
the tunnel of the TBM Avenger.
Courtesy of Simon Brown -
Platinum Fighter Sales, Warbird
and Classic Aircraft Broker.

In the TBM Avenger's tunnel, Andy Winnegar turned his attention to the ZB receiver unit's homing signal as they began the search for the USS White Plains. The escort carrier had been steaming on since they had catapulted at 0600 hours. Pat's plotting board and dead reckoning should bring them right back to the carrier as long as she hadn't changed course. Unfortunately, it wasn't always that simple as Pat tended not to keep his plotting board in working order which meant the ZB radio was their ticket home to the USS White Plains.

At least there won't be any debriefing. We can head straight to the mess for some chow and treats as long as we can find the ship!

Andy listened in on the carrier's radio ZB homing signal and heard a "dit-dah" or "A," indicating they were to the left of the correct course back to the White Plains. Andy felt Pat correct the TBM's heading to the right seeking the sweet spot and the ZB hum that would bring them home.

A few minutes later, the ZB unit switched to a "dah-dit" or "N" signal as they were now to the right of the correct course. A slight heading correction a few degrees to the left brought them back to the sweet hum.

"OK, Pat. Now, let's hold that course to the White Plains," Andy called out over the intercom to his friend.

"Sure, Andy. If you want to fly Sierra Sue, then you should go to flight school!"

"I just might look into that," Andy laughed. "You see the White Plains yet?"

"Negative, but we've been flying around for three hours, and meanwhile, she's been steaming on towards Saipan."

Figure 107 Grady Gatlin. Yearbook photograph.

"As long as we have the sweet hum on the ZB homing radio, we're golden."

"What's your rush to get back, Andy?" Grady Gatlin asked from the turret.

Grady Gatlin was a Marine Captain in the VMO-4 spotting squadron who came along for the ride replacing their gunner, Maurice Hie, who usually operated the turret's .50 caliber machine gun. Once they got to Saipan, Gatlin would be in charge of spotting the enemy and directing artillery fire from the vantage point of their TBM Avenger.

"Gotta get in line for my "Pogey Bait! A boy's gotta eat," Andy laughed.

"What's bogie bait? Some kind of navy aviator version of the salmon eggs we used fishing for trout back home?"

"No, Captain. It's Pogey Bait, not Bogie Bait. I guess it's just a Navy expression meaning candy."

"Why didn't you say so? I'll join you after I file my report with our squadron CO, Nathan Blaha."

"OK, but don't hold me up. Those treats don't last long with all the hungry sailors and aviators on board the White Plains."

"Ok. I see the White Plains, dead ahead," Pat reported. "So far, that

ZB homing signal has never failed us.,"

"I heard about a Jap pilot who got lost and had run out of fuel. The Zero was flying on fumes. He picked up a homing beacon and landed his Zero on one of our escort carriers," Andy related. "Talk about nerve!"

Maintaining radio silence, Owens descended and approached the carrier, passing it along its starboard side before turning back onto his downwind leg with his landing gear and tail hook down.

Flying downwind along the ship's port side allowed the Flight Officer on the White Plain's bridge to inspect the plane to confirm that the landing gear was down and the tail hook deployed.

Looking to his left, Owens waited for the green light, indicating that all gear was down and the tailhook was deployed.

There's the green light. Let's land this Avenger.

Owens decreased power as the Avenger passed the ship's stern and immediately began the short rounded descending turn to the left, lining up with the flight deck.

He increased power and the angle of attack on the short descent, dragging the airplane with power rather than gliding towards the deck.[49]

Picking out Lt. Pine, the landing signal officer, Pat spotted his two flags positioned over his head, indicating that their approach was too high.

OK. Bring her down.

Pushing the stick forward, Pat got Sierra Sue onto the correct glide path, and the landing officer lowered the flags to the straight and level horizontal position.

"Ok! Now we're in the groove," Pat called out as the TBM dropped toward the carrier.

As the Avenger crossed over the deck's threshold, the landing officer crossed his right flag across his body, the signal to chop power.

---

[49] Letting the engine pull the plane through the air rather than gliding, assures that when the pilot "chops power" the plane will fall out of the sky onto the carrier deck.

Figure 108 Landing signal officer and TBM Avenger. World War Photos.

Pat immediately pulled the throttle all the way back, cutting power, and the Avenger fell out of the sky, making a solid three-point landing.[50]

The tail hook missed the first cable and bounced over the second cable before finally grabbing ahold of the third of the five arresting cables. The hydraulic cables pulled out, quickly stopping the Avenger with a jolt. The entire sequence from entering the approach to engaging the cable took only 20 seconds.

"Well, boys, we walked away from another teeth-jarring landing!" Owens announced. "Looks like we won't be needing the barriers on

---

[50] The entire landing sequence on the carrier is carried out in radio silence to avoid detection by the enemy. On the downwind leg, the Green Light from the bridge confirms that gear and tail hook are down. The Landing Flight Officer's two flags control the descent plane towards the carrier's deck. In the event that radio communication is needed, the White Plains call sign is "Convict Base" and Owen's Avenger is "Convict 7."

this flight!"[51]

Climbing out of the Avenger's side door, Winnegar waited for Gatlin, who descended out of the turret into the tunnel.

"Watch your step and keep your feet off my radio transmitter!" Andy called out as Gatlin wormed his way out of the turret into the Avenger's tunnel.

"Well, Captain, how'd you like flying with the Navy today?"

"Not bad for a first ride. What happens when the enemy starts shooting at us?" Gatlin asked outside the plane, wiping beads of sweat off his forehead.

"Our Avenger is a fighting machine, so we shoot back! We've got three .50 caliber machine guns, my .30 caliber stinger, rockets, bombs, and torpedoes."

"I guess you'll have to check me out with that .50 caliber in the turret."

"Sure thing, Captain Gatlin. Be my pleasure. Now, do you still want some of that Pogey Bait?"

"Sure. You guys serve better chow than the Marines' C-RATS," Gatlin laughed. [52] "Also, you can drop the Captain stuff in private. Grady is fine in the plane."

"OK, Grady. Then stash your stuff in your locker, and meet me below the hangar deck at the canteen. You are about to experience a real Navy tradition."

The canteen was crawling with unhappy-looking sailors.

"What do you guys mean? You ran out of Pogey Bait!"

"That's impossible! What do you expect us to eat around here?"

"Yeah! Come on! We live for this junk food. I've been looking

---

[51] The carrier had three barriers that were in the down position, but raised rapidly if the landing was long.

[52] C-RATS or C-Rations were developed in 1938 and consisted chiefly of canned corned beef or bacon and cans of hardtack biscuits, as well as ground coffee, sugar, salt and tobacco with rolling paper.

forward to this treat all day!"

After a few tense minutes, the crowd of disappointed sailors slowly filtered away, leaving Andy and Gatlin alone in front of the canteen.

"Sorry about this, Captain."

"Yes. I was looking forward to the Navy tradition of post-mission Bogey Bait."

"It's Pogey Bait, Captain, but we'll try again tomorrow if we can get Mr. Owens to head home a little earlier."

They turned and were walking towards the exit.

"Pssst! Winnegar!"

Andy stopped and turned around, looking for the source of the voice."

"No! I'm over here in the canteen!"

Andy looked back at the now-empty canteen and spotted a black Messman, motioning for him to come over. "Yeah! Come on over here."

As Winnegar and Gatlin approached the canteen, he spotted the Messman and laughed.

"Willie, what are you doing back there?"

"I thought you might be coming, so I saved you some geedunk. And here's some for your Captain."

"Hey! Thanks, Willie!"

"What's a geedunk? I thought we wanted Pogey Bait."

"No, Captain. Geedunk is even better. It's ice cream!"

"Thanks, Willie!" Andy smiled.

"Don't mention it to anyone. Me and the guys think you're OK, Winnegar. Maybe we can spar again sometime."

"Sure thing, Willie. I think you guys are alight and darn good boxers."

"Go on and get out of here before someone sees us and gets me in trouble for holding out the geedunks. They'd go nuts if they knew we had more back here."

As they walked back up to the hangar deck, enjoying their geedunks, Winnegar's thoughts were interrupted.

"How do you know the Black messmen?"

"Long story, but it has to do with boxing."

"You mean here on the ship?"

"Yeah, and back home in New Mexico. I fought a lot of black boxers in Golden Gloves and admired their heroes like Joe Louis. They're good people. Different from us but still good people. I guess I try to treat them the way I would want to be treated."

"What do you mean?"

"The way I see it, they got the short end of the stick their whole life through no fault of their own. So, it seems like the least I can do is treat them like people."

"Well, it looks like you are being paid back one geedunk at a time, Winnegar."

"Guess you're right, Captain," Andy smiled as he polished off the last of his chocolate ice cream. "But I can't eat too much of this stuff. Gotta stay in boxing shape!"

Figure 109 WWII Navy sailors enjoying geedunks. US Naval Institute Photo Archive. Wikipedia.

Chapter 14

CRAPS, SCUTTLEBUTT AND TORPEDO ATTACKS – JUNE 12 1944

Informal interactions between the officers and enlisted men aboard the White Plains were rare, unplanned, and could lead to unexpected consequences like Winnegar and Gatlin's surprise geedunks or something more.

Thursday, 12 June, was a non-flying day for Owen's TBM Avenger crew. Andy Winnegar had spent the morning cleaning the .50 caliber wing guns and was now reading in his bunk. Andy read a lot. In fact, he read everything he could get his hands on. He was looking into signing up for a correspondence course, but that would have to wait.

Winnegar was on his way to the ship's library with his usual stack of books to return. The library was in the ship's stern on the fourth deck below the flight deck. The ship's librarian was a Naval officer Lt. Widoff, who did double duty as the White Plains' chaplain.

"Winnegar, are you back again? You must like to keep me company. Most of the ship's crew comes in here looking for comic books or porn, and we don't have either."

"Well, that's a relief. Do you have any books on speaking German?"

"You want to be a spy, Andy?"

"No. I'm just naturally curious and can't stop reading."

"Well, you average a book a day by my accounting. How are your tests for Flight School coming along?"

"Dr. Donelson gives me a test every week and says I'm doing well. I'll be able to take the tests in German soon," Andy laughed as he headed out with his new stack of books.

Figure 110 TBM Avenger. Cleaning machine guns Public Domain. Low Family Collection.

Winnegar had just settled into his bunk, filling out his application for a correspondence school, when a familiar voice interrupted his reading.

"Andy, come down to the hangar deck for a craps game," Steve Walley called out. "You can make some money to pay for all the books you read!"

Walley was Andy's best friend and the radio operator in another TBM Avenger piloted by Rocky Carson, the sometimes-boxing referee for Winnegar's demonstration matches with Goldberg.

"No way I'm going to give away my hard-earned money. Your games of chance are probably rigged with loaded dice," Andy laughed.

"Come along anyway for some company. We can check for geedunks afterward."

"OK. I guess I can finish up this application later."

"You're smart enough, Winnegar. You don't need any more school," Steve laughed.

Andy encountered a most unusual sight as they approached the illegal craps game on the hangar deck. A group of ten enlisted sailors and aviators were crouched around the game as expected, but right in the middle of the group was Lt jg Pat Owens, his pilot.

"Oh, man! This is going to be bad. Those guys are busted, and it's my pilot doing the busting. I'll never live this down!" Andy moaned.

"We better head the other way," Walley suggested.

"No. It's too late. We've been spotted. Look. Tigner's waving for us to come over."

As they drew closer, Andy heard Owen's voice commanding the sailor's attention.

"You see, fellas. It's all in the wrist. You put a little English on it as you roll the dice. Let's say this is the come-out roll for a pass bet," Owens explained as he tossed the dice against the wall.

The two dice bounced off the deck, hit the far wall, and clattered to a stop.

"See! A perfect '7.' It works every time."

Owens looked around the group sternly before continuing. "You know that playing craps aboard ship is against Naval regulations. I should report you to the skipper."

The smiles quickly faded, and the men shuffled uneasily, hoping for a reprieve or a way to make a quick escape.

"However, you seem like a good group of guys. Not a bubblehead amongst you."

"Yeah, lieutenant, have a heart and show us more of your skills."

"Well, I'll tell you what. I promise not to report you if," Owens paused for effect as he looked each man in the eye.

"If you let me be the shooter, and you keep your mouth shut. Now get your money out, boys!"

"OK. I'll bet ten dollars on "Pass." Who wants to cover my bet?" Owens asked, grinning.

"I'll put down two dollars on "No Pass," Tigner replied.

"Me too. Here are another two dollars on "No Pass.""

"You guys are crazy. Didn't you see the lieutenant roll those dice? I'm with him. Here are two dollars on "Pass.""

After a round of bickering and cajoling, the bets were covered, and side bets were made. Finally, the moment of truth had arrived.

"Come on, lieutenant, make me some dough! Roll those dice with your English!"

Owens cupped the dice in his right hand, blew on them for effect, and with a flick of his wrist tossed them against the far wall.

The men were silent as they waited for the dice to stop.

"Seven! I told you guys to trust the lieutenant!" the lucky sailor shouted amidst the cheers and groans of the sailors.

"OK. This time I'll give you guys two to one odds if you want to bet against me. You can't pass up those odds, fellas!" Owens laughed.

"Here's ten dollars on "No Pass." Come on, guys, put your cash on the deck!" Owens continued.

The next roll of the dice came up "8," and Owens collected his winnings again.

"Someone else want a turn being the shooter?" Owens asked.

"No, lieutenant. You keep rolling until you lose. Those are our Navy regs," Tigner laughed.

Over the next 30 minutes, Andy watched as his pilot skillfully cleaned up and took all the sailors' money. He let them win a few rolls but soon had wads of cash in front of him. The glum looks of the sailors told the story. Owens was right. There were no bubbleheads in this group.

Owens looked around the group of unsmiling men. "Well, boys. In appreciation of your hard-earned cash, let me give you a few more lessons about playing craps so you can fleece your shipmates."

"Yeah! Thanks, lieutenant. You're alright!" they called out, gathering around to learn tips from the master craps player.

"Oh, and here's your money back, boys." Owens smiled as he pushed the wads of cash back into the center of the deck. "And remember, keep your traps shut about our little game."

"Sure thing, Mr. Owens. You're alright!"

"Next time we're in port in San Diego, I'll take you boys out to the "Pirate's Cove" for a real night out on the town. Now, who wants to learn how to put some English to these dice?"

The following day in the officer's mess, Lts. Owens and Carson were finishing up breakfast with the other squadron pilots. The conversation turned to the mystery of their final destination.

"Pat, you wanna bet on where the navy is sending this convoy?" Carson asked.

"That's too easy, Rocky. We're going to war, courtesy of Uncle Sammy," Owens laughed.

"No. Really. Haven't you been listening to the rumors?"

"Not worth the effort. But I'll bite. Where are they sending this armada, Rocky?"

"Well, the scuttlebutt[53] is that the White Plains and our VC-4 Squadron will park off some tropical island paradise. Then, we'll establish a forward Navy airbase complete with hula girls and mai tai cocktails!"

---

[53] Scuttlebutt in slang usage means rumor or gossip, deriving from the nautical term for the cask used to serve water or a water fountain. The term corresponds to the colloquial concept of a water cooler in an office setting, which at times becomes the focus of congregation and casual discussion. Water for immediate consumption on a sailing ship was conventionally stored in a scuttled butt: a butt (cask) which had been scuttled by making a hole in it so the water could be withdrawn. Since sailors exchanged gossip when they gathered at the scuttlebutt for a drink of water, scuttlebutt became Navy slang for gossip or rumors

"I may have to learn how to play the ukulele," Pat laughed.

"I'm not joking, Pat. Someone overhead the skipper talking to White Plains' Captain Weller, and he swears he heard it clear as day."

"I guess we'd be like the Navy version of the Marine's Pappy Boyington and his Black Sheep Corsair Squadron flying off Vella Lavella the Solomons."

"Yeah, except we've got better planes and pilots!" Rocky boasted.

"Those Japs won't know what hit 'em once they tangle with some grumpy Navy aviators."

"We'll call our base Evins Eagle's Nest," Rocky suggested getting into the spirit of the moment.

"I think Hitler already claimed that name," Owens remarked.

Their bantering was interrupted by a blaring "General Quarters" alarm.

"General Quarters! General Quarters! All hands man your battle stations!"

"Convoy is under submarine attack. Incoming torpedoes. All hands brace for shock. Pilots, man your planes."

Rocky Carson and Pat Owens ran to the Ready Room, grabbed their gear, and headed to the flight deck where the flight crews had already assembled.

"Looks like we've got some action today, Andy," Owens greeted his radio operator. "Where's Hie," he asked, looking for his gunner.

"Last time I saw Maurice, he was playing craps, I mean cards with you," Andy blurted out.

"Yeah, well, find him, and let's get Sierra Sue in the air."

Maurice came running across the flight deck between rows of TBM Avengers with their propellers spinning.

"Watch where you're going, Maurice. You're headed for a close shave running past those spinning props," Owens warned.

Maurice was already through Sierra Sue's side door and was halfway into the turret before Owens finished his warning.

Figure 111 F4F Wildcats on Aircraft carrier flight deck.

"No problem, Mr. Owen's. I still got my head attached, and my trigger finger's ready to squeeze off a few .50 caliber rounds."

Andy had followed Maurice into the Avenger's tunnel and was seated at the radio operator's console.

In rapid succession, the catapult-launched eight TBM Avengers off the port bow of the White Plains. The eight FM2 Wildcats took off directly from the flight deck and were in the air first. Each Wildcat paired up with a TBM Avenger and immediately began their search for the Jap submarines responsible for the attack.

"Keep your eyes peeled, guys. That Jap submarine is still out there somewhere. They spotted two torpedoes, but both missed." Owens said. "What type of armament do we have onboard, Andy?"

"We've got four 500-pound depth charges and eight three-inch

Figure 112 TBF Avenger dropping 1975-pound torpedo. US Navy Photograph.

rockets to deal with any submarine threat," Andy replied.[54]

"What sector are we flying, Pat?"

"We'll be out 75 miles, straight ahead of the convoy, flying lazy figure 8's," Owens replied.

"That Jap sub is still out there, so keep a sharp lookout and let's go sub-hunting."

Following the three-hour ASP, their return to the White Plains was too late for evening chow. Fortunately, Lt jg Atkinson looked up the Chief Master-at-Arms, who in turn located the Chief in charge of the galley.

"Hey, Joe. Can you fix our flyboys something to eat? They've been out looking for Jap subs while everyone else was chowing down your gourmet cuisine."

"Sure, thing, lieutenant. You fellas, take a seat while I fix you

---

[54] The three-inch anti-submarine rockets had steel tips and were designed to penetrate the water to thirty feet and then travel horizontally through the water.

something special. No SOS for you this evening."

The sizzling sounds and the smell of fried food from the galley were intoxicating.

A few minutes later, Joe returned with a dinner of fried eggs, bacon, jelly, and apricots served on regular plates. It was the best meal the guys had had since coming aboard the White Plains.

Chapter 15

MESS AND MEALS ABOARD THE
USS WHITE PLAINS

Life aboard the USS White Plains was centered around trips to the mess hall. Walking across the hangar deck, Winnegar, Hie, Walley, and Fuller descended a ladder to the enlisted men's mess hall located one deck below the hangar deck or two decks below their compartments. They made this walk three times a day unless they were out on a mission. Entering the large mess hall that seated several hundred of the ship's crew and aircrew, they funneled into a line of about 50 men with trays in hand.

"Hey, Steve! You forgot your tray. Better pick one up. Otherwise, you'll have to hold out your hands and tell the mess man, 'I'll have one serving of SOS, please,'" Andy laughed.[55]

Walley looked up and grinned, "Didn't get enough shut-eye last night. Still sleepy."

Winnegar handed him the metal tray with its six built-in compartments to keep the food separated.

---

[55] SOS – shit on a shingle was really chipped beef on toast.

Figure 113 Navy mess hall 1943. University of Missouri Savitar Yearbook Photograph.

The commotion and laughter at the other end of the room drew their attention and halted the cafeteria line.

Even from that distance, they recognized what was happening. The sea of men parted as a huge shape came strutting through the mess hall.

Oh, man! Ed Wysoki is not going to be happy with this! Bob Fuller sighed.[56]

The uproar of laughter filled the room as Rocky Carson came strutting through the hall wearing his wooden chicken beak, head bobbing forward with each step.

"The slop they're serving today is not fit for farm animals. I might as well go pick with the chickens!"

"Bawk! Bawk! Bawk"

Good-natured Rocky didn't complain about much, but the food in the mess hall was another matter and a constant source of irritation for Rocky and entertainment for the men watching his chicken antics.

"Hey, Rocky! You eat with the officers. Your food has to be better

---

[56] Ed Wysoki from New York was the chief chef aboard the White Plains.

than this." [57]

"If it were, I wouldn't be looking for the chicken coop now, would I? But at least my chickens don't lay green eggs!"[58]

The laughter in the room grew with chants of "Rocky! Rocky!"

The food was actually not too bad, depending on how long the White Plains had been at sea. Three squares a day, serving food that was considerably better than Marine field rations. Breakfast was powdered eggs and powdered milk except for Saturday when breakfast was beans.

"We learned to like beans for breakfast," Winnegar remembered.

"If we had to get up early for a flight at 0330 or 0400, for breakfast, we got real eggs any way we wanted them, over easy, or straight up with bacon. That was a real treat," Winnegar recalled. "It was a regular breakfast served on a plate."

Another crowd "favorite" for dinner was chipped beef on toast, aka "SOS," which most guys detested. Still, Andy Winnegar liked it because growing up in Missouri, he enjoyed biscuits and gravy every morning. So, to Andy's way of thinking, SOS was a close cousin of his favorite biscuits and gravy.

"When we were fresh out of port, we would have steaks for a while, but we ran out of those pretty quick. Same with fresh vegetables and fruit," Winnegar recalled.

After a few weeks at sea, the steaks, fresh vegetables, and fresh fruits were a faded memory, replaced with canned goods and whatever else was left.

For other dinners, they served lamb. Then, of course, Friday dinner was always fish if they had it. Finally, they brought out turkey with all the trimmings for a memorable holiday dinner on Christmas and New Year's. It wasn't like mom made, but it was a close second for the men on the White Plains.

---

[57] Chief Petty Officers had a different mess and officers were served by Steward mates in the Wardroom. There was not a lot of difference in the main courses. Differences would have been in the furnishings, appetizers, and desserts we all ate well when supplies were available.
[58] The men referred to the powdered eggs as "Green Eggs."

Figure 114 Admiral Halsey messing with sailors aboard the USS New Jersey Thanksgiving 1944. US Navy Photograph.

As every sailor learned quickly, selection in the mess hall did not exist. If you were in line in the mess hall, you ate whatever they were serving, or you went hungry.

Andy recalled, "There was a time when we were off Saipan when food supplies were at the bottom of the barrel. All we had to eat was beans and rice. We had rice in the morning with cream or powdered milk and sugar. We had rice and beans at lunch and rice and beans for dinner. This went on for 7-10 days until we were finally resupplied from Saipan. There was lots of grumbling that week!"

Hey, Fuller! Have some of this raisin bread. It's delicious!" Andy called out to his bunkmate.

"No way, I'm falling for that one, Andy," Bob Fuller laughed as he held the "raisin bread" up to the light, revealing dozens of weevils embedded in the slice. Maybe I'll eat the crust, and I'm not even sure that's safe."

"A little protein is just what the doctor ordered," Winnegar encouraged with a smile.

Coffee was readily available in colossal quantities with the milk already pre-mixed. The men called it "mud" and drank it down by the gallon. For Winnegar, coffee was also available in CIC or the Radio Room if he remembered to bringbut still his own cup.

Rows upon rows of folding tables and backless benches filled the mess hall. The aircrew and the ship's crew ate separately for the most part. But, regardless of whom you ate with, the mess hall was a place to refuel and socialize and hear the latest scuttlebutt.

Lately, the scuttlebutt was all about Saipan, drawing closer every day. What lay ahead for the men of VC-4 and the USS White Plains was anyone's guess, but it certainly was going to involve fast planes, big guns, and a tenacious enemy.

Chapter 16

SAIPAN INVASION – 15 JUNE 1944

The USS White Plains arrived at Saipan before dawn on 15 June 1944, the day of the invasion of the Japanese-held island by the 2nd and 4th Marine Divisions. The battle-tested 2nd Marine Division had seen action in the Pacific in bloody battles during the invasion and defense of Guadalcanal and Tarawa. The 4th Marine Division was officially activated on 16 August 1943 at Camp Pendleton, Oceanside, California. They had seen action in the occupation of Kwajalein and Majuro Atolls on 1-8 February 1944. Saipan would be the 4th Marine Division's first assault on an enemy-held island.

In the waters off Western Saipan, 34 LSTs were unloading 719 Higgins Boats and LVT amphibious tractors in four lines headed for the eight assault beaches along with southwest Saipan. The landing craft would form up in lines 4,000 yards from the beach in preparation for a 27-minute gut-wrenching ride to the assault beaches.

During the invasion of Saipan, the air squadron VC-4 from USS White Plains would provide cover for the fleet against enemy torpedo and air attacks, strafe the beaches, and spot enemy shellfire.

Figure 115 Aircraft carrier squadron ready room WWII. Library of Congress.

Onboard the White Plains, Naval aviators and a handful of Marine leathernecks packed the squadron-ready room. Nineteen-year-old Andy Winnegar looked around the USS White Plains from his cushioned leather seat in the back of the ready room.

The Wildcat and TBM Avenger pilots of Composite Squadron VC-4 filled the seats ahead of him. Young and confident, the pilots engaged in loud, good-natured bantering. Some snoozed. All felt the butterflies as this would be their first experience with actual combat. Training had prepared them for every contingency and battle scenario, but the stakes were a thousand times more real now that an enemy would be shooting back at them.

"Hey, Winnegar! How ya doin' this fine day?" Rocky Carson asked with a wide Louisiana grin. Make sure you make it back today. We need you to entertain the crew with your boxing prowess."

"Thanks, Mr. Carson. I'll try to keep my head on straight," Andy laughed. "Besides, I'll be needing my head intact if the Navy accepts me for flight school."

Maurice Hie sat down next to Winnegar. "How you doing, Andy?"

"What do you mean, Hie?"

"Well, this is D-Day on Saipan. First combat mission and all."

"Can't say I've given it much thought. It's not that big a deal. I don't know what to expect. I just don't want to mess up."

"Mess up? You're more ready than any man here and cool as a cucumber."

"Captain Gatlin sent for me last night to review my duties on today's flight. I'm supposed to copy Shackle code,[59] take pictures, watch our ship's gunfire, throw out leaflets, strafe enemy troops, and keep the radio operating at its maximum output. I'm going to have my fingers crossed. I'd rather be shot than make a serious mistake."

"I'd give anything to go. I begged Owens for permission to ride along in the center cockpit, but he refused. I can't believe I'm going to miss the invasion!"

"Don't worry. You'll get your chance, Hie. Actually, Captain Gatlin was giving me every opportunity to back out of the mission today. He said we'd be flying low and slow over an enemy that is armed and doesn't much like us."

"Sounds dangerous and exciting, Andy,"

"Yeah. If the Japs burn the cane fields and we have to fly low, it could be more than dangerous. But there's no way I'm going to abandon Owens. I'm his radioman. If he goes, I go."

"Well, you'll be going up in the second wave this morning. So, hang on to your hat."

---

[59] A shackle code is a cryptographic system used in radio communications on the battle field by the US military and the Rhodesian Army. It is specialized for the transmission of numerals. Each of the letters of the English alphabet were assigned a numeric value. A number could have several letters assigned. – Wikipedia.

Lt Comdr. Robert C. Evins, the commanding officer of Composite Squadron VC-4, entered late, stood at the front of the briefing room, and waited. The bantering stopped immediately.

"Men, we have 20,000 Marines going ashore this morning along southwest Saipan at Red, Green, Blue, and Yellow Beaches," Evans said, pointing at a map of Saipan.

Continuing, "VC-4 will be flying a CAP/Strike[60] mission. We will patrol the air over the invasion armada and beaches and engage any Jap aircraft intent on harming our leatherneck and grunt brothers. The Zeros will be coming from the Aslito Airfield along the island's southern end. We also have reports of carrier-based enemy fighters, so watch your backs."

"We'll fly at different assigned altitudes to shorten the response time to engaging the enemy. Those Marines have a rough day ahead of them. Your job is to neutralize the enemy airpower. All of it. Do you understand?"

"Yes, sir!" came a raucous reply. "Let's go!"

Figure 116 TBM Avenger on carrier flight deck. US Navy Photograph.

---

[60] CAP – Combat Air Patrol

"Not so fast, boys. Your secondary role today is to strike the enemy gun emplacements and Jap troops wherever you find them. We need to soften them up so strafe and bomb the enemy at will. They have some big-time artillery down there, and we want to silence those cannons."

The men let out another raucous cheer.

"Three TBM Avengers will be flying with Marine spotters from VMO-4. Your mission is to patrol for Jap submarines and to locate Jap artillery emplacements. Call in the coordinates to direct Naval strikes against these targets. Make sure you know where our guys are before you start raining down the firepower from our Naval artillery."

"Any questions? No? Well, then God Speed and happy hunting, men!"

"Come on, Andy. Let's go and check out the flight deck," Maurice said.

"You can't get enough excitement, Maurice," Andy laughed.

On the flight deck, everything was hustling aboard the ship. The deckhands were getting Wildcat fighters off for fighter strikes. The steam-driven catapult on the port bow of the White Plains was busy launching the first wave of torpedo bombers. Some of the flights got off earlier if they were on strike missions to fire rockets and drop bombs.

Gatlin came up behind them. "We go out on the second wave today. Our mission is to observe troop movements and artillery fire for the commanding general. You need to be taking photos of the front lines."

"I have my KC-20 camera ready and loaded with film," Andy replied while adjusting the large camera.

Later that morning, on the flight deck, Owens started and warmed

Figure 117 TBM Avenger air craft carrier catapult launch. Public Domain. World War Photos.

up the Avenger's Wright Twin Cyclone engine. Gatlin was in the turret and Winnegar in the Avenger's tunnel. Then, taking their position on the White Plains catapult, Owens called out, "Let's go to war, boys."

The catapult officer gave Owens the one-finger turn-up signal.

Owens nodded, advancing the throttle to full take-off power. The engine roared, straining against the restraining hook. In the tunnel, Andy sat up straight and grabbed the back of his neck.

Can't reach the damn catapult grips with this tight shoulder harness. "Let's get this show on the road!" Andy hollered.

Gatlin, in the turret, braced himself and grabbed onto the .50 caliber gun grip.

Then, with the final launch signal, the Avenger catapulted down the deck and off the end of the flight deck. Owens's head snapped back. They were airborne in two seconds as the plane dipped down, passing over the carrier's bow, and then ascended into the air towards Saipan.

When they arrived at the west coast of Saipan, the chaos of the beach landings by the 2nd and 4th Marine divisions was evident. The landing had been underway for about one hour, and the Japanese

Figure 118 Saipan Invasion 15 June 1944. Landing craft waiting to go in. Saipan, Marianas. Public Domain. Coast Guard Photo 222-19

shelling pinned down the Marines on the beach. Several of the Amtraks were held up offshore on the coral reef.

An eerie quiet had preceded the initial assault on Saipan's beaches as the 31,000 Japanese held their fire until the Americans passed over the coral reef and entered the lagoon. Then, all hell cut loose as the deafening barrage from the concealed coastal artillery commenced. Japanese artillery hit three "amphibs" almost immediately, stranding two near shore and leaving the third smoking 100 yards offshore. The beaches' congestion and chaos made the Marines an easy target for Japanese mortar and machine gunfire. The fighting was fiercest on the southern Yellow beaches, where after a full hour of battle, the 1st Battalion Marines were still pinned down on the beaches. Still, by nightfall, 20,000 combat-ready soldiers had landed on Saipan at the cost of up to 3500 American lives.

Figure 119 Saipan Beach Landing with wrecked amphibious tractors 15 June 1944. Public Domain.

"Those Marines and Amtraks are being creamed by the Jap shell fire," Andy said.

The amphibious tanks they hoped would take them off the beach couldn't penetrate far. Most were stuck on the beach, pinned down by Japanese artillery and mortar fire.

"Man, I feel bad for our Marine brothers down there. Those guys are taking it in the shorts and can't even get off the beach," Owens said.

"Well, let's fly low over the island and spot enemy artillery so we can call in Naval strikes," Andy said.

"Not too low or too slow. Those guys down there will be shooting at us," Gatlin observed nervously.

"Gotta do our job, Grady. The mission is to get in close and take photographs. We can't do much good from up here," Pat replied as he descended to 600 feet. "Don't worry. We have plenty of firepower."

Figure 120 Buffalo Amtrak landing on Saipan beach 15 June 1944.

Andy was busy in the Avenger's tunnel preparing his KC-20 camera when he noticed something he had never seen before. A pencil beam of sunlight shone in from the Avenger's skin, bouncing off his radio equipment.

That's weird! I wonder where that light's coming from. It's kind of pretty.

In the next instant, Andy got his answer as a 7.7 mm bullet from small arms ripped a hole in the bottom of the plane, tore off the zipper on his jungle pack, and continued out the other side of the Avenger's fuselage. Now there were two pencil beam shafts of light shining through the tunnel.

"Holy crap! Those guys are shooting at us! A round just passed through the tunnel and struck my jungle pack," Andy yelled into the intercom.

"I'm a little busy up here, Andy. Deal with it," Owens replied.

Figure 121 Marines pinned down on Saipan beach 15 June 1944.

"Get your camera out and take photos of the front line on the next pass," Gatlin instructed, climbing out of the turret into the tunnel. "Are you OK?"

Andy was staring at the pencil beam shaft of light streaming into the Avenger. "Yeah, I guess."

Gatlin could not shake the image of the shaft of sunlight and the holes in Sierra Sue's fuselage as he climbed back up into the turret. His hands were shaking as he gripped the .50 caliber machine gun, and beads of sweat formed on his brow.

The next shell could be for me! Stop it, Grady. Shake it off!"

He felt the heaving in his stomach at the same time as the bitter taste arrived at the back of his throat. In the next instant, Grady was heaving his green egg breakfast all over his flight suit.

Picking up the intercom, Gatlin called out to Pat, "I'm airsick, Pat. Can you ease up on the dives and turns?"

"Are you barfing in the turret? Andy, get Grady something to puke into. I'll head out to sea while you settle down your stomach."

Andy quickly looked around the tunnel for a bag and then spotted his bag of trusty hand grenades. Emptying the six hand grenades onto the deck of the tunnel, Andy took the green canvas grenade bag, handing it to Gatlin.

"Here, Grady. Use this bag for your puke. The green color will match your eggs from breakfast," Andy quipped.

A few minutes later, Grady checked in. "I'm doing better, but Andy's grenade bag is a mess."

"No problem, Grady. Let's get back to work," Pat replied as he headed the Avenger towards Saipan's shore.

Andy took the now full and foul-smelling grenade bag, opened Sierra Sue's side door and chucked the bag into the slipstream. "Here's a little gift for the emperor, boys!"

Directing the K20 aerial camera out the side windows of the tunnel, Winnegar photographed the area ahead of the advancing Marines. At the same time, he kept his eyes peeled for enemy pillboxes and artillery emplacements.

As they skirted the coastline looking for enemy activity near Garapan, Winnegar called out, "Looks like we got some action up ahead!"

"Whoa! That ack-ack is thick as a swarm of angry wasps," Pat replied, noting the black puffs of smoke filling the sky. "Think I'll change our altitude before they get us bracketed in."

Owens entered a tight right turn on the third pass over the Japanese line near Garapan. Andy had his camera in his hand and was leaning back to cock it when a 37mm shell passed through the Avenger's side door, hitting the camera. Scattered pieces of aluminum hit the right side of Andy's helmet and forehead.

"I've been hit. It feels like my head's been struck with a

Figure 122 Saipan Invasion 15 June 1944. Ack Ack artillery fire. Public Domain. Coast Guard Photo 222-18.

sledgehammer," Andy yelled with blood streaming down his face. His ears were roaring from the impact.

Immediately, Gatlin came down out of the turret and tore open the first aid kit before Andy had finished talking with Owens. He jerked out a compress, removed Andy's helmet, and bandaged the wound.

"Wound must be pretty bad if you're using so much compress."

In the meantime, Pat had it wide open and was throwing the Avenger all over the sky to avoid the anti-aircraft shelling.

"Cherokee, this is Leo 3. We have a wounded crew member. Request relief from station. Over."

"Leo 3, Cherokee here. Permission granted, Wilco and out."

"Andy, how's your wound?"

"OK, Pat. That 37mm shell passed within two inches of my head. Had we been 200 feet higher, it probably would have exploded in the tunnel."

Figure 123 37 mm shell hole in door of Number 27 TBM Avenger 15 June 1944. Saipan. Courtesy of Andy Winnegar.

"You have the luck of the Irish, Andy. Let's head on back to the White Plains."

Flying back to the White Plains, Andy noticed the massive hole in the bottom of the fuselage where his 37mm shell had exited the Avenger. As they flew back to the White Plains, the slipstream was rushing through the hole, sending the red and black leaflets flying all over the inside of the tunnel. Andy was supposed to drop the flyers for the Saipanese civilians but had been preoccupied. So now the red leaflets covered the windows.

As they entered the White Plains' flight pattern, the flight surgeon, Dr. Donelson, peering through binoculars, saw the Avenger's windows covered with red. "My god! Andy's blood is all over the windows! Get him to sickbay immediately."

Upon landing, Dr. Donelson met the crew. "Where's Winnegar? His blood is all over the tunnel."

"I'm OK, Doc. I just got a scratch over my right forehead. The red on the windows is from these flyers I was supposed to drop for the civilians," Andy explained, handing a red leaflet to the flight surgeon

"Really, I'm OK."

Maurice Hie greeted Andy as they exited the flight deck. "Hey, Andy. Go to sickbay so Donelson can recommend you for a Purple Heart."

"There's no way I'm going to sickbay for this scratch just so I can get a Purple Heart. We saw plenty of Marines getting shot up today. Those guys deserve the Purple Hearts. Not this little scratch!"

Figure 124 Lt. Martin Donelson Jr. White Plains VC-4 Flight Surgeon. Courtesy of Andy Winnegar.

The second hop at 1330 was to be strictly observation. Andy became intrigued with Gatlin's searching for enemy targets, and he peered intently out the side windows of the tunnel, searching for his own target.

As they passed over the center of the island near Mount Tapochau, Andy spotted a group of American tanks cresting a steep rise. As they ascended the embankment, their guns were aimed at the sky, exposing their underbelly to the enemy fire. He immediately spotted the Japanese artillery camped out on the other side of the rise, waiting for a juicy target.

"Grady! Look at those tanks cresting that rise. They're sitting ducks with that Jap artillery poised to blow them up! We gotta do something quick."

"Nice pick-up, Andy. We don't have time to call in an artillery strike. Pat, see if you can get permission to take out that Jap artillery before he makes burnt toast out of those tanks."

"Cherokee, Leo 3 here. Request permission to engage hostile Japanese artillery about to attack exposed tanks cresting a rise near Mount Tapochau. Over."

"Leo 3, Cherokee here. Permission to engage is denied. Those tanks will take care of themselves. Out."

Pat was fuming. "We can knock out that Jap emplacement in a heartbeat!"

The Japanese artillery fired on the first tank. The second tank over the rise saw the threat and fired a round at the Japanese emplacement, missing the enemy.

"Screw this! Let's lend some firepower to this party," Pat yelled as he dove the Avenger at the Japanese artillery.

"Grady! Shoot those suckers with your .50 caliber machine gun! Do it now!"

Gatlin had no experience firing the .50 caliber turret machine gun and had not trained in gunnery tactics, let alone firing from a moving TBM Avenger. Nevertheless, he pulled the trigger, but the results were pathetic and ineffective.

"Damn it! Andy, get up into the turret and take out that Jap artillery!"

Andy wasn't sure what to do, so he waited for the chaos to blow over. Fortunately, the American tanks scored several direct hits on the enemy artillery in the next moment, completely destroying the emplacement.

The rest of the afternoon was uneventful until Pat decided to unload their ordinance on a juicy target at the end of the flight.

"Let's head over to Tinian. I saw some Jap Betty bombers on the airfield."

They covered the three-mile distance between Saipan and Tinian in a heartbeat.

"See! I told you. There's a whole row of Betty Bombers just waiting for some action," Pat called out as he entered a steep dive, strafing the Bettys with his wing-mounted .50 caliber machine guns.

As the Avenger entered its 4-G pullout, Andy had a clear no-deflection shot into the hanger and unloaded several long bursts from the .30 caliber stinger.

"Take that!" Andy exclaimed as he noticed the tracers and puffs of pink smoke surrounding Sierra Sue from the Japanese anti-aircraft guns.

Suddenly, the Avenger shook with a jolt as she caught a 37mm shell in her port elevator, shearing off a 14" x 18" piece of the plane when the shell exploded.

"How bad is It, Andy?" Owens asked.

"We're missing a big chunk of our port elevator."

Figure 125 TBM Avenger with damaged port elevator. World War Photos.

That evening Grady and Pat invited Andy to "Officer Country" for a shot of whiskey to calm his nerves. Officers' quarters are separate from enlisted berthing. Andy politely declined, but a few minutes later, Dr. Donelson showed up to evaluate his patient and to see if the battle stress was getting to him.

"How are you doing, Andy?"

"I'm doing great, Doc. Why does everyone keep asking me that?"

"Because you just sustained an injury in a war zone and almost got your head blown off."

"Well, when you put it that way. But, no, I'm fine, Doc. I'm ready to go back up tomorrow. There's nothing I can do to change it, so let's get me back up in the air."

"Alright. But first, let me examine you. Hold your hands out in front of you. Nice and steady."

"Alright, Andy. I concur that you do not need whiskey tonight. But you take care of yourself. We have to get you into flight school."

At 1750, CIC identified bogeys approaching the White Plains, and a CAP led by Lt. Kurz was sent to investigate. They intercepted five Japanese Jills and shot down two at 29 miles and the other two as they approached the White Plains, with the fourth shot down five miles from the ship. The fifth Jill broke through, and Lt Henry C Palmer scrambled his FM-2 Wildcat off the deck to support Lt Kurtz's division. The Jill attacked another Taffy 3 escort carrier. Palmer engaged the enemy with a flat rear approach at 100 feet above the water, firing at 1000 feet. He hit the Jill's fuselage and starboard wing, but only one of his guns was firing.

"Crap! Let's go around and recharge the guns!" Palmer yelled.

Palmer banked to the right, recharged his .50 caliber wing guns, and closed on the Jill with all four guns blazing. Four Wildcats from VC-68 joined the fight, attacking from above, and a heavy barrage of anti-aircraft fire from our destroyers helped to finish off the enemy. The Jill burst into flames and crashed in full view of the White Plains port bow, five miles from the ship.

In landing the CAP FM2-Wildcats, Lt Solon N. Bales crashed into the sea over the port side in an attempted night landing. As he struggled to extricate himself from the sinking plane, his parachute harness became entangled in his jungle pack. Finally, out of the plane, someone threw him a signaling light as the White Plains steamed away. The light saved his life as he signaled a destroyer escort and was recovered uninjured by the DE, who later put him aboard the White Plains by breeches buoy.[61] The White Plains crew had a busy time as another enemy plane broke through just above the water, presenting a difficult target in the mounting dusk. The White Plains 20-mm and 40-mm guns repulsed the invader without damage.

So ended the first hectic day of battle during the Saipan invasion for the USS White Plains and VC-4. The stakes were high, and all bets were final as both sides were playing for keeps.

Figure 126 Fred E. Kurz FM-2 Wildcat pilot. VC-4

Figure 127 Henry C. Palmer, FM-2 Wildcat pilot VC-4. Courtesy of Andy Winnegar

---

[61] A breeches buoy is a rope-based rescue device used to extract people from wrecked vessels or to transfer persons from one place to another.

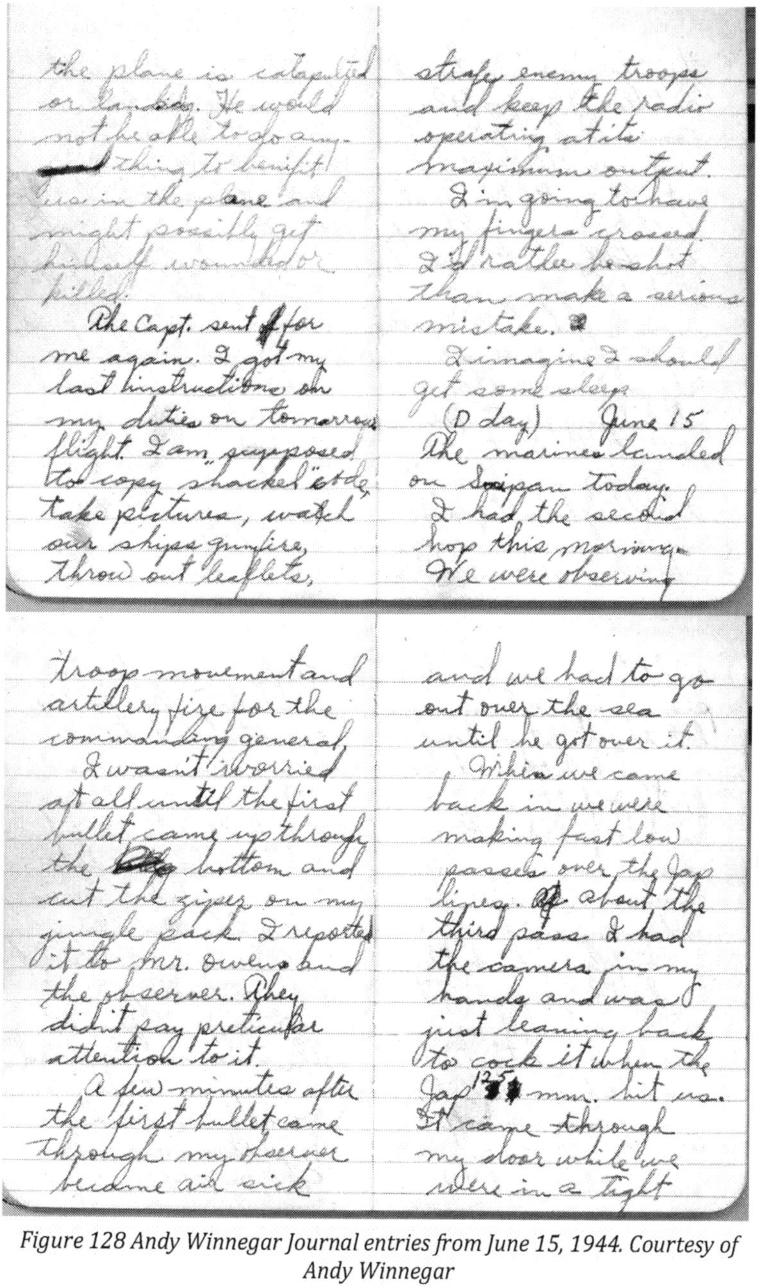

the plane is catapulted
or landed. He would
not be able to do any-
thing to benefit
us in the plane and
might possibly get
himself wounded or
killed.
    The Capt. sent off for
me again. I got my
last instructions on
my duties on tomorrows
flight. I am supposed
to copy shackel code,
take pictures, watch
our ships gunfire,
throw out leaflets,
strafe enemy troops
and keep the radio
operating at its
maximum output.
I'm going to have
my fingers crossed.
I'd rather be shot
than make a serious
mistake.
    I imagine I should
get some sleep.
(D day)   June 15
The marines landed
on Saipan today.
I had the second
hop this morning.
We were observing

troop movement and
artillery fire for the
commanding general.
I wasn't worried
at all until the first
bullet came up through
the bottom and
cut the zipper on my
jungle pack. I reported
it to Mr. Owens and
the observer. They
didn't pay particular
attention to it.
    A few minutes after
the first bullet came
through my observer
became air sick
and we had to go
out over the sea
until he got over it.
    When we came
back in we were
making fast low
passes over the Jap
lines. At about the
third pass I had
the camera in my
hands and was
just leaning back
to cock it when the
Jap 25 mm. hit us.
It came through
my door while we
were in a tight

*Figure 128 Andy Winnegar Journal entries from June 15, 1944. Courtesy of
Andy Winnegar*

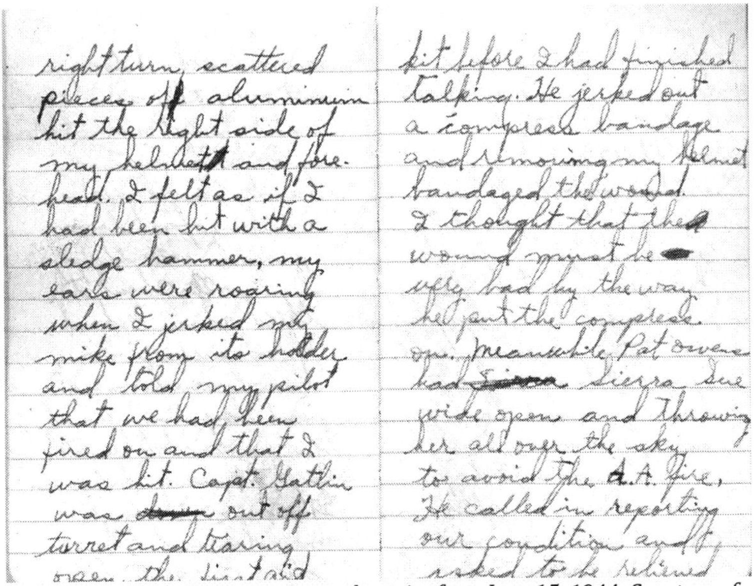
right turn, scattered pieces of aluminum hit the right side of my helmet and fore-head. I felt as if I had been hit with a sledge hammer, my ears were roaring when I jerked my mike from its holder and told my pilot that we had been fired on and that I was hit. Capt. Gatlin was [illegible] out of turret and tearing open the first aid

kit before I had finished talking. He jerked out a compress bandage and removing my helmet bandaged the wound. I thought that the wound must be ugly bad by the way he put the compress on. Meanwhile Pat Owens had [illegible] Sierra Sue wide open and throwing her all over the sky to avoid the A.A. fire. He called in reporting our condition and asked to be relieved

Figure 129 Andy Winnegar Journal entries from June 15, 1944. Courtesy of Andy Winnegar

Chapter 17

THE SKIPPER IS MISSING –
17 June 1944

Robert C. Evins, command-
ing officer of Composite
Squadron VC-4, was a
Southerner from Hartsville,
South Carolina. His slight build
belied the heart of a lion, evident
in his exploits at Annapolis in
Battalion Boxing and Battalion
Football. Bob, or "Sweet Pea," a
man of many facets, loved theater
and was cast in "Medicus" and
"Rome and the Modern World" at
Hartsville High School.

Figure 130 LCDR Robert C. Evins

Aboard the USS White Plains,
Lt CMDR Evins was the beloved

Figure 131 Japanese twin engine plane shot down attacking USS Kitkun Bay CVE 71. June 18 1944. Public Domain.

leader of VC-4. A direct, quiet, and down-to-earth man, Bob led from the front as squadron CMDR and FM-2 Wildcat pilot. An excellent pilot, he never once missed an approach for a carrier landing and had the complete confidence and loyalty of his men and the love of his wife, Mary Elizabeth.

17 June 1944 is a day never to be forgotten in the annals of the USS White Plains.[62] The buildup of Japanese aircraft and activity in the vicinity of the Marianas and the Philippine Sea made it clear that something was brewing. Japanese Admiral Ozawa had steamed his fleet from Tawi Tawi on 13 June, shadowed by American submarines who regularly reported the activity to American Admiral Spruance. Ozawa had gathered together 440 aircraft onboard nine aircraft

---

[62] On 17 June 1944 seven FM-2 Wildcats from the VC-4 squadron were lost, the largest single-day loss in the entire war for VC-4.

carriers, forming the Japanese Naval Mobile Fleet supplemented by Japanese island garrisons. The larger American aircraft carriers were sent to meet Ozawa's Mobile Fleet. For the Americans, Admiral Spruance commanded 905 fighters, torpedo, and dive bombers from 15 carriers. The ensuing Battle of the Philippine Sea would not take place for two days on 19-20 June 1944. History shows that the lopsided battle and the "Great Mariana Turkey Shoot" would severely cripple the Japanese naval fleet with minimal American losses.

The USS White Plains remained in place off Saipan to support the invasion forces. 17 June 1944 was a busy day with FM-2 Wildcat fighters flying CAP strike missions to engage and neutralize the increasing Japanese air power in the area. During the day, a few of the Japanese Kates and Vals broke through with intentions to attack and sink the White Plains. However, none was successful as the White Plains' anti-aircraft guns and the firepower of the Destroyer Escorts destroyed the attacking aircraft. Nerves were on edge with repeated calls to General Quarters throughout the day.

By evening the fighters began to return to the White Plains and the other escort carriers. As darkness fell, the situation became chaotic, with American fighters and torpedo bombers sometimes returning to the wrong carrier. A fighter pilot from another carrier attempted to land on the White plains just after sunset. When the pilot flared out and pulled the stick back, he hadn't turned off his gun switch. The pilot accidentally pulled the gun trigger, firing his wing .50 caliber machine guns across the flight deck.

Winnegar and Hie were on the White Plains flight deck preparing to dismount and clean the Avenger's two wing machine guns when the Wildcat's .50 caliber bullets sprayed wildly over the deck.

"Crap! Andy, that Wildcat pilot's got his gun switch jammed!" Hie yelled as bullets from both wing guns rained destruction across the flight deck.

"We gotta get out of here," Andy yelled as they took cover behind their Avenger.

The flight deck was chaotic, with bullets ricocheting off the deck at

Figure 132 Edward Billinghurst FM-2
Wildcat pilot VC-4. Courtesy of Andy
Winnegar.

850 rounds per minute as crewmen and deckhands dove behind whatever cover they could find.

The shooting finally ceased as the FM2 Wildcat came to a stop.

"I think the flight deck isn't such a great place to be right now. Let's go down to the weather deck."

"I'm with you, Andy. Let's get our butts out of here before they get riddled with bullet holes," Hie laughed.

From the Weather Deck, Andy and Maurice watched the next FM-2 Wildcat approach.

"He's coming in way too fast, and his flaps aren't down. He's not going to make it!" Andy yelled

The FM-2 Wildcat piloted by Ens. Edward Billinghurst of VC-4 had been damaged by .50 caliber gunfire that had also struck Billinghurst. The Wildcat barreled headlong towards the White Plains with no time to correct his approach as Lt. Pine, the landing signal officer, frantically waved the plane off.

"He's not going to make it. He's coming in way too high and fast!" Maurice yelled as the Wildcat missed all five cables, hit the deck, and bounced over the barrier cables, landing in a fiery crash amongst the planes parked at the end of the flight deck. The fire and explosions were felt throughout the ship.

"Whoa! That's right where we were standing ten minutes ago!" Andy exclaimed.

"Someone's injured down there!" Maurice yelled. "I hope it's not one of our guys!"

Eighteen-year-old Roger R. Albright, a gunner for Lt. Flateboe's TBM Avenger, was removing the wing .50 caliber machine guns for cleaning when disaster struck. He was crushed and severely burned that night when Billinghurst's plane crashed on USS White Plains. Albright was taken to the sickbay but succumbed to his injuries later that night. Albright, born in Texas, had grown up in an orphanage in Pasadena, California, run by the Boys and Girls Aid Society. Roger, who had always dreamed of flying, was the first airman of Composite Squadron VC-4 killed during the war. Unfortunately, he would not be the last. In the same crash, James M. Lancaster AMM3/C was lost over the side and was not recovered.

Just before sunset, enemy raiders attacked just after 1800. At 1809 the White Plains scrambled eight FM-2 Wildcats led by Lt CMDR Robert C Evins. Evins' flight was to reinforce a flight of four FM-2 Wildcats from the White Plains on a similar CAP / Strike mission. The weather was clear, with scattered cumulus clouds at 5,000 feet in a moonless sky.

The Wildcats pursued the enemy, encountering four single-engine Japanese bombers 16,000 yards south of the White Plains. In the confusion of night fighting, none was splashed.

Figure 133 Lt CMDR Robert C. Evins. Public Domain.

Two bombers dove at the White Plains, which took violent evasive actions with all of her starboard anti-aircraft guns blazing. One "Kate" bomber was probably shot down. The second enemy pulled out of his dive and passed overhead 2,000 feet to starboard, his bombs falling harmlessly into the water. During the hour and a half raid on the White Plains, the gunners fired 5,000 rounds of 20-mm and 40-mm ammunition and 15 rounds from the 5" gun on the fantaiO.[63]

As sunset approached at 1845, the two FM-2 Wildcat divisions were split up and vectored out by the controlling fighter director officer. Neither division made further contact with the enemy. Thirty-five minutes later, at 1920, all aircraft were recalled preparatory to recovery and were instructed to turn on running lights[64] to signify friendly character. Five FM-2 Wildcats of Composite Squadron VC-4 landed aboard the USS White Plains between 1923 and 2005, and two more landed safely aboard other carriers.

At 2145 Evins contacted the White Plains.

"Convict Base, this is Convict 1. I have an oil leak. Vision is totally obscured by oil covering the windshield, over." [65]

"Convict 1, Convict Base here. Land aboard the ship if you can read the landing signals—otherwise, land in the water alongside our Destroyer Escort. Do not land in the water until instructed to do so. Turn on your running lights, over."

A minute later, Convict Base repeated the instructions.

"Convict 1, Convict Base. Acknowledge. Land aboard the ship if you can read the landing signals—otherwise, land in the water alongside

---

[63] The USS Fanshaw Bay was hit and had to retire. Three of her planes unable to land on the damaged flight deck, landed on the USS White Plains. Rear Admiral GF Bogan USN transferred to the White Plains on 18 June, making this his flag ship.

[64] "Turning on. Running lights" is coded instructions for the pilot to turn on their IFF that would send out a signal every two seconds that showed up on the ship's radar identifying the plane as a "friend."

[65] Radio silence was maintained so the enemy would not learn the name and position of the carrier. If direct communication was necessary, code names were used. Convict Base was the USS White Plains, Convict 1 was the VC-4 plane contacting the White Plains.

our Destroyer Escort. Do not land in the water until instructed to do so. Turn on your running lights, over."

"Convict 1, Convict Base. Acknowledge instructions, over."

At 2150 Evins finally acknowledged the orders and then added. "I believe I can land aboard by putting my head out of the cockpit, Out."

This was the last transmission received from him. Lieutenant CMDR R. C. Evins was last seen by his wingman, Lieutenant William A. Mudgett, at about 2150 when he made a normal breakup ahead of USS White Plains in preparation for landing.

Figure 134 William A. Mudgett. FM2 Wildcat pilot VC-4. Courtesy of Andy Winnegar.

Pushing back the Nacelle cockpit cover, Evins put his head out of the cockpit.

"Yeah! I can do this! Evins said as he strained to place his head out of the cockpit.

Darn oil leak. It may have been friendly fire.

As he approached the White Plains, Evins saw the lights on the deck and began to have second thoughts about his plan.

If I mess up this landing, I could put the flight deck out of commission and cripple the White Plains.

OK, Bob. Do the right thing. Land in the water alongside the carrier. They'll pick you up.

Evins veered his Wildcat to the left and glided for a forced water landing along the port side of the White Plains.

In the darkness of night, the water landing was abrupt and rough as the Wildcat skipped along the swells and came to a stop.

Removing his harness, Evins climbed out of the cockpit onto the port wing. He inflated the Mae West, turned on the emergency beacon, and wrestled the life raft into the water. As he looked up, the huge dark shape of the White Plains receded into the distance as she steamed into the night. He was soon alone in the expansive Philippine Sea as the Wildcat sank to the bottom of the ocean

Onboard the White Plains, the observer with binoculars in hand yelled out, "I see a beacon in the water on the port side. It must be Lt CMDR Evins!"

The White Plains did not stop for anyone and continued on into the night. They communicated Evins' presumed position to their Destroyer Escort. In the night, the search of the dark waters of the expansive ocean was challenging. The odds of being recovered after a night water landing were slim.

Figure 135 Lt CMDR EK Fickenscher. Public Domain.

As Andy and Hie entered the squadron ready room the next morning, the room was silent and gloomy.

"What's going on in here, Fuller? This place is like a mortuary."

"The Skipper is missing," Fuller replied. "He made a water landing last night but hasn't been found. It's not looking good."

Lt. Edward R. Fickenscher Jr., VC-4's executive officer, assumed command of the squadron and addressed the men.

"We have a job to do, men, so let's get to it. I need some volunteers to fly anti-sub patrols today. I know a lot of you are tired from yesterday's missions, but we need to press on."

En masse, the entire squadron stood. "We're ready to fly today, Skipper," they replied.

Fickenscher gazed at the young airmen, nodded, and wondered if he would ever command this type of loyalty.

Figure 136 FM-2 Wildcats of VC-4 Squadron USS White Plains.

Pilots, man your planes."

The anti-sub patrols and, in fact, nearly every flight launched from the White Plains that day were really a search and rescue mission as the men desperately searched the ocean for their beloved Skipper. It was some time before the gloom that fell over Composite Squadron VC-4 slowly began to lift. Lt. CMDR Robert C. Evins was 25 years old when he was declared Missing in Action. His body was never recovered.

Chapter 18

COMBAT INFORMATION CENTER (CIC) – JUNE 1944

The White Plains' Command Information Center or CIC was located a few steps from Winnegar's compartment on the way to the Ready Room. The CIC was the strategic heart of the White Plains. It was also a convenient place to stop for coffee as long as you brought your own coffee cup.

Andy entered the brightly lit CIC and looked around for his friend, eighteen-year-old Donald Crounse. He nodded at Ens. C.L. Lohman the CIC Watch Officer. The CIC was a different world from the rest of the ship, filled with nine men hovered around ground-searching and air-searching radar scopes, radio equipment, plexiglass plotting boards, and maps. Radarmen like Crounse and Radiomen like Homer Roos were at home in the CIC's tactical command center.

The purpose of the CIC is to collect data from multiple sources and supply that information to the commanding officer regarding the location, identity, and movement of friendly and enemy aircraft and surface ships within the area. Accordingly, ships were plotted on the horizontal plotting board while aircraft were indicated on the vertical plexiglass plotting board.

Figure 137 CIC. Command Information Center. WWII Aircraft Carrier. 1946. United States Navy. Public Domain. Wikimedia Commons.

Lt. Austin W. Kivett was the officer in charge of the CIC. Kivett, born in 1898, was more than 20 years older than the men in his charge and was the closest thing to a father figure aboard ship for most of them. Kivett was always calm and never got riled up, a calming figure in the CIC's at times chaotic world. Kivett had served in WWI and was a practicing attorney in Milwaukee before signing up for the last great war. Austin Warren Kivett was a rare gentleman in the US Navy whose men in CIC would have followed him into battle anywhere.

At Kivett's side was Lt A.W. Slater, the Fighter Direction Officer (FDO), who used air-searching radar and radio voice commands to direct the FM2-Wildcats to intercept the enemy bogeys depicted on the vertical plotting board.

Andy spotted Crounse hovering over his radar scope. Hey, Don. Do you have any fresh coffee?"

"Did you bring your mug?"

"Sure thing," Andy replied, posing with a smile on his handsome face.

"No! Not that mug, your coffee mug," Don laughed.

"Sure did," Andy replied, bringing out his WP coffee mug. "You guys make the best coffee, a lot better than the "mud" they serve in the mess.

"Help yourself," Crounse replied, not looking up from his radar scope. "I'm kind of busy right now. We're tracking some inbound bogeys headed straight for the White Plains."

"Let me see," Andy said, crowding around the scope to take a look.

Crounse moved aside, giving Andy a view of the radar scope. Three blips on the scope were headed for the White Plains.

Figure 138 Donald Crounse, Radarman in the White Plains CIC. 1943. Courtesy of Don Crounse.

"They're a ways out, maybe 60 miles, but they definitely do not have IFF lights turned on, [66] and they're headed right for us," Don added, pushing Andy out of the way. "I have to get back to work, Andy."

Crounse relayed the information about the possible bogeys to the plotter, who used a grease pencil to annotate the aircraft on the edge-lit plexiglass vertical plotting board. Next, Lt. Austin Kivett and FDO Lt. Slater evaluated the information. Kivett then picked up the on-ship intercom and spoke directly with the Commanding Officer on the bridge.

"It is so weird how those plotters write backward and right to the left on the back of the plotting board," Andy marveled.

"That way, the officers can read it from the front without having to look through the plotter," Donald explained. "It does take a while to

---

[66] IFF (Identification Friend or Foe) is an identification system designed for command and control. It enables military radar to identify aircraft as friendly and to determine their bearing and range from the interrogator. With the IFF system turned on, the appearance of the plane on the radar scope indicates it is "friend." With the system is turned off, the radar cannot distinguish a friend from a foe.

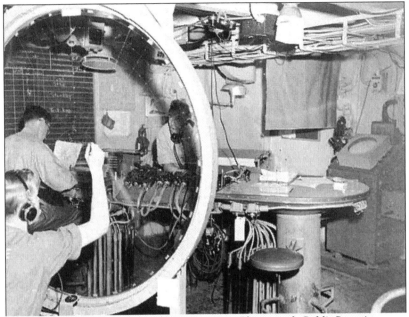

Figure 139 CIC WWII. United States Navy Photograph. Public Domain.

figure out the plotter's job. We rotate jobs, so these seven radar men in here will end up doing everything. They only let us sit in front of these radar scopes for 30 minutes at a time."

"You guys are playing musical chairs all day long," Andy said.

"I guess they're worried that the radar will harm our eyes."

"I wonder why they haven't sounded GQ for the bogeys," Don remarked with a puzzled expression.

"The Captain thinks your bogeys are a flight of TBM Avengers from St Lo with their running lights turned off," Kivett explained.

"I still call those bogeys," Crounse muttered. "And they're getting close. Bogeys are only 10 miles out now."

In the next moment, there was a blaring call on the White Plains' ship-wide overhead speakers, "General Quarters! General Quarters! All hands, man your battle stations."

Crewmen dropped everything, running to their battle stations. The galley mess men were already poised and ready at the Oerlikon 20mm anti-aircraft guns.

*Figure 140 Oerlikon 20-mm
antiaircraft gun crew.*

Gazing out to the western horizon, Willie exclaimed, "Here they come! Three Jap zeroes at 3'oclock, coming in low."

The tracers from the blazing guns on the port-side of the White Plains lit up the sky. The zeros were closing at 300 miles per hour as the sailors fought back to save their "Take that! Willie yelled as his 20-

Figure 141 Bofors 40-mm antiaircraft guns

mm shells found their target, taking out the lead zero, which plummeted to the ocean in flames, leaving a trail of black smoke. [67]

"All right! Splash one," Willie yelled, pumping his fist into the air.

"Stop celebrating, Willie. We gots two more Zekes coming in fast."

The other two Zeros split up and attacked from the bow and stern through the hail of anti-aircraft fire. The White Plains five-inch gun went into action, shooting down the second Zeke striking from the bow. The final Zeke dove at the White Plains stern and then broke off with his engine smoking, flying low over the water towards the horizon.

"Wow! We showed those Japs not to mess with the White Plains' fightin' mess men!" Willie shouted.

Back in the CIC, Crounse and the other Radarmen were busy at the six radar scopes, plotting the ships and aircraft, looking for the next attacking enemy. Then, Andy, who had gone topside during the attack, entered the CIC with his coffee cup in hand.

"Looks like you called those Bogeys right," Andy Winnegar said with a smile. "Good work, Don."

---

[67] The Oerlikon Cannon: 20 mm antiaircraft gun. The gun can fire 450 rounds per minute making the barrels glow red hot. A handler wearing asbestos gloves changed out the barrel whenever the gun was being reloaded. The hot barrel was placed in a tube to cool. The 20-mm guns could fire at a maximum range of 14,000feet or 2.73 miles at a 35-degree angle.

CHAPTER 19

FM-2 THE WILDER WILDCAT

The General Motors FM-2 Wildcat fighter flown off of the USS White Plains was the third generation of the original GM FM-1 fighter built in 1942-43. The subsequent second-generation GM F4F-4 Wildcat made by Eastern had only four wing-mounted .50 caliber machine guns instead of six but was otherwise unchanged. The Eastern FM-2 Wildcat with a more powerful Wright 1820 radial engine was lighter, climbed faster, was more maneuverable, and had a more extended range than its predecessor. The increased power of the FM-2 required a distinctive taller vertical tail. Overall, the FM-2 Wildcat was a vastly superior plane, with over 4,000 built between 1943 and 1945.

All United States Navy FM-2 fighters operated exclusively from the small CVE escort carriers. They were paired up with the larger TBM Avenger to fly antisubmarine patrols, and to provide air cover for invasion forces and close air support for ground troops.

The plane captain started the Wildcat engine with a cartridge, like a shotgun shell, that fit into a breech behind the right front landing gear. If that failed, there was a large crank on the side that you could

Figure 142 FM2 Wildcat VC 4 White 5, Dottie 15 and 7 on patrol over USS White Plains. 1944 Public Domain. US Navy Photograph.

spin, although it took a lot of energy. Unlike the heavier TBM Avenger, which required a catapult launch, the Wildcat took off directly from the carrier deck.

On the TBM, all controls are electric or hydraulic, while on the Wildcat, everything is manual. For example, to raise or lower the landing gear, the pilot had to lean forward in the cockpit and reach down on the right to locate the crank. It took 26 turns of the crank to raise the landing gear. Folding the wings on the Wildcat was also a manual operation, creating more work for the "plane pushers."

Armed with four wing-mounted .50 caliber Browning machine guns, two 250-pound bombs, or six five-inch rockets, the FM2 Wildcat could pack quite a punch. With a top speed of 332 mph, the Wildcat had a range of 900 miles. In comparison, the Mitsubishi A6M Zero had a top speed of 351 mph and a range of 1600 miles.

Over time, the Wildcats learned to hold their own, flying head-to-

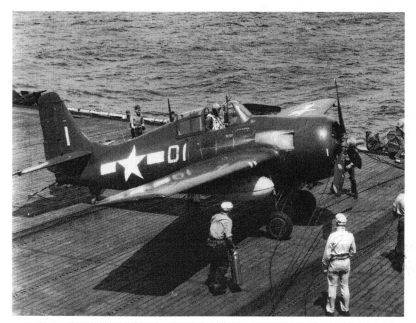

Figure 143 General Motors FM 2 Wildcat. VC 79. White D1 BuNo 55592 USS Sargent Bay. 1945 US Navy Photograph. Public Domain.

head with the Zero. The lighter Zero allowed it to fly farther.

Still, the Zero's lack of armor and unsealed gas tanks made it infamously vulnerable to disintegrating and bursting into flames after sustaining only light damage. The Wildcats learned to take advantage of their superior diving speed by attacking the Zeros from above. Finally, a maneuver called the "Thatch Weave," in which two Wildcats flew a figure eight in tandem as a "bait" and "hook," was wildly successful in downing the entrapped Mitsubishi A6M Zeros.

Air to Air combat resulted in dogfights that led to two WWII Wildcat Aces, including one who flew for VC-4 off the USS White Plains.

The White Plains' FM-2 Wildcats were in the thick of battle beginning in Saipan. The first contact with the enemy occurred on 13 June 1944 when Lt James A. Huser, flying a TBM, sighted a Japanese

Betty bomber. The twin-engine bomber dove to avoid contact and soon disappeared.

The real Wildcat battles began on D-Day on Saipan on 15 June 1944, as remembered by Lt Russ Wood of the VC-4 squadron on the White Plains.

"We arrived on station well in advance of the first wave of Marines, which started toward the beach at 0800. VC- 4 and our carrier were very much in evidence from the outset. Support missions for troop landings got off to an early start and continued throughout the day. Later in the evening, members of our combat air patrol each bagged a Japanese Jill, now 30 miles ahead of the ship. Another Jill broke through, and Lieutenant Henry C. Palmer immediately engaged the enemy firing at 1000 feet. He hit the Jill's fuselage and starboard wing root, but only one of his four guns was firing. He drew to the right, recharged his guns, and closed with all four blazing. At this point, four FM- 2 aircraft from VC- 68 made joined the attack, and the Jap was subjected to a heavy barrage of anti-aircraft from one of our destroyers. The enemy burst into flames and crashed in full view off the port bow of our carrier Lieutenant Palmer credited the kill to either the destroyer or the FM- 2

Figure 144 Lt. Russ Wood. FM-2 Wildcat pilot VC-4 on the USS White Plains. US Navy Photograph Public Domain.

Figure 145 Frank C Srsen. FM-2 Wildcat pilot VC-4 USS White Plains. US Navy Photograph. Public Domain.

group overhead."

The personality of the VC-4 Wildcat pilots matched their aircraft's name. They were young, cocky, confident, bold, and at times spoiling for a fight. Each pilot had a handle or nickname that their squadron often bestowed on them. For example, "Dunk" Maloney received his name after two unplanned water landing off the coast of California during training. Other handles just sounded good, like Dennis "The Duke" Durick. There was also Leo "Lucky Pierre" Ferko, Curtis "Slim" McGaha, Fred "The Hot" Kurz, Frank "Tiny Tim" Srsen, and Edward "The Deacon" Fickenscher.

Figure 146 Francis J "Dunk" Maloney. FM-2 Wildcat pilot. VC-4 White Plains. US Navy Photograph. .

Srsen, from Tacoma, Washington, was small in stature but had the heart of a lion. He played football at Lincoln High School and at St Mary's College, where he was a Little All-American. Srsen, whose parents immigrated from Czechoslovakia, had a fighting spirit on the gridiron and in the air as a Wildcat pilot.

The Wildcat's bravado was only matched by their loyalty to each other and the squadron. "One for All and All for One" could have been their motto borne out in many a bar fight.

In mid-June, just after D-Day, "Dunk Maloney was flying over Saipan with Ltjg John Bear, Ltjg. Lee R Pool,

Figure 147 Lt. Leo "Lucky Pierre" Ferko FM2-Wildcat pilot for VC-4 on the USS White Plains.

and Lt. Leo Ferko.

Suddenly, Maloney broke off and was in hot pursuit of a flight of the strangest enemy planes he'd ever laid eyes on. It was a beast, as large as a TBM Avenger, and there was a whole flight of them 1,000 feet below. [68]

"Man! Will you look at those pregnant Jap fighters? They're sitting ducks. I'm going to be an ACE in one day!" Dunk yelled as he dove towards the flight of unsuspecting enemy planes.

"Take that, you devils!" Maloney yelled, firing his .50 caliber wing guns into the flight.

"Stop! You idiot! Those are friendlies!" Ferko screamed.

Figure 148 Dennis E. Durick. FM-2 Wildcat pilot VC-4. USS White Plains. US Navy photograph

Maloney broke off his dive and headed out to sea. "Those aren't any American plane I've ever laid eyes on."

"They're P-47s, "Dunk." Brand new fighter."

"Come on. Those guys are landing at Aslito. We better explain "Dunks" welcome wagon," Bear said.

After landing their planes at Aslito, the four VC-4 Wildcat pilots headed for the Officer's Club adjacent to the field. Although they came in peace, the results were predictable as soon as they walked through the Officers' club doorway.

Eight P-47 Thunderbolt pilots of the 318th Fighter Group jumped to their feet as the four Wildcat pilots entered the Officers' Club.

"What the hell were you Navy yoyos doing up there shooting at us!" yelled the Thunderbolt flight leader.

"Settle down, boys," Ferko answered calmly, trying to defuse the

---

[68] Francis "Dunk" Maloney FM-2 Wildcat Pilot VC-4 USS White Plains

situation.

"Settle down my ass! You Navy boys need to learn some manners!" a P-47 pilot screamed as he hurled a chair across the room.

Bear grabbed the chair out of the air and stood with it raised over his head, glaring at the Army Air Force pilot. Bear, who was 6'2" and built like a linebacker, got people's attention when he spoke calmly. When he was riled up, people got out of his way.

"You boys want trouble?" Bear demanded. "Because if you do, you'll have to answer to me first!"

Figure 149 John H. Bear. FM-2 Wildcat pilot. VC-4. Courtesy of Andy Winnegar.

"No, we just want the head of your pilot who dove on us, firing his .50 caliber guns. Which one of you Navy swabbies was it?"

"You'll have to come through me to find out!" Bear hollered as he violently heaved the chair into the Thunderbolt pilots.

The Thunderbolt pilots charged. Their flight leader was stopped cold when "Dunk" Maloney cold-cocked him with a right cross to the chin, dropping him to the bar floor.

Ferko, Bear, and Pool were at Dunk Maloney's side throwing punches and butting heads with their Army Air Force brethren.

Figure 150 Lee Ross Pool. FM-2 Wildcat pilot. VC-4. Courtesy of Andy Winnegar.

Two Army pilots grabbed Pool, restraining him while their buddy punched him in the stomach.

"Oomph!"

"That's not a fair fight, you chicken shits!" Dunk yelled as he crashed a chair over their heads, rescuing Pool.

"Thanks, 'Dunk.' I had them right where I wanted them."

"Yeah, sure, Dunk. Let's finish these guys off!"

Ferko and "Wildman" Bear were backed into a corner when Bear charged his assailants and cracked one over the head with a beer bottle.

"How does that feel, you losers?"

After a hurricane of punches and head butts, bodies and broken chairs were strewn across the Officers' Club. The humiliation of the Army pilots was not complete until "Dunk" uttered the final insult. "Your plane looks like an ugly fat toad!" [69]

All of the men still standing were bent over and gasping for air. The fight was over. Other than a few black eyes and bloody noses, the combatants were no worse for wear. Both sides gave as good as they took, and for the most part, egos were intact.

After a round of drinks paid for by "Dunk" Maloney, the men shook hands and headed back to their planes.

"Welcome to Aslito, boys!" Ferko hollered at the P-47 pilots as he climbed into his Wildcat and headed back to the White Plains.

---

[69] The P-47 Thunderbolt's nickname was the "Flying Jug."

Figure 151 Two P-47 Thunderbolt of 318th Fighter Group taking off at Aslito Airfield, flying over Aviation Engineers. Wikimedia Commons.

Chapter 20

STRAFING, BOMBING, AND TRYING TO GET HOME – 22 JUNE 1944

Flying observation missions over Saipan with Captain Gatlin was becoming more routine, but you never knew what excitement or problems the next hop would bring. There were now only two TBM Avengers flying the dangerous observation missions. Coll McClean took himself out of the rotation after they were shot up on 17 June, requiring an emergency landing at Charon Kanoa. That left Owens, call sign Leo 3, and Rocky Carson, call sign Leo 1, to fly all of these missions, tempting fate and any enemy combatant with a firearm to take a pot shot at their Avengers. Leo 1 and Leo 3 played tag team by continually relieving each other every three hours. Not surprisingly, the bond between the crews grew as they together faced the dangers of low and slow flights over an armed enemy that didn't much care for them. They kept the metalsmiths on the White Plains busy patching up the new bullet holes in the Avenger. Sometimes the damage was so extensive that they simply pushed the plane over the edge of the flight deck into the ocean.

By 22 June 1944, the Marines had pushed inland during the week since D-Day on 15 June. However, the Japanese resistance was still

Figure 152 TBF Avenger firing HVAR Holy Moses rockets. World War Photos. Public Domain

fierce as they withdrew towards central Saipan, dominated by Mount Tapochau, the highest point on the island. Bloody battles gave rise to colorful names for adjacent landmarks, including Death Valley and Purple Heart Ridge.

Winnegar recalled, "We were relieved by Leo 1 at 12:10 and were told to help another TBM destroy a Jap emplacement. So we fired our eight rockets at the emplacement, located othe side of a gorge. We scored some near-hits."

"At 1445, we took off again to relieve Leo 1. This time we directed artillery on Japs, gathering for a counterattack. My pilot spotted some Japs near a farmhouse, and we directed Pittsburgh fire on them. We were almost hit by artillery shells several times, both on this and the morning hop. Then, having no rockets or bombs, we directed a final

Figure 153 TBM Avenger over Saipan at dusk. Public Domain

volley of Pittsburgh artillery at 1810 and headed for where our ship should be."

"Those clouds are closing in," Pat noted as he headed out over the Pacific Ocean in search of "Home" and the White Plains as the downpour started.

"I can't see a thing out here, and it's getting dark. Hope we can find the White Plains," Andy added.

"The navigation equipment on this rental plane is on the fritz," Pat grumbled. "The ZB homing radio is out of commission."

"Use your plotting board and dead reckoning," Andy suggested.

"The plotting board is broken. I wish we were flying #27. I don't trust this VC-68 plane from the Fanshaw Bay," Pat complained. [70]

---

[70] On 17 June 1944 at 18:52, a Japanese Kawasaki Ki-61 Tony fighter made a run on the Fanshaw Bay, dropping a 500-pound bomb as it flew about 1,500 ft above the carrier. The bomb penetrated into her aft aircraft elevator, punching through the wooden decking, and detonating within the hangar bay. On 18 June, at 11:30 in the morning, her 14 dead were buried at sea in a ceremony. Fanshaw Bay retired from operations and proceeded to Pearl Harbor for a long period of repairs.

"Lots of VC-68 planes landed on the White Plains when that Jap 500-pound bomb blew up in the Fanshaw Bay's aircraft elevator," Andy explained.

"How much gas do we have, Pat?" Grady asked, changing the subject.

"We're running low, and we're consuming more gas every second. We'll be running on fumes soon," Pat replied.

"Time to break radio silence and call in for a vector," Grady suggested.

"Convict Base, Convict Base. This is Convict niner one. Come in, please. Over."

"Convict niner one, this is Convict Base. Over."

Convict Base. This is Convict niner one. Request vector. Over."

"Convict niner one, this is Convict Base. Turn on your running lights. Wilco. Out."

Andy turned on the IFF system identifying them as a friend.

"Convict niner one, this is Convict Base. Heading 050 degrees, 30 miles."

It was now pitch-black outside, and the squall had picked up with the wind and rains buffeting the TBM Avenger. Finally, after keeping the heading for a few minutes, Pat spotted a plane on the starboard side.

"Bogey at 2 o'clock low," Pat called out.

Convict Base. This is Convict niner one. We have a bogey on our starboard side. Over."

"Convict niner one, this is Convict Base. We have no friendlies in your vicinity. Advise you investigate. Over."

Pat glanced at the fuel gauge and then dove towards the bogey. The bogey saw him coming, opened up the throttle, and took off like bat out of hell."

Convict Base. This is Convict niner one. Bogey is going like hell, and I can't catch him. Over"

"Convict niner one, this is Convict Base. Plane identified as a friend. Come on in. Heading 070 degrees 12 miles. Wilco. Out."

"Hope we find the White Plains soon. We're out of fuel," Owens reported. "We may have to ditch this plane."

Andy looked out the TBM window. *Man, it's dark out there! No way a DE is going to find us out here in this storm.*

Pat was staring into the storm, desperately searching for the White Plains. "Convict Base, Convict niner one here. We're out of gas. We may have to ditch this plane."

The engine sputtered and then restarted as the TBM began to drop out of the sky.

"Convict niner one, Convict Base here. "Continue on present course. One minute. Out."

In the next few seconds, Pat finally spotted the White Plains and sighed in relief as he tapped the gas gauge, with its needle now on empty. "OK. I see the ship. We're almost home."

"Come on, get us home. Only a little further," Pat coaxed the TBM as they dropped out of the sky. "We've got one shot at this landing, boys."

Andy and Grady silently waited as the plane descended through the darkness. Pat dropped the TBM onto the White Plains flight deck, making a beautiful night landing. The tailhook grabbed the third arresting cable, bringing the TBM to an abrupt stop.

Home at last!

That night Andy received a message from Dr. Donelson to reserve one hour the following day for his next Navy Flight School examination.

Reporting to Sickbay the next afternoon, Andy found Dr. Donelson finishing up with a crewman who looked a bit green around the gills.

"Stop drinking that blasted *Torpedo Juice*, or you're going to end up with a lot worse than a hangover."

"Yes, sir."

Andy smiled. "It looks like those loaves of bread aren't filtering all the contaminants out of their torpedo alcohol."

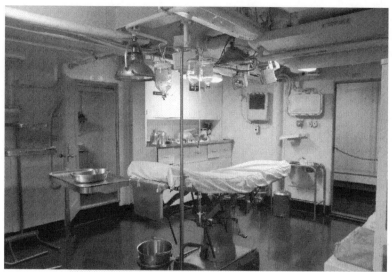

Figure 154 Sickbay in World War II Air Craft Carrier

"Never mind them. Are you ready for your next exam, Winnegar?"
"Ready as I'll ever be, sir!"

Andy spent the next hour working through problems in math and physics and finished 15 minutes early. He rose and handed the test to Dr. Donelson.

"Are you sure you don't want to check your answers?" Donelson asked with a worried expression.

"Nope. I'm sure."

"OK. Then have a seat, and I'll grade your exam right now," Donelson replied, reaching for the answer sheet.

Donelson looked up from the test a few minutes later, "Well, you missed one, Andy. Your score is 98%. You're doing great, but don't get cocky."

Chapter 21

THE DECK APES ON THE WHITE
PLAINS FLIGHT DECK

Figure 155 The Plane Director in Yellow Jersey and cap instructs the catapult crew in green jerseys and caps on the flight deck of a WWII aircraft carrier. Public Domain. National Archives.

I t requires many men performing countless different jobs to keep an aircraft carrier operating smoothly. The Airedales are the aircrew who fly the planes off the carrier deck. Pilots, aerial gunners, and radio operators/bombardiers are essential for prosecuting the war from the skies. On the USS White Plains, these were the men of Composite Squadron Four. Their missions were only possible because of the hundreds of ship's crew who worked on and around the White Plains' flight deck. Their colorful jerseys and headgear identified their jobs in the intricately choreographed dance that occurred dozens of times daily in the launching, landing, rearming, fueling, and relaunching the White Plains squadron of TBM Avengers and FM2 Wildcats.

Deck Apes

The Deck Apes are crewmen of the ship's company who work on the flight deck engaged in numerous jobs indicated by the color of their jerseys and cap. The ability of the crews to quickly launch,

Figure 156 Flight Deck Officer in Yellow Cap and vest directing plane handlers. National Archives.

Figure 157 Flight Deck Officer. National Archives.

land, refuel, rearm, and then relaunch their aircraft was a deciding factor in determining the outcome of the Pacific War.

Lt Cdr. K.H. Holcomb was the White Plains' Air Officer or Air Boss, who usually worked on the White Plains' tower or bridge, where he had a nearly unobstructed view of the entire White Plains flight deck. Hollering instructions through a megaphone, Holcomb was in charge of all aspects of operations involving the aircraft on the flight deck, the hangar deck, and all airborne aircraft out to five nautical miles from the USS White Plains.

Flight Deck Officers,

Wearing the yellow jersey and cap, flight deck officers like Lt jg Donald H. Schmitt were responsible for directing all aircraft movement on the hangar and flight decks

Plane Handlers wear blue jerseys and blue caps. These crews worked on either the flight deck or the hangar deck. A letter "H" on

Figure 158 Plane handlers in blue jerseys and caps pushing plane on hangar deck.

their back indicates their plane handling job is on the hangar deck on the carrier. The number on the front of their jersey divides the plane handlers into different groups. They are responsible for moving and respotting planes and for tying them down securely.

Catapult Crew

The shorter flight deck of the CVE escort carriers made the catapult an essential part of naval flight operations. While the lighter FM2 Wildcat typically used a direct fly-away take-off from the White Plains' flight deck, the heavier TBM Avenger always required a catapult-assisted take-off to become airborne. The Catapult Officer, Lt jg JO Karstrom, Jr., supervised the Catapult Crew, who wore green jerseys and caps, as did the Arresting Gear Crew. He was responsible for all aspects of catapult operation. Karstrom checked the wind direction and speed to assure that the pilot would have sufficient speed for take-off at the end of the catapult stroke. When everything was set, he

Figure 159 Catapult Crew wearing green caps and jerseys. National Archives

signaled the pilot to take off as he assumed the "shooters" pose.

The steam-driven catapult track was located along the Port Bow of the ship on the White Plains. The catapult crew used wooden positioning chocks to quickly and reproducibly position the planes on the track with a minimum waste of effort or time with front and tail wheel chocks.

The stop chock in front stopped the forward motion of the plane while it was being attached to the catapult. The hold-back-and-release unit connects to the plane from a fixed socket in the deck, keeping the aircraft in position against the full power of the plane's engine until the catapult is fired. In anticipation of firing the catapult, the crew removes the stop chock. The bridle is attached to the front of the plane and to the shuttle in the catapult track. A bridle catcher is placed on the forward end of the track to catch the bridle as the aircraft becomes airborne.

Below deck, the crew maintains and operates the piston-driven steam catapult machinery. The force of compressed air is transferred to a hydraulic cylinder with wire rope linkage to the shuttle, pulling the plane down the track. The catapult control officer on the flight deck presses the fire button, which is relayed below deck to the catapult machinery room. On deck, the First Ready, Standby, and Final Ready lights are activated sequentially, communicating between the flight deck and the catapult machinery room.

On deck, the pilot is given the one-finger check. He nods OK and advances the throttle to takeoff power. The pilot gives a final ready signal to the Catapult Officer, Lt jg Karstrom, who assumes the Shooter's pose. With his right leg bent, he squats with his left leg extended behind and his left arm behind his back. With a final motion, the "Shooter" extends his

Figure 160 Flight officer directs take off.

right arm with two fingers pointing down the catapult track. Fire!

The plane is launched into the air. This intricately choreographed dance involves teamwork between many men on the catapult crew above and below deck. A well-trained catapult crew can accomplish this series of tasks with only a few minutes between catapulted planes.

However, an escort carrier's catapult was only 45 feet long, and the best the carrier could do into the wind was 19 knots. "We would come off the catapult at 90 knots—barely flying speed," recalled turret gunner James Gander. "We would dip down when we left the deck until we got our speed up." [71]

For the FM-2 Wildcats, communicating with flag and hand signals, the launch officer directs the pilot to "hold the brakes" until given the signal for takeoff. High seas could swamp low flying planes, so the moment of lift-off was timed to coincide with a rising deck.

---

[71] Stephen Wilkinson. Tough Turkey. Why Grumman's TBM Avenger was the Ultimate Torpedo Bomber. History Net.

Figure 161 A U.S. Navy General Motors TBM Avenger torpedo plane is catapulted from the escort carrier USS Makin Island (CVE-93), in 1945. US Navy Photograph

Landing Signal Officers (LSO), Lt Robert E. Pine and Lt jg Joseph M. French, were responsible for guiding a landing plane down to a safe landing on the carrier flight deck. He controlled the approach of the aircraft through arm signs with his paddles. The signals provide information to the pilot regarding lineup with the deck, height relative to proper glide slope, and angle of attack. The LSO is positioned on the aft end of the carrier in front of a square canvas that makes him more visible to the landing aircraft pilot. In July 1944, Pine was promoted to Assistant Air Officer, moving to the bridge.

Figure 162 Landing Signal Officer guides plane to a safe landing. US Navy photograph.

Arresting Gear Crew

Arresting Gear Officer, Lt jg Robert F. Johnson, supervised the arresting gear crew, including the men like AMM 3/c Walter Ryan, who maintained and deployed the cables and wire barriers that brought to a stop the aircraft landing on the carrier's flight deck. The arresting gear officer monitors the status of the flight deck area, determining if it is "clear" and ready for landings or "foul"

Figure 163 Lt jg Bob Johnson Arresting Gear Officer USS White

and not ready for landings. The arresting gear engines are adjusted to apply varying resistance to the arresting cables depending on the aircraft's weight. With turnaround times of 60 seconds, the arresting gear crew has a very stressful and dangerous job. The arresting gear crew wears green caps and jerseys like the catapult crew.

Figure 164 USS White Plains Lt jg Bob Johnson (center) and Arresting Gear Crew. Courtesy of the Bob Johnson Family

Figure 165 Landing of a U.S. Navy Grumman TBF-1 "Avenger" on the escort carrier "USS Card (ACV-11)" on 9 December 1942. Wikimedia Commons

On 24 August 1944, one of the new TBMs broke an arresting cable, landing on the White Plains. An end of the cable whipped across the port catwalk, hitting one arresting crew sailor across the forehead. It cut a gash about three inches long and an inch deep in his head. He was fortunate to survive. The Tail Hook Man is a member of the arresting gear crew responsible for unhooking the tailhook from the moving aircraft. The tailhook man may have the most dangerous job on the ship. On 22 October 1944, while bringing planes onboard the White Plains, a tailhook man, Bill Willson, was knocked down, fracturing his skull. He died before morning and was buried at sea the next day.

Figure 166 Wire barriers operated and maintained by the arresting gear crew.

The flight deck crew achieved remarkable efficiency with practice, needing only 13 seconds for a landing, twenty-six seconds for a deck launch, and forty-five seconds for a catapult launch. [72]

Crashes during aircraft landings on a CVE escort carrier put the arresting gear crew at significant risk due to the small size of the flight deck and the challenges of landing fighters and bombers on the short deck of a pitching escort carrier.

Fueling Crews

These men are identified by red caps and jerseys and refuel the planes on the flight deck. Gasoline Officer R. Defranco was in charge of the Fueling Crews. Aviation fuel is pumped up to the flight deck from

Figure 167 Refueling Crew in red caps and jerseys.

huge tanks positioned along the bottom of the aircraft carrier's hull, providing ballast. The smoking lamp is out during aircraft fueling.

---

[72] Walter E. Skrzynski. Minority Plus 2: Life in the Navy; 1941-1947. A true and personal account as I remember it.

Ordinance Crews,

Ordinance crews, including seamen like Charles A. Lee, dressed in white jerseys with red caps, bring out the replacement ammunition trays for the .50 caliber wing and turret machine guns and the .30 caliber TBM stinger, feeding the belts into the guns. Bombs and torpedos are loaded once the planes are moved aft on the flight deck after landing.

Figure 168 Ordinance crew rearming a TBM Avenger with a torpedo aboard the USS Wasp 13 October 1944. National Archives.

Plane Captains

Plane captains wearing brown caps and jerseys are assigned to individual aircraft. They are responsible for preparing the plane for flight and starting up the engine before the crew arrives for takeoff. Upon landing, the plane captain secures the plane and is in the cockpit whenever it is being moved on the flight deck by the plane handlers. AMM Cooper was the plane captain for the TBM #27 flown by Lt jg Owens. AMM Wesley Townsend was the Plane Captain for FM-2 Wildcats flown by Lt Palmer and Lt jg Robertson.

Figure 169 Plane Captain in brown jersey and cap secures the TBM Avenger on the flight deck. National Archives

The flight deck was a scene of multicolored orderly chaos with multiple flight deck crews, each with a different job and colored jersey and cap. The teams worked side by side as they prepared the aircraft for the next mission. Refueling crews, ordinance crews, plane handlers, arresting gear and catapult crews, plane captains, and flight deck officers all intermixed as they work together to prepare the Wildcats and Avengers for the next flight.

Figure 170 F4F Wildcats with flight deck crews aboard USS Enterprise early 1942.
US Navy Photograph.

Recovering and Re-Spotting Planes on the USS White Plains

The success of the USS White Plains to carry out its mission depended upon the precision and teamwork of its flight deck crews to rapidly take off, land, rearm and refuel its aircraft. The highly choreographed procedure involving hundreds of men accomplished these tasks in a matter of minutes.

As the aircraft return to the White Plains, the Plane Captains for

Figure 171 Lt. Robert Pine (left) White Plains LSO and Lt jg Joseph French LSO

each aircraft, the Handling Crews, Chock Men, and Wing Folders, stand at the ready on the catwalks along the edges of the flight deck. Crash gear is ready.

Barriers are raised. Tailhook Release Men and Plane Directors are at their stations. Arresting Gear Men raise the five arresting gear cables spanning the flight deck. The Landing Signal Officer and his assistant man their station to guide the planes onto the flight deck. A Green Flag on the bridge indicates the While Plains is ready to receive her aircraft. The Flight Deck is clear of all personnel and gear. Lt Robert E. Pine and Lt jg Joseph M. French, the Landing Signal Officers (LSO), bring the planes aboard, giving the chop power signal as the plane drops onto the flight deck catching one of five arresting cables.

Immediately, the tailhook men run out to disengage the tailhook from the arresting gear cable—the Plane Director signals for the pilot to fold flaps. The plane quickly is directed to taxi up the flight deck to the next Plane Director, where the chock men and wing folders scramble out of the catwalks. For the FM-2 Wildcat, five wing folders on each wing fold the left wing slightly ahead of the right wing and then run off the deck back to the catwalks. The TBM Avenger has its wings folded by the pilot using a hydraulic control system when signaled by the Plane Director.

Figure 172 FM2 Wildcat landing with tailhook down on USS Makin Island. Landing
Signal Officer and wind screen in the background. Wikimedia Commons

The chock men follow along by each wheel to stop the plane in an emergency. Another Plane Director uses hand signals to spot the aircraft towards the bow of the flight deck. The tail wheel is locked. "Cut the engine, chock it up!"

The Plane Captain puts on the tie-down lines to secure the plane and attaches the ground wire. Next, the Fueling Crews in red and the Rearming Crews in white with red caps begin the task of preparing the aircraft for its next mission. The next plane has already landed and begins the same process with a short thirty-second turn-around time between landings.

After the last plane is aboard, the Red Flag goes up. Re-Spotting Plane Handlers in Blue Jerseys reposition the planes aft in preparation for the next take-off under the direction of a Yellow-Vested Plane Director. The larger TBM required two eight-man Plane Handler Crews to reposition the 10,500-pound torpedo bomber. Finally, the planes are secured, refueled, and rearmed for the next flight.

For those men on the White Plains who "work on the roof," every flight day is 12-14 hours long with no such thing as spare time. Recovering, respotting the deck, servicing, and reloading every plane, and performing preflight checks for several launches each day make for a very long day.

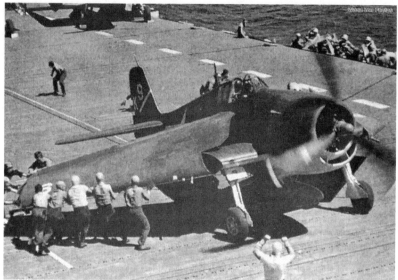

Figure 173 Flight deck crew of USS Yorktown folding the wing of a F6F-3 Hellcat. Public Domain. World War Photo

CHAPTER 22

MARINE PATROLS AND SOUVENIR HUNTING ON SAIPAN – 24 JUNE 1944

The USS White Plains' steam-powered catapult launched Owens' Avenger into the early morning sky, headed for Saipan's Aslito Field. Maurice Hie was up in the turret, and Andy Winnegar was in the tunnel tuning the radios and checking out his .30 caliber stinger machine gun.

"We'll be picking up Grady Gatlin at Aslito, Hie, so you'll have to find something to keep yourself occupied while we're flying our observation mission today," Owens advised his gunner.

"No problem, Cap. I met a bunch of Marines who are all too happy to have a Navy-trained gunner along to keep them safe and sound. We go out on patrol looking for Jap snipers."

"You're a crazy man, Hie! You can't get enough excitement in the air, so you have to go out looking for trouble on the ground!"

"I just hope I'm not too late. Those Marines don't wait for anyone."

Figure 174 Plane captain on the wing of a TBM Avenger waits for his crew, including the radio operator, the pilot with the seat parachute, and a Marine observer on the left. For Andy's crew, this would have been Winnegar, Owens, and Gatlin.
USMC Photograph

At Aslito, Hie was ready to hop out of the TBM when Andy grabbed his shoulder. "Don't forget to take off your flight suit. Otherwise, you'll be a target for every Jap sniper on Saipan. They love to shoot up flyboys."

"No problem!" Hie replied. "I wore my dungarees underneath the flight suit."

Hie stripped off his flight suit, grabbed a duffle bag, and made a beeline for the 4th Division Marine squad bivouacked along the edge of the field. The seven Marines didn't have a tent. They were camped out under a field tarp tied to a tree. Running up to the tarp, Hie discovered that it was oddly quiet.

Crap! I'm too late. Those guys already went out on patrol!

"Hie! Get your butt over here. We're about to take off. What's in the duffle bag?"

Hie looked towards the voice and smiled when he spotted his Marine buds on board their M3 Half-Track with its 37mm gun upfront. The Marines were ready to roll. Running to catch up, Hie bounded up onto the vehicle taking his place behind one of the .50 caliber machine guns. "Duffle bag is a gift from the White Plains' cooks. They sent you some fresh fruit and vegetables and other good Navy grub."

"Terrific! What do they want in return?" Richter asked.

"Jap souvenirs for the Navy cooks in exchange for fresh fruit and vegetables for the Marines," Hie quipped.

Put this helmet on, soldier," Sgt Richter ordered. "We need you to keep your head on so you can shoot straight and take out the Jap snipers. We'll find plenty of Jap souvenirs for the cooks."

"You can count on me, Sergeant. Let's roll!"

Figure 175 M3 Half Tracks WWII on Saipan June 1944. Public Domain

Figure 176 M3 Half-track with dual .50 caliber machine guns in back and the forward-facing 37mm gun.

Traveling north of Aslito, the Half-track or SPM (self-propelled mounts), as the Marines called the vehicle, headed across the plains of Saipan. A few sugar cane fields broke up the otherwise flat landscape.

"What's our mission today, Sergeant?" Hie asked.

"We're hunting Jap bunkers and snipers. See that bunker over there? The concrete's two feet thick. Even our 37mm gun can't touch it. Last week, we had to clear it out with flame throwers."

They were only half a mile from Aslito, but the landscape had rapidly changed, with burned-out tanks and vehicles littering the countryside. The Americans had removed their dead, but the Japanese had so far left their men where they fell. The grotesque shapes of the enemy, distorted by war, were now given over to the flies and scavengers. Hie looked away, but the smell of death still permeated his senses.

Thirty minutes later, Sgt Richter warned, "We're crossing into enemy territory. Keep your eyes open and your wits about you. Call out the enemy!"

The half-track crossed the fields north of Aslito, rolling over and around bomb craters, abandoned Japanese artillery, and blasted out armored vehicles.

Figure 177 Maurice Hie 1940s. Courtesy of Chrissy Hie

Suddenly, the noise of the rumbling half-track was interrupted by the staccato of gunfire.

"Keep your heads down, men," Richter instructed. "We've got a firefight up ahead."

Hie gripped the .50 caliber machine gun and swung it towards a group of trees about 200 yards in front of them.

"Our guys are pinned down. Must be snipers in those trees."

Hie waited until he saw the muzzle flash in a tall tree, and then he let loose with a long burst from his .50 caliber machine gun. The sound was deafening and spent cartridges littered the floor of the half-track.

"What are you shooting at, Hie?" Richter demanded.

"The sniper, Sarge," Hie shouted.

"I didn't see anything. You sure? Which tree?"

Before he could answer, Hie saw another muzzle flash as the sniper's bullets rained down on the trapped Marines.

"Here, take this one for your emperor!" Hie shouted as he unloaded another machine gun burst into the tree.

"You're crazy, Hie!" Richter shouted just as the sniper's limp body suspended by a rope came tumbling out of the tree.

"Not so crazy, Sarge. Just good peepers," Hie laughed. "You gotta see things quickly when shooting at the enemy from our TBM."

"OK. Look for a second shooter, men," Richter said as their half-track advanced towards the Marines.

A squad of ten 2nd Division Marines came out from behind rocks and fox holes as the half-track approached.

"You guys showed up right on time. Thanks for taking out that sniper. We couldn't get a bead on him."

"No problem, Lieutenant. You can thank our Navy gunner friend, Hie. Kid's got keen vision and a steady hand."

"We have wounded. Can you get them back to Aslito?"

"Where are your casualties?"

"Our Navy corpsman, 'Onion Head,' is tending to them. One Marine is in critical condition and needs immediate evacuation."

"What did you call him?"

"Corpsman Dings, but we all call him Onion Head. He's one hell of a corpsman. Let me tell you, a lot of wounded Marines on Tarawa and Guadalcanal owe their lives to Dings."

"Dings, how's he doing?"

"He's lost a lot of blood. This plasma will stabilize him for now, but he needs evacuation ASAP."

Figure 178 Navy Corpsman Robert Dings 2nd Marine Division. Courtesy of Karen Dings Low.

Figure 179 Navy Corpsman Pharmacist's Mate Robert "Onion head" Dings giving plasma to a wounded Marine.

"Move him onto the half-track for now. Then, we can call ahead and have a litter jeep meet us. They can transport your friend back to the infirmary at Aslito faster, or they can have him evacuated to a Navy Hospital ship ASAP," Richter explained.

Dings finished applying a field dressing to the Marine's wounds and hung another bottle of plasma. Pulling out a syringe, he then administered more intravenous morphine.

"That should make you more comfortable, Joe."

They transferred the wounded Marine by stretcher onto the half-track, doing their best to make room on the crowded vehicle.

"OK, 'Onion Head,' hop up here and keep your friend alive while we head back to Aslito," Richter instructed.

Halfway back to Aslito, the litter jeep met them and then sped away with the wounded Marine and Corpsman Dings.

"I hope that Marine makes it," Hie said softly.

Marines are tough as nails, but he'll need a bit of luck as well to

Figure 180 Navy Corpsman Dings transporting a wounded Marine back to Aslito on a 'litter jeep."

survive that wound," Richter said somberly.

"Nice shooting today, Hie. You kept that damn sniper from harming any more of our Marine brothers. You can come back and ride with us anytime."

"Say, Sarge. Can you get me one of your Marine M1 carbines?" [73]

"Consider it done. Maybe in exchange, you can teach our guys some Navy gunnery tactics."

Hie smiled, "Sure, Sarge. As you put it, they just need sharp eyes, steady hands, and nerves of steel."

Back on Aslito, after Hie went off with the Marine patrol, Andy still had a couple of hours to kill, so he headed for a nearby Marine ordinance tent searching for more firepower. He left his .38 caliber sidearm in the Avenger.

Sargent. I'll be here for a couple of hours, and I don't have a weapon. What do you have for me?"

"Sure, son. How about this Springfield bolt action rifle?"

"I want something that will fit in my pocket. That Springfield is a

---

[73] Maurice Hie came home with an M1 Garand, a gift from Marine Sgt Richter, as well as his .38 caliber revolver.

little bit too large to conceal.

"Well, take it or leave it."

"Are you sure you don't have a 1911 .45 caliber sidearm?"

"Let me look around. We have all kinds of weapons from wounded Marines and infantrymen. They won't be needing any more firepower. Most of them are done with this war."

"Say, Sarge. Would you like me to bring you and your men anything from the White Plains?"

Figure 181 Andy J. Winnegar. VC-4. Courtesy of Andy Winnegar

"What do you have?" the Marine asked with growing interest.

"Well, the geedunks wouldn't make the trip, but we have candy bars, and ..."

"Bring us some Pogey Bait – chocolate bars, and I'll get you any kind of firearm you want."

"My pleasure, Sarge. My next trip to Aslito will be the Hershey's Express!"

Still in search of more weapons, Andy then proceeded to a different Marine ordinance tent, picked up a carbine, and took it back to the Avenger

Before his scavenger hunt was over that day, Andy had scrounged a 1903 bolt action Springfield, a 1911 .45 caliber sidearm, a Carbine, and an M1 Garand semiautomatic rifle. Back on the White Plains, Andy placed securely into a crate his souvenirs of WWII and Saipan. As fate

Figure 182 1911 .45 caliber handgun. Wikimedia Commons.

would have it in the end, Andy got shipped back to Flight School and never again saw his arsenal. Bob Fuller was supposed to take care of the guns, but somehow, they never did make their way to Winnegar, and Andy never could find Bob Fuller after the war.

Figure 183 1903 Springfield rifle. CC0. Wikimedia Commons

Two days later, on 24 June 1944, Pat, Andy, and Maurice landed on Aslito by 0700. Maurice and Andy set about cleaning the Avenger's windows. Then, anxious to refuel their TBM Avenger, they hustled over to the gas drum refueling station and got in line. However, a last-minute change in assignments sent Gatlin on an observation mission with pilot Lt. Shields and radioman Davis.

With no mission to fly and unexpected time on their hands, Andy and Maurice set out to explore the area around Aslito.

"Come on, Andy. We've got some time to kill. Let's take a walk and

Figure 184 Japanese block house near Aslito Field

go exploring." Hie said as they slid out of the side door of the Avenger at Aslito field.

"Sure, but first, I have to deliver this bag of Hershey's candy bars to a leatherneck friend.

Afterward, we can be the first tourists in this tropical paradise. We just need to bring along a camera and a gun."

After Andy returned, Hie told him, "I saw a Jap block house not far from here. Let's go and take a look. Did they like their Pogey Bait?"

"Like kids in a candy store," Andy replied. "Smiles all around. It felt like Christmas on Saipan."

*Figure 185 Entrance to
Japanese Block House.*

The Japanese bunker was a round concrete building about half a mile from Aslito. The roof and walls were all constructed of thick solid concrete. An encased stairway led down into the bunker, where an open door was on the left. Entering from the bright sunlight, Winnegar and Hie were blinded in the bunker's pitch-black interior

At the bottom of the stairs, Maurice and Andy paused on either side of the door before entering. It was eerily quiet and absolutely dark. Andy had his loaded and cocked .38 caliber revolver in hand as they stood concealed by the darkness.

"Strike a match, Hie.

"You strike a match."

"I don't have a match. You know I don't smoke. You do!" [74]

"Oh. Alright!"

In the glow, Andy spied a box at his feet on the bunker floor half full of candles.

Picking up several candles, Andy instructed, "OK. Let's light these things so we can see what's in here."

Each man lit two candles and began exploring the interior of the bunker.

To their surprise, the bunker floor was covered with an array of raincoats, sandals, gas masks, and books.[75]

---

[74] Neither Maurice or Andy wanted his face lit up to become a target for a Japanese sniper.
[75] The raincoats or slickers were actually designed as protection from toxic gas or chemical attacks.

"Come on, Andy. Let's get this stuff back to the Avenger."

The half-mile walk back to Aslito was a bit longer than they remembered. Each man was loaded down with souvenirs.

"Hey! I gotta take a breather. These souvenirs are getting heavy. How do you do it, Winnegar? You're hardly breaking a sweat."

"A boxer's got to stay in shape. One never knows when the next big match is coming," Andy smiled.

Neither man noticed the Japanese sniper lurking in the shadows, carefully following their path, waiting for the right moment to strike.

"Quick! Throw this stuff in the tunnel," Andy instructed.

Owens and Gatlin showed up just then, poking their noses into the plane and inspecting the haul filling the tunnel.

"What do you two have in here? Where's this stuff from?" Owens asked.

Oh, man! After all that trouble, these officers are going to pull that crap on us and claim our bounty.

"Can you get us some?" Gatlin asked.

Andy smiled. "Sure, we have a little time to spare. Hie and I can hike back to the blockhouse and pick up more souvenirs."

"Yeah, we can go back and get you some cool stuff," Maurice added.

As they passed a taxi strip heading for the blockhouse, Andy noted the ditch by the side of the road.

At that moment, the sniper who had them in her sights stuck with a vengeance.

"Ping! Ping!" The sniper's bullets flew over their heads as Andy and Maurice dropped to the ground and rolled down the embankment into the ditch.

"I heard one shot."

"No. I heard two shots clear as day."

After a few minutes that seemed like an eternity, Andy poked his head up, looking for more sniper fire.

"Hey! Get back down here before you get your head shot off."

"Here, place my helmet on the end of this stick and wave it around," Hie instructed.

Figure 186 Japanese gasmask WWII. Auckland Museum CC1.0. Wikimedia Commons.

"OK. Here goes."

The helmet-on-a-stick routine did not draw any fire.

"Looks like it's clear. Let's get the hell out of here."

As they hurried down the ditch towards the bunker, Andy looked back at Hie.

"What's that on your shirt collar?"

"I can't see it. What are you talking about?"

Stopping to look more closely, Andy whistled. "That bullet grazed your collar! Looks like this is your lucky day, Hie."

As they approached the bunker, Andy paused. "Get your gun out. Who knows what's down there?"

With guns drawn, Andy and Maurice descended the stairs into the darkness.

"No one's down here. "Let's load up and head back to Aslito. We got enough Jap junk to last the officers and us for quite a while.

As they ascended the stairs, Andy froze.

"Psst! Look! There's a foot! Must be the sniper!"

"Should I shoot him in the leg?"

"No, let's sneak up behind him and take him out!"

As they cautiously ascended the stairs with guns drawn, the two souvenir-laden airmen were prepared to shoot the Jap sniper.

Sneaking up behind the enemy, Andy placed the barrel of his gun squarely in the sniper's neck.

The man jumped a foot in the air dropping his apple to the ground.

"Don't move. Or I will end this for you right here! Now turn around slowly!"

As the enemy turned around, Hie shouted. "Don't shoot him!"

In the sunlight, the enemy combatant turned out to be an apple-eating infantryman.

"What the hell are you two doing out here?" he asked, eyeing the two loaded down with Jap souvenirs. "You went inside that thing?" he demanded incredulously.

"Don't you yoyos know, this is exactly how the booby traps will get you. You two risked your lives over some piles of junk!"

"Yes, sir. We'll be more careful."

"Say. Can I have one of those gas masks?

"Sure. Help yourself. There's plenty more down in the bunker."

Back at Aslito, Andy and Maurice unloaded their most recent haul, filling the Avenger's tunnel.

"OK. Let's get out of here," Andy said.

"First, tell us about the sniper," Pat and Grady demanded in unison.

"Well. He almost put a permanent crease in Hie's neck," Andy proclaimed, pointing at Maurice's collar.

"Whew! That was a close call."

"I heard they did find a sniper along that road. It was a girl hiding up in a tree," Gatlin reported.

Figure 187 WWII Japanese helmet with Rising Sun.

238

"She was a Japanese civilian."

Andy was rummaging through the haul in the tunnel.

"Here it is!" Andy proclaimed, placing the Japanese helmet on his head.

"Andy, I want a Hara Kari knife. Think you can find one for me?" Pat asked.

Sure, Pat. I saw one with jewels in the hilt, but the guy wanted $1500. That's more than I make in a year."

"We'll just need to barter and get the price down."

"No problem, Pat. Nothing's too good for my pilot."

The TBM Avenger, loaded down with Saipan souvenirs, rolled down the Aslito runway and was soon airborne, taking its treasure trove of riches back to the USS White Plains. Or so they thought.

As they passed over the end of the runway at Aslito with their load of souvenirs, Pat turned North over enemy-controlled territory. They arrived back over station, where Andy took several pictures of searchlight hill.

While in a slow turn to the left, Andy felt a sickening jar, pushing the Avenger to the side.

"Crap! What was that?" Pat yelled. "What do you see, Andy?"

Looking out the port side window, Andy inspected the plane for damage.

"There's a huge rip in the leading edge of the port wing. "

"What was it?" Pat yelled.

"It might have been a large bird."

"No way! I think it was an OY-1. Those poor devils didn't stand a chance. We cut their little plane in half right behind the cabin," Hie called out from the turret.

"I saw two guys trying to bail out, but they were only 500 feet above the deck. No time. They were looking right at me!" Hie added.

"That poor little OY-1 was fluttering down to earth like a dying eagle."

"God help those poor devils."

The next day, Gatlin and Hie investigated the crash site of the L5, the Army equivalent of the OY-1. The victims were an Army Colonel and a 2nd Lieutenant. They were behind enemy lines and were still strapped into the L5 when they were found. These small unarmed observation planes could quickly become a death trap in a theater of war. The Japanese had found them first and had not treated them well. The gruesome image stayed with Hie for the rest of his life.

After returning to Aslito Field, Executive Officer Flateboe, a wannabe fighter jock, flew Pat's damaged Avenger back to the White Plains. Meanwhile, Pat, Andy, and Maurice hitched a ride to the White Plains in the tunnel of Shields' TBM Avenger.

Souvenirs, snipers, and a deadly midair collision were all in a day's work for the VC-4 Squadron's TBM Avenger

The next day on 25 June 1944, at 1000, two of the White Plains' TBM Avengers, four FM2 Wildcats, and two F6F Hellcats from another

Figure 188 TBM Avenger piloted by Lt. Fickenscher of USS White Plains sinks Japanese merchantman Shoun Maru with a Mark XIII aircraft torpedo off Rota in the Mariana Islands 25 June 1944. Note the torpedo's wake.

carrier went to the harbor at Rota Island to finish off a Japanese cargo ship initially attacked on 23 June 1944. It took only Lt. Fickenscher's TBM Avenger armed with a 1950-pound torpedo to sink the ship within three minutes. The F6F Hellcats dropped their bombs on the airfields and city of Rota. VC-4 took the nickname *Deacon's Demons* in honor of their fearless leader, Lt. Edward "Deacon" Fickenscher.

CHAPTER 23

CRICKETS IN THE SKY
MARINE OBSERVATION STINSON OY-1
- JUNE-SEPTEMBER 1944

The 2nd and 4th Division Marines utilized the small, fixed-wing Stinson OY-1 Sentinel as a spotter observation plane. The Army version of this plane, designated the L5, was the victim of the midair collision with Owens' TBM over Saipan. Lightweight, slow-flying, and capable of making tight turns, the unarmed Stinson OY-1 flew with a crew of two men, a pilot and an observer, seated in tandem. A six-cylinder 190 horsepower Lycoming O-435 engine powered the fabric-covered plane. With a top speed of 135 miles per hour, the Stinson could cruise at a pedestrian 89 miles per hour with a range of 375 miles.

The Marine Corps' VMO-2 and VMO-4 spotting squadrons were attached to the 2nd and 4th Marine Divisions. Their mission was to provide essential tactical reconnaissance, spotting enemy artillery emplacements on Saipan and Tinian, directing naval, air, and land artillery strikes against the enemy.

Saipan and Tinian Campaigns - 1944

The USS White Plains was home to the eight VMO-4 Stinson OY-1 planes. While the Marines preferred the term OY-1 observation aircraft, the Navy aircrew called the small planes the "Cricket Circuit," referring to their diminutive size and chirping engine.

The first two planes of VMO-4 left the White Plains 150 miles offshore on 17 June 1944, heading for Saipan. The first Stinson piloted by Lt. Thomas Rozga of Milwaukee, Wisconsin, landed on a thick sandy road opposite Yellow Beach 1, about a half-mile from the front line.

"It's a good thing I was in full stall configuration because it was like landing in peanut butter, which stopped my OY-1 in a hurry," Rozga recalled.

Figure 189 Stinson OY-1 prepares to take off from esc ort carrier USS Petrof Bay September 1944

Figure 190 Stinson OY-1 taking off from USS White Plains CVE-66. 17 June 1944. US NAVY Photograph. Public Domain.

Next, Captain George Hooper and 1st Lt. Leonard Wollman landed their Stinson OY-1 on the dirt strip at Charon Kanoa between Green Beach and Blue Beach. Both planes immediately began their mission to provide tactical reconnaissance for the 4th Marine Division.

The OY-1s were pressed into service immediately, calling in artillery fire to protect the 4th Marine Division. Flying at around five hundred feet but constantly adjusting altitude to avoid the Japanese gunners, the small OY-1 was still an easy target for anyone with small arms or an anti-aircraft canon.

"After a while, I lost count of how many holes I had in my airplane. Thankfully most of them whizzed through the fabric covering and kept right on going!" Rozga remarked.

Suddenly, a naval shell came roaring overhead, passing just above the little Stinsons.

"Rozga, let's get the hell out of here before we get shelled by our own ships!" George Hooper yelled.

The blast of the shells landing inland shook the Stinsons.

"Roger that, let's head back to Charon Kanoa – Out," Rozga replied.

The remaining aircraft were brought ashore in wooden crates two days later.[76] By 22 June, all eight Stinson planes were in operation, flying from Aslito Airfield, providing vital spotting for the artillery strikes.

Initial strategic plans called for the small observation planes to fulfill their role while remaining safely behind front lines at all times,

Figure 191 Stinson OY-1 being assembled in wooden crate. Public Domain. National Archives.

avoiding the dangerous anti-aircraft artillery fire. It was immediately evident that this approach was ineffective and not practical. The VMO-4 and VMO-2 pilots instead flew deep behind the enemy lines directly over the enemy to spot targets and direct artillery fire. The OY-1 had to remain in this precarious position while observing the artillery strikes to make proper adjustments. To accomplish their mission, these long, low, and slow flights over the enemy put the small unarmed OY-1 and her two-person crew directly in harm's way.

From the outset, bad luck seemed to plague the VMO-4 squadron. This black cloud continued throughout its deployment in Saipan. Within days, they lost four of the eight Stinsons destroyed by enemy

---

[76] Stinson OY-1 being assembled in wooden crate. Public Domain. National Archives. Photo by Stan Piet.

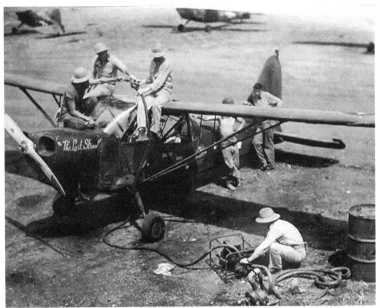

Figure 192 Stinson OY-1 being refueled on Saipan from 53-gallon barrel.
Public Domain. National Archives.

fire or accidents. The unarmed, fabric-covered "Warbug" was agile but was no match for Japanese Zeros and ack-ack guns.

Even on the ground, the VMO-4 squadron was not safe. On the night of 26 June 1944, Japanese Betty bombers attacked the squadron at Aslito airfield. This raid killed three enlisted men of VMO-4 and injured three officers, including squadron CMDR Nathan Blaha. Lieutenant Thomas Rozga succeeded Blaha in command.

In a predominantly Polish neighborhood, Thomas Paul Rozga was born in 1922 in Milwaukee, Wisconsin. His grandparents, Szczepan and Alma, immigrated to the United States in 1881 and 1870, making their way to Milwaukee, where they married in October 1883. Szczepan or Stephen started a funeral home business in Milwaukee that continues today. His son John J entered the business when he was fourteen years old.

His grandson, nineteen-year-old Thomas Rozga, enlisted in the U.S.

Figure 193 Stinson OY-1 flying mission over western coast of Saipan directing naval gunfire. History of War. Public Domain.

Navy in late December 1941, less than one month after the Japanese attack on Pearl Harbor. After Boot Camp, Rozga followed his older brother Tony's footsteps and attended flight school. Rozga was commissioned as a 2nd Lieutenant in the US Marine Corps in December 1943. His initial assignments were to fly the F4U Corsair and PBY-Catalina. He was then attached to the VMO-4 Marine Observation Squadron of the 4th Marine Division.

Some VMO-4 pilots, including Captain Grady Gatlin, alternated between flying the Stinson OY-1 and performing the same role as an observer aboard the VC-4 TBM Avengers in the Marianas. Lt Pat Owens, Lt Hugh "Rocky" Carson, and Lt Coll McLean volunteered to fly their TBM Avengers on these dangerous observation missions. However, if flying low and slow observation missions over an armed enemy was hazardous in the TBM Avenger, the same mission flown in the unarmed Stinson OY-1 was borderline suicidal.

For the Stinson OY-1, the dangers posed by groundfire with armed enemy combatants firing anything from small arms to anti-aircraft artillery were matched by the risks of air attacks from Japanese planes or accidental mid-air collisions in the congested airspace over Saipan. The small "Cricket" would not fare well in any of these encounters.

In the last week of June 1944, the OY-1 flown by Captain Hooper and Lt. Wollman encountered a Japanese Zero near Aslito Airfield.

After a morning of directing Naval artillery fire against Japanese holed up in caves near Naftuan point, Hooper and Wollman were headed back to Aslito airfield. Suddenly, a lone Japanese Zero appeared low on the horizon over the blue Pacific Ocean. Wollman saw the Zeke streaking towards them at 300 miles per hour.[77]

"Let's get the hell out of here, George. "That Zeke's got us in his sites."

"Roger. It's only four miles to Isley Field," Hooper called out, advancing the throttle, climbing towards the clouds for cover.

They could make out Isley Field in the distance when the Zero struck with a hail of 7.7 mm bullets and tracers lighting up the sky around the Stinson. The plane's left wing and tail were laced with bullet holes as the Zero streaked past the slowly-moving spotter plane.

"He's coming back around, George! We'll never make it to the field!"

The Zero assaulted the Stinson head-on with guns blazing. A hail of bullets ripped through the windshield and engine cowling. Smoke filled the cockpit.

"George, you're losing altitude. Pull up!"

Wollman looked ahead at Hooper, slumped forward with blood streaming down his face.

Everything was spinning as the Stinson plummeted towards the

---

[77] Personal account of events by Leonard Wollman.

Figure 194 Captain George E. Hooper. VMO-4. US Marine Corps. Public Domain

ground. Wollman desperately grabbed the stick, struggling to pull it out of the steep dive. Smoke poured from the engine, leaving a black streak behind the dying plane

Hooper, the pilot, was killed in the crash, while Wollman survived, although it required years of surgeries and rehabilitation to recover from his crushed lower legs. The following month, VMO-4 pilot, 2nd Lt. John A. Cameron, from Minnesota, was killed on 30 July 1944 when his Stinson OY-1 (60504) was shot down over Tinian. The U.S. Navy posthumously awarded twenty-three-year-old Lt Cameron the Distinguished Flying Cross.

The Japanese propaganda about the baby-eating murderous Americans caused fear and panic amongst the native population and Japanese civilians on Saipan. They were ordered to commit suicide by jumping into the ocean from cliffs high above the sea. In early July 1944, Rozga and other OY-1 pilots flew their planes over the northern end of Saipan with loudspeakers, attempting to convince civilians not to jump to their deaths. For the most part, the attempts were unsuccessful, as one thousand perished at Suicide Cliff on Marpi Point.

While VMO-4's artillery spotting was a crucial component in the American's successes in the Marianas, they paid a high price for their role. However, the legendary story of these heroic Marine aviators flying their small unarmed Stinson Grasshoppers over the Pacific battlefields was far from over.

CHAPTER 24

AMMUNITION DUMP FIREWORKS & TAIL HOOK MISADVENTURE – JUNE - JULY 1944

F or the TBM Avenger, glide bombing and low altitude horizontal bombing were the order of the day. In dive-bombing, made famous by the SBD Dauntless and the Curtis Helldiver, the plane dove directly at its target with a near vertical attack angle. The TBM Avenger was not designed for dive bombing and took a different approach with glide bombing and low altitude horizontal bombing. If dive bombing is like dropping a marble into a cup, then glide bombing is like pitching horseshoes, while horizontal bombing is more like skimming stones where the TBM is coming in low and flat over the target, dropping the bombs on train.

Glide Bombing

As the pilot approaches the glide bombing run, he makes evasive jinking S-turns to avoid the AA fire. The glide bombing run starts at 4,000-5,000 feet at 200 knots. Flying parallel to the target, the pilot places the target on his right wing. He pushes over and begins a 45-

degree dive to the right with the target centered in his gun sight. At 3,000 feet, the pilot begins strafing with the .50 caliber wing guns, using the tracers to determine where the bomb will strike. The pilot brings the nose up just before releasing the bombs at 1500 – 2,000 feet. The goal is to escape without being hit by antiaircraft fire from this point on. The pilot pushes the nose down to gain speed, diving off the final 1500 feet, taking evasive maneuvers, finally pulling up ten feet above the deck. Flying low over the water between the enemy ships with their guns blazing, there was little room for error. Staying low, the pilot flies jinking S-turns towards the horizon that is fifteen miles away and then climbs to regain altitude with a glance back at the hopefully smoking enemy target. The evasive maneuvers throw the plane all over the sky while the poor radioman in the TBM tunnel bounces around like a ball in a pinball machine. Winnegar never strapped in and recalls "hanging on for dear life." Owens executed a glide bombing attack on an ammunition dump 21 June 1944.

Low Altitude Horizontal Bombing

Typically performed at less than 1,000 feet, for low altitude horizontal bombing, the pilot establishes the path over the target and calls out the speed and altitude, to the radio operator/bombardier sitting at his console in the tunnel. The bombardier enters this data and sets the interval between bombs.

Winnegar recalled, "It was like setting a timer on a stove. You turn one dial for 200 knots, another for the altitude, and another dial for 15, 20, or 100 feet apart, determining the spacing of the bombs. Usually, for 100-pound bombs, I'd set them pretty close. There was no need to set the interval any wider than 50 feet because the shrapnel wouldn't cover that area. You want it to overlap, and you want to get the biggest concentration of firepower."

Just before the plane reaches the target, the pilot pushes the release button. Each of the bombs released in train will hit the target at the same instant that the airplane is passing over it. On 4 July 1944, Owens and Winnegar set up a horizontal bombing run on Saipan that gained them considerable notoriety.

Glide Bombing on Saipan– 21 June 1944

Following their observation missions, the Avenger crew had a green light to drop their ordinance on the juiciest target they had spotted during the day. At the end of 21 June 1944, they were flying just east of Mount Tapochau in an area named Death Valley.

In the words of Col. Albert K. Stebbins, Jr., 27th Division chief of staff: The cliffs and hillsides were pocketed with small caves and large caves. The wooded area was rough, filled with boulders, and excellent for defensive operations. The enemy laid bands of fire thru the underbrush and in such a manner as to make it most challenging to discover their locations: Well-placed, hostile guns only fired when troops passed and striking our forces in the rear disrupted the attack.

The Japanese were well hidden within caves with brush concealing the openings. They were armed with automatic weapons, light and heavy mortars, and 75mm mountain guns. American infantry advancing through Death Valley had difficulty rooting out the enemy

Figure 195 Mount Tapochau Saipan 1944.

while taking on fire from the concealed caves.

"Grady, checkout that mound on the starboard side. I think it's an ammunition dump," Andy called out over the intercom.

"I agree, Andy. Let me call in a Marine artillery strike."

"Pittsburgh, this is Leo 3, Can you handle a fire mission? –Over."

"Leo 3, this is Pittsburgh, Affirmative, –Over."

"This is Leo 3 Grid location 4 Bravo. – Over."

"This is Pittsburgh. Grid location 4 Bravo. Test round fired –Over."

The first test artillery round was beyond the target 150 yards and to the right 50 yards. Gatlin called in the report.

"This is Leo 3. Down 150, left 50."

"This is Pittsburgh. Round fired. –Over"

"This is Leo 3. Fire for effect. HE is possible –Out."

Subsequent artillery rounds were no more effective, and the Marine artillery company quickly moved on to other targets.

"Pittsburgh, here. We got a shit load of damn targets to shoot at! – Out!"

"Forget those guys. We'll take care of that ammo dump the Navy way with 500-pound bombs," Pat exclaimed.

Entering his glide bombing run at 4,000 feet, Owens pushed the stick forward and to the right, entering a 45-degree glide, keeping the ammunition dump centered in his gun sight. Flying at 200 knots, he pulled the nose up slightly and released the bombs at 1500 feet. The first 500-pound bomb hit pay dirt with an explosion that shot smoke, dirt, and debris 1200 feet into the air. The blast shook the Avenger with black smoke encircling the plane as they took evasive action to avoid the anti-aircraft fire and the exploding ammunition dump.

"Whoa! What a blast! That was fun. Let's come around and do that again," Andy said.

"Maybe we'll drop the next bomb from a higher altitude," Pat noted. "We should have taken a photo of that explosion for our Pittsburgh leatherneck brothers."

The next three 500-pounders exploded on target without the drama of the first bomb.

"Well, that's all in a good day's work, boys. Let's head back to the White Plains for chow," Pat said.

Horizontal Bombing Run on Saipan – 4 July 1944

Two weeks later, on 4 July 1944, Owens's TBM Avenger flew a strike mission that made the crew famous for their "Fourth of July Bombing Run." Targeting a row of enemy tents and gun emplacements near Saipan's Death Valley, Andy prepared for a low altitude horizontal bombing run.

"OK, Andy. There's our target. I don't know what's in those tents, but take them out!" Pat instructed, spotting rows of enemy tents lined up along either side of a road at the edge of a palm grove, covering the length of a football field.

Figure 196 Lt jg Pat Owens standing next to TBM Avenger #27. Plane captain, Cooper, is on the wing. Courtesy of Andy Winnegar

"Aye! Aye! Skipper. Setting the bomb interval for 15 feet. Altitude 600 feet, speed 200 knots."

Pat lined up the row of tents with his gunsight as they flew straight down the road leading to the rows of tents.

"Andy, release the bombs. Now!" Pat called out.

"Man! Will you look at that! Andy yelled as he gazed out the bomb bay as the ten one hundred-pound bombs were released on train in rapid-fire succession. They could feel the concussion from the impact of each bomb.

"Whoa! What a strike," Andy yelled as he watched the devastation through a plexiglass window looking out the bomb bay.

"Yeah! We were really close on that run. What a show," Hie called out.

"We lined them up perfectly," Pat called out as the bombs destroyed the road and the shrapnel took out the tents and gun positions on either side of the road.

Winnegar remarked, "We didn't realize we were shooting ourselves up so badly from the exploding shrapnel that it took out our tail hook. Otherwise, I wouldn't have been watching the spectacle through that little plexiglass window."

After completing their bombing run, Owens had eight rockets left. TBMs flown by Lt jg Hearn and Lt jg Carson joined up each with ten bombs and eight rockets.

"Cherokee, Leo 3 here. We have ordinance remaining. Over."

"Leo 3, Cherokee here. Feel free to cruise around to find your targets."

"Wilco. Out."

"Well, boys we have the green light. Let's go hunting," Owens said.

"I see some building and installations on Marpi Point at the Jap airstrip," Hie reported from the turret.

Pat started a dive towards Marpi Point followed by Hearn and Carson's TBM Avengers.

All three TBM unleashed their fury on the target with the explosions from the rocket fire and the wing .50 caliber guns destroying the buildings.

As Pat pulled out just past the target, Andy felt the 4-G force as he grasped the spade grip of his .30 caliber stinger, keeping his chin on the handle for control. He struggled to keep the gun centered on the target, and then he let it fly with a roar of machine gun fire directly

Figure 197 Garapan Saipan exploding ammunition dump 1944.
World War II Database

into the buildings. His teeth felt the jarring of the gun, as smoke filled the tunnel and spent cartridges clattered to the deck.

"Whoa! That was fun! Let's do it again, Pat."

"Anything to keep you happy, Andy. I have ammo left for the wing

Figure 198 Marpi Point Northern Saipan. US Navy and Marine Corps Museum. Public Domain.

guns. Going around," Owens replied as the three Avengers circled and climbed out over the ocean, preparing for a second pass.

When they got back to the White Plains, Pat entered the downwind leg, flying by for the tower to inspect his landing gear and tail hook.

"Leo 3, your landing gear is down and locked, but you haven't deployed your tailhook," the landing signal officer reported.

"It is down! It's in the down position."

"You don't have a tailhook then. So, you can't land."

"Hie, get down out of the turret and see what's wrong with our tail hook," Pat ordered his turret gunner.

"What'd you do to the tail hook, Andy?" Hie joked as he climbed down out of the turret into the tunnel.

"I didn't do anything. I just dropped the bombs."

A motor raised and lowered the tail hook using a chain similar to

Figure 199 Two TBM Avengers with tail hooks deployed approaching air craft carrier. US Navy Photograph. Public Domain.

but larger than a bicycle chain connected the motor and tail hook.[78]

"Well, here's the problem. The chain's cut! The shrapnel from your bombs really did a number on our tail hook."

"Pat, I found the problem. Andy's shrapnel sheared off the tailhook chain," Hie reported.

"It's not my shrapnel!" Andy objected.

"We're headed back to Aslito to repair the tailhook," Pat interrupted.

On Aslito, Hie and Winnegar headed over to a wrecked TBM by the side of the runway.

Climbing into the tunnel, Hie found the intact tail hook chain, removing a one-foot section.

"Here. This piece ought to fix us right up."

Hie returned to their Avenger and spliced the chain segment into their severed tail hook chain."

"There you go. Just like new! That ought to fix it so we can land on the White Plains."

"Hey! Nice work, Maurice," Pat said, admiring Hie's handiwork.

"Let's test it out, Pat. First, lower and then raise the tail hook."

"Perfect! Nice work, Hie," Andy said.

"I was inspecting the rest of the Avenger, while you two were scavenging parts. There are lots of dings from the shrapnel."

Inspecting the damage, Andy whistled, "Man! I'm lucky it didn't blow back through my Plexiglass window."

After departing Aslito at 1445, they headed for the USS White Plains.

"Looks like we have some company, boys, Pat called out. "I see enemy bombers coming in. We need to land before they call General Quarters, or they'll shut down the landing operations, and we'll be stuck up here."

---

[78] The chain has a master link that can be disassembled to lengthen or shorten or repair the chain.

After circling the White Plains until 1545, Pat flew the downwind leg and was given the green light to land with landing gear and tailhook deployed. Pat made a textbook landing on the White Plains with the newly repaired tail hook working flawlessly, catching the second cable. Once word of their day's exploits got around, they became famous as the crew that sheared off their own tail hook.

The TBM Avenger was a beast with enough firepower to deal with most situations. While ten 100-pound bombs worked well on that mission, the most common Avenger payload was four 500-pound bombs used against land targets. The TBM Avenger could also carry one 1,000-pound bomb. For attacks against submarines, they carried four 500-pound depth charges or rarely a single 1950-pound torpedo. The concept of torpedo bombing never worked out in practice. In fact, Winnegar recalled that the only submarines they ever spotted were American.

Four smoke canisters could be deployed to drop a smoke cover for invading troops. Other armament included eight three-inch rockets, five-inch rockets, two wing-mounted .50 caliber machine guns, a turret-mounted .50 caliber machine gun, and the rear-facing .30 caliber machine gun fired from the tunnel.

Glide bombing was the most common technique used by the Avenger. The TBM Avenger crews never used the Norden bombsight because they were never high enough to perform horizontal bombing.

On the ground, after three weeks of fierce fighting, the American forces were in control of three-quarters of Saipan, having driven the enemy to the northern corner of the island by the beginning of July. For the Japanese, surrender was an unthinkable option. So, with no place left to retreat, General Yoshitsugu Saito ordered a final fanatical suicide Banzai charge of the 4,000 remaining Japanese soldiers. The

Figure 200 Lt. Col William O'Brien. Recipient Congressional Medal of Honor. WWII. Public Domain

officers were followed by thousands of Japanese soldiers who came in seemingly endless waves. The charging Japanese overwhelmed the American forces, bursting through their lines and fragmenting the American counter-attack. The Japanese just kept coming.

With two pistols in hand, Lt Colonel William O'Brien of the Army's 105th Infantry Regiment shouted encouragement to his men being overrun by the Japanese hordes.

"Stand your ground and fight, men. Do not give up an inch of ground!"

When his ammunition ran out, O'Brien, although severely wounded, threw down his pistols and jumped up to a jeep-mounted .50 caliber machine gun, blazing away at the charging enemy. O'Brien was surrounded by a crazed horde of Banzai-charging Japanese when his machine gun ammunition ran out. More than 30 Japanese bodies lay scattered around the Jeep. Lt. Col O'Brien's last stand allowed many of his men to retreat and regroup. Incredibly, this was only one of several acts of selfless heroism by O'Brien on Saipan, for which he was posthumously awarded the Congressional Medal of Honor.

Nearby, the seven Marines from Aslito Field, including Hie's friend Sargent Richter, were concealed from the Japanese in a slit trench. The noise of the Banzai charge was deafening.

Richter stuck his head up over the edge of the trench. What he saw was the stuff of nightmares as hundreds of Japanese infantries swarmed over the surrounding field. Suddenly, a Japanese officer appeared on the opposite side of the trench with his sword raised over his head. He swung violently at Richter's head, but the blade twisted in his hand, and the flat of the blade struck Richter's back.

Startled, Sargent Richter stumbled forward and then turned, glaring at the enemy. Richter grabbed the blade with his bare right hand, wrenching it away from the Japanese officer.

With one motion he threw the sword into the air, caught it with both hands and swung the weapon at the enemy, decapitating him. "Take that for your emperor!" Richter growled.

By 1800, after more than 12 hours of intense and bloody fighting, the Americans had regained the 1000 yards lost to the Japanese Banzai attack. The human toll for both sides was staggering. A total of 4,311 Japanese soldiers were killed. The toll was also grim for the Americans, with 406 dead and 512 wounded, almost wiping out the first and second battalions of the 105th Infantry Regiment.

By 9 July 1944, all enemy activity on Saipan ceased, and Saipan was declared secured as they raised the U. S. flag on the northern end of Saipan a little after 1600. The action had proven to be longer and costlier than anyone had initially imagined, but this strategic island was now under American control. That day, the Marine observation OY-1 Crickets came out and buzzed the ships in celebration.

On the next day's ASP, Owens' crew found something far better than an enemy submarine. Andy picked up a short-wave broadcast from San Francisco in the United States of America.

"Hearing those four words, United States of America, was a real thrill," Andy recalled with moist eyes.

For boys thousands of miles from home, listening to the music from home and hearing the baseball scores clarified why they were at war.

"The San Francisco announcer said that we had taken Saipan in a four-week battle that was the costliest battle of the South Seas." At that moment, the boys knew the folks back home appreciated their sacrifice.

Pride filled their hearts and their plane as they gazed at the Stars and Stripes flying over Saipan on 10 July 1944. Flying over the island towards Aslito, they looked down and spotted troops using flame throwers on caves and blockhouses where the Japanese were still holding out. Mopping up operations continued for months, rooting out pockets of stubborn resistance from Japanese soldiers who had taken refuge in Saipan's countless caves.

Figure 201 Raising the flag at Marpi airfield, 9 July 1944.
USMC photo

CHAPTER 25

TINIAN INVASION AND MIDAIR COLLISION– 24 JULY 1944

The invasion of Tinian, located three miles south of Saipan, began on 24 July 1944. The battle for Tinian was over in nine days. The 15,600 men of the 4th and 2nd Marine Division encountered much less Japanese resistance than greeted them on Saipan's D-Day 15 June 1944. American casualties during the Tinian invasion included 326 killed and 1,593 wounded. For the Japanese forces, 5,542 soldiers were killed and 252 taken prisoner. In addition, over 4,000 Japanese civilians perished, many by suicide. As on Saipan, TBM Avengers from the USS White Plains and Marine Observers played a crucial role in identifying the enemy and directing naval and ground artillery strikes at the enemy.

Pat Owens and Rocky Carson were two Avenger pilots who carried out these dangerous observation missions during the Battle for Tinian.

Figure 202 The Curtiss SOC Seagull was an American single-engine scout observation seaplane, designed by Alexander Solla of the Curtiss-Wright Corporation for the United States Navy. The aircraft served on battleships and cruisers in a seaplane configuration, being launched by catapult and recovered from a sea landing. Public Domain. Wikimedia Commons.

"Pat, turn left and go back over that group of the Japanese infantry," Gatlin instructed.

"I can see them just fine from here. Why do we need to fly low and slow over the enemy just so you can take pictures, and they can shoot at us?" Owens complained.

"Because I'm the Marine Captain in charge of this mission!"

"Aye! Aye! Captain Bligh. Turning left and descending over the enemy," Owens replied.

The TBM turned to the left, passing through a slight mist and a small cloud. Then suddenly, the Avenger was knocked aside violently.

"Crap! What was that?" Pat called out from the cockpit.

Riding backward in the turret, Andy had a perfect vantage point to observe the skies. On his right, Andy spotted an SOC seaplane flying in

Figure 203 Photograph Curtis SOC Seagull alongside the USS Memphis 1942. Public Domain. US Navy Photograph

the opposite direction with three feet of its upper port wing missing. In addition, the Avenger's port elevator was fluttering, and the stabilizer had a good-sized dent in it. However, the worst of the Avenger's damage to the port wing was not visible from the turret.

Gotta tell Pat! Where's that darn turret mike? Still not working!

Climbing down from the turret into the tunnel, Andy found Gatlin looking out the stern window for the Japanese infantrymen.

"Grady! Didn't you feel that jolt? We just had another midair collision!"

"What are you talking about, Andy?"

"We just clipped an SOC. Ripped out a big chunk of its port wing."

"What's our damage?" Gatlin asked.

"Part of our port elevator is missing, and we have a big dent in the vertical stabilizer."

"There's got to be more than that," Gatlin said, looking out the port window.

"What do you see?"

"A big chunk of our port wing is missing!"

"I better talk to Pat. Where's your mike?"

"Hey, Pat. Didn't you see that collision? We clipped a SOC seaplane."

"Hi, Andy. No, I didn't see a thing. So, what's our damage report?"

"A chunk of our port wing is missing, and the port elevator is damaged as well as the vertical stabilizer."

"Did you see the other plane?"

"Yeah. She was still flying with a section of her port wing ripped away."

"Well, good thing it wasn't another L5. The last one didn't fare too well after our midair collision last month."

"I'm going to land at Aslito to check out the damage to '27'," Pat replied.

Landing immediately at Aslito, Pat, Gatlin, and Andy hopped out to inspect the Avenger's damage.

"Whoa! Look at that left-wing, Gatlin said.

"That's a pretty big hole on the leading edge of the port wing, and here's another on the bottom of the wing," Pat noted.

"The props got a bunch of nicks," Andy observed.

The vertical stabilizer and port elevator damage was just as Andy described from the turret.

"We're lucky it wasn't an engine-to-engine head-on collision, Andy whistled. "I can't believe you didn't see them coming."

"I just hope those other guys survived," Pat said.

"I saw them heading for their cruiser along the west coast of Tinian," Andy added. "I'm pretty sure those guys made it back." [79]

---

[79] The SOC seaplane used a catapult to launch. Landing the seaplane was a bit tricky, The cruiser made a sharp turn, creating a wake and smooth area for the SOC to land. The plane was then recovered with a hook and crane. The crane operator on the ship lowered a hook. At this point, the radioman/gunner would climb forward from the after cockpit and stand upright over the pilot in order to grasp the crane's hook. The pilot would hold on to the radioman/gunner's ankles to prevent him from falling off the aircraft which would now be swaying back and forth in the wind. After the radioman/gunner slipped a steel loop from the upper wing of the aircraft

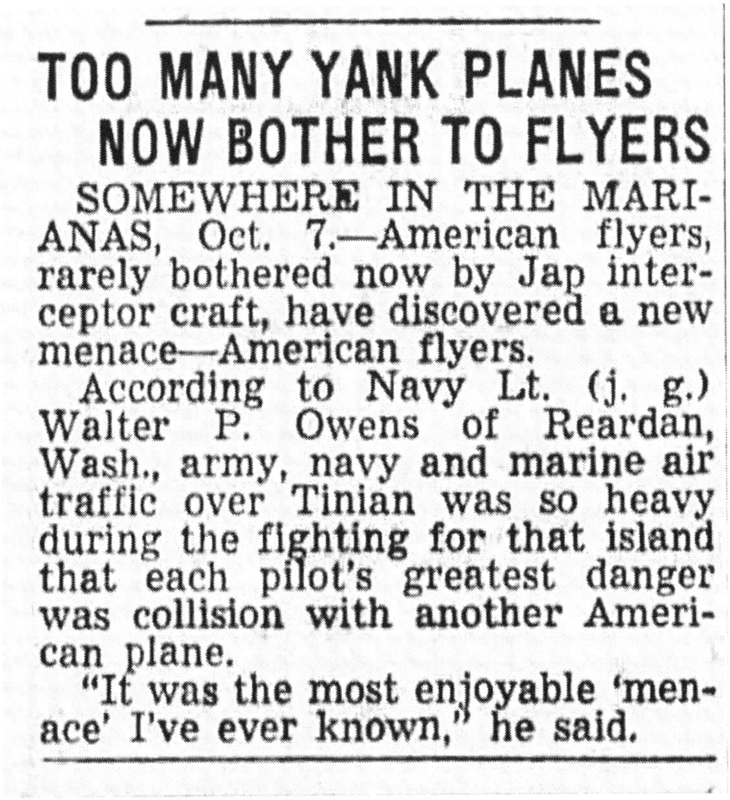

TOO MANY YANK PLANES NOW BOTHER TO FLYERS

SOMEWHERE IN THE MARIANAS, Oct. 7.—American flyers, rarely bothered now by Jap interceptor craft, have discovered a new menace—American flyers.

According to Navy Lt. (j. g.) Walter P. Owens of Reardan, Wash., army, navy and marine air traffic over Tinian was so heavy during the fighting for that island that each pilot's greatest danger was collision with another American plane.

"It was the most enjoyable 'menace' I've ever known," he said.

Figure 204 8 October 1944. Spokesman Review – Spokane Washington.

"Well, it looks like we'll be spending the night here on Aslito, while the guys make repairs," Pat said.

"We better borrow some mess kits. They won't serve us otherwise, and you can't carry chili beans in your hands," Andy laughed.

"Let's head to the Army mess tent. We can borrow some mess kits from the TBM Avenger service tent."

---

over a hook lowered by the ship's aircraft-handling crane, the seaplane was hoisted aboard ship and secured to the catapult amidship.

Ongoing nightly raids by isolated Japanese soldiers put the American planes parked at Aslito at considerable risk. The Japanese would break through the line, bayonet the American planes' belly tanks, and then light them on fire, creating a spectacle of destruction. These raids had been going on for several weeks, and Andy and Hie had no intention of letting "27" go up in flames.

"No Jap's going to mess with our Avenger tonight!" Andy said as he and Hie headed out to the parked Avengers from the White Plains.

"Yeah. There's no way she's going to end up like Hed Up n' Locked. The ball-of-flames crap at the hands of some crazed Jap banzai will not happen on my watch!" Hie shouted, waving his .38 caliber handgun

At the Avenger, the guys set about securing the perimeter.

"I'll sleep in the turret to have a bird's eye view of any Japs sneaking upon us," Hie explained.

"OK. I'll sleep in the tunnel and keep a sharp lookout for any enemy activity."

"Bam! Bam! Bam!"

Oh no! Looks like we're in for a rough night of artillery fire. We're shelling Tinian, and the Japs are returning the fire, shell for shell."

"I think we're right under the flight path for those artillery rounds!"

Andy and Hie stayed awake until the early hours. No enemy combatants appeared. Instead, they let the unrelenting swarms of Saipan mosquitos do their dirty work.

"Man! I'm being eaten alive!" Andy yelled into the intercom.

No problem here. The turret is sealed, so no skeeters up here."

"I tried crawling under a parachute, but the little buggers keep finding a way in! They must like the taste of Winnegar."

The TBM Avenger was intact by morning, but the Saipan mosquitoes had covered Andy Winnegar's body with welts and bites.

"Hope I don't get malaria, dengue fever, or yellow fever," Andy exclaimed.

On Saipan, mosquito-borne diseases like malaria were endemic. If you stayed long enough, you would eventually come down with malaria. The newly formed Malaria Control Unit, affectionately called the "Skeeter Beaters," did its best to combat the pests. They sprayed diesel oil on swamps to choke larvae and fumigated planes and huts with newly invented aerosol "bug bombs." They encouraged Marines to take the hated Atabrine pills and forced local plantation workers to relocate so mosquitoes could not spread malaria from them to troops. [80] Hence, the short-lived miracle of DDT,[81] a pesticide used to combat mosquitos on Saipan, DDT was sprayed from planes, killing all insects on the island. Soldiers and sailors by the millions were carrying small cans of DDT powder to protect themselves from bedbugs, lice, and mosquitoes. They came to love the stuff, especially in the tropics. Millions of DDT aerosol bombs were used to spray the interiors of tents, barracks, and mess halls. The side effects of DDT were not appreciated until the 1960s.

Figure 205 WWII Saipan and Malaria & Epidemic Control Unit. US Navy Photograph. Bureau of Medicine and Surgery. Public Domain.

---

[80] In the Solomon Islands and at Gonadal Canal, in 1942-43 malaria put more Marines out of action than did Japanese fire.
[81] DDT (dichloro-diphenyl-trichloroethane) was developed as the first of the modern synthetic insecticides in the 1940s

CHAPTER 26

ROCKY CARSON – 1 AUGUST 1944

Augut 1, 1944 was the final day of the Battle for Tinian. Rocky Carson, the gentle giant from Louisiana, flew a final observation mission over Tinian with his radioman Steve Walley and Marine Observer Captain James Motley. For the most part, the fighting was over, but the dangers of war can strike at any time as they did on this Tuesday morning.

Carson flew over Tinian with Motley in the tunnel and Walley in the turret. They were waiting to be relieved by Lt jg Owens.

"Come on, Rocky! Let's unload our ammo on one of those fuel dumps," Walley pleaded while rotating the turret's .50 caliber machine gun right to left.

"Sure thing, Steve. I saw some juicy targets on our passes over the island."

"James, get ready with the .30 caliber stinger," Rocky instructed his Marine Observer.

"Alright, boys! We have an ammunition storage facility dead ahead. Get your guns ready. Let's have some fun. Yeeha!"

Rocky put the TBM Avenger into a steep dive, firing the Avenger's

Figure 206 TBM Avenger over Tinian July 1944. Public Domain.

5-inch rockets and .50 caliber machine guns. Then, he pulled back on the stick, passing the ammo dump, initiating a 4-G pullout.

"Alright, boys! She's all yours. Take her out!" Rocky ordered as the Avenger climbed high into the clouds, providing a perfect shot for the rear-facing turret .50 caliber machine gun and the .30 caliber stinger.

The devastation was complete as the ammunition dump exploded into a flaming inferno. Rocky did a fly-by so the guys could admire their handiwork.

"Here! Take that!" Steve exclaimed, unloading another burst from the turret .50 caliber gun.

The fun's not over yet, boys. I hope you saved some ammo. We have a gasoline storage complex to take out," Rocky said.

Rocky initiated the same dive and 4-G pullout with rockets and machine guns blazing away. The results were spectacular, with gasoline drums exploding and setting fire to the enormous aviation fuel tanks. As they turned back over the exploding gasoline tanks, a huge black mushroom cloud extended hundreds of feet into the air.

"Well, that's one to write home about, boys! Nice work."

Figure 207 Exploding ammunition dump on Tinian from attack by Navy TBM Avenger. Public Domain. National Archives.

In the turret, Walley felt a thud.

"What the hell was that? Did we hit a bird?"

From the tunnel, Captain Motley called Carson, "Rocky, make a turn to the right so I can see if the Japs moved the panels on that one sector."

No answer.

"Rocky, turn to the right so I can check out that panel. I think the Japs have moved it."

No answer.

Meanwhile, in the cockpit, Rocky looked down at his abdomen. The blood-soaked flight suit told the story.

"Looks like I'm gonna need some help."

"Leo 3, this is Leo 1," Carson called out into his radio

"Leo1, this is Leo 3. What's up, Rocky? We're on our way to relieve you and should be in your sector in two minutes."

"I've been hit by machine-gun fire, Pat. It looks pretty bad. What should I do?"

"Head for the water, Rocky. Try to put her down with a water landing, and I'll call Cherokee to have a destroyer escort pick you up. What's your position?"

"Feelin' kind of faint, Pat. I'm flyin' over Western Tinian headed due west towards the water,"

"You can make it, old friend. Help is on the way."

Over the intercom, Rocky called out, "I've been hit bad. We're headed out to sea for a water landing."

Carson put the Avenger into a glide. The flaps weren't working, so the angle was steeper than he wanted.

Figure 208 Captain James Coleman Motley Jr. USMC. With the 8th Marines Motley fought at Guadalcanal, Tarawa, Saipan and Tinian.

"Hold on, boys! We're going in! We're at 700 feet. Too low for parachutes."

Walley and Motley braced themselves for impact.

The Avenger's nose and the right-wing struck the water, spinning the plane around.

Walley struggled to release the plexiglass hatch from the turret. Partially out of the turret, a breaker swept over him, wrenching his leg. He climbed out of the turret onto the port wing. As sea swells washed over the plane, the Avenger was barely still afloat.

Walley took two steps on the wing towards the cockpit, where he found the nacelle cover slid back. Rocky was slumped forward over the controls, and his flight suit was a bloody mess.

"Rocky! Are you OK? We gotta get you out of here," Walley shouted, reaching down to unfasten Rocky's harness.

At that moment, a huge swell crashed over the Avenger. The bottom dropped out, and the ocean swallowed up the plane and Rocky.

Figure 209 TBM Avenger water landing. US Navy Photograph.

"No! Rocky!" Walley called out, reaching for his friend as he bobbed on the surface with his Mae West inflated.

Overhead, Owens' TBM Avenger watched the scene unfold. Carson's plane was on the surface briefly, and almost immediately, it disappeared and sank into the sea.

"Cherokee, this is Leo 3. Carson's TBM is in the water. Send DE to look for survivors."

"Leo 3, this is Cherokee. Are there any survivors?"

"Unclear. The plane just sank.," Owens replied.

Cherokee relayed the position of the crash scene to a nearby destroyer escort that was blasting coral to create access to Tinian. The destroyer escort dispatched two Higgins boats with divers to search for survivors.

Owens' Avenger flew past the crash scene and then circled back. By the time they were once again over the crash site, the Higgins boats were gone, and Carson's Avenger was at the bottom of the sea. *God, please let Rocky be OK.*

"Andy, blinker the destroyer and see if there were any survivors."

Figure 210 Blinker communication with ship. US Navy Photograph.

Winnegar set about communicating with the destroyer.

"Just one," Andy said to Pat.

"Who?" demanded Owens.

A few tense minutes passed while information was communicated by blinker

"Well! Who is the survivor, Andy?" Pat demanded.

"Walley," Andy softly replied. "Sorry, Pat."

In the cockpit, Pat was stunned that his friend, Rocky Carson, was gone. His stomach was tied in knots, and he wept silently for his friend.

Rocky was a bear of a man who was larger than life. He was invincible.

I can't believe he's gone. Pat whispered a prayer for the soul of his departed friend and fellow Avenger pilot.

I guess I'll have to write his mother in Texarkana.

Harold 'Rocky' Carson, the gentle giant from Spring Hill, Louisiana, who had a smile that could light up a room, was 26 years old. Captain James C. Motley Jr USMC was 24 years old.

Walley was flown from Saipan to Eniwetok in a twin-engine Navy CMDR. He rejoined the White Plains two weeks later on their way to Espiritu Santo. When Walley came aboard, he told Winnegar the details of the crash. Walley was still shaken and felt terrible that he could not save his pilot, Rocky Carson. However, the bond of friendship between these two men had seemed unbreakable. In training and combat, Steve Walley and Rocky Carson had flown 307 hours together in their TBM Avenger. The loss of his pilot and friend stayed with Walley for the rest of his life.

Figure 211 TBM Avenger pilots of VC-4. 2nd Row: Col McLean, Pat Owens, Rocky Owens. Courtesy of Andy Winnegar.

Figure 212 Harold "Rocky" Carson TBM Avenger pilot and Steve
Walley Radioman. Courtesy of Andy Winnegar.

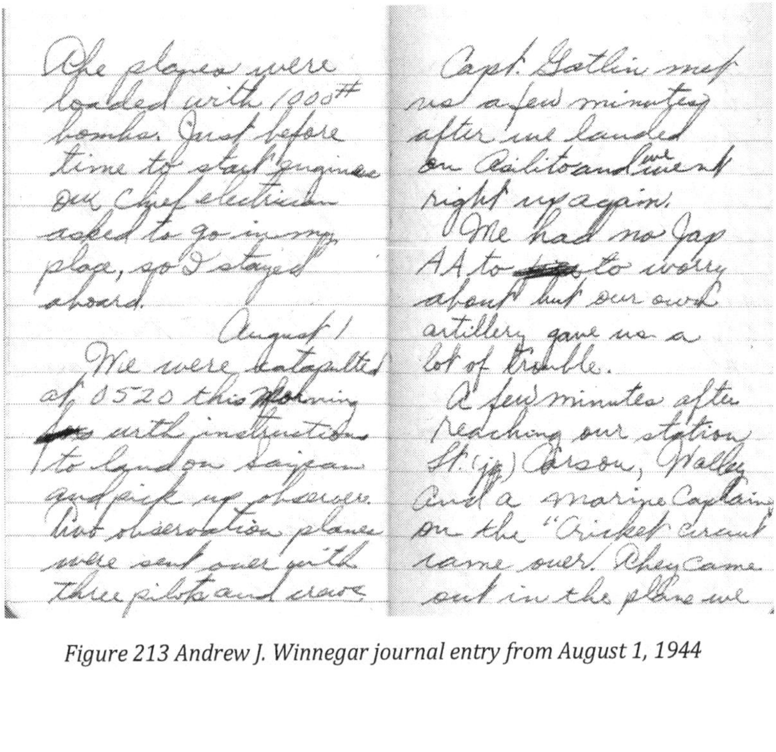

Figure 213 Andrew J. Winnegar journal entry from August 1, 1944

had flown over but had grounded because of a locked control stick. After we took off he had fixed the stick control.

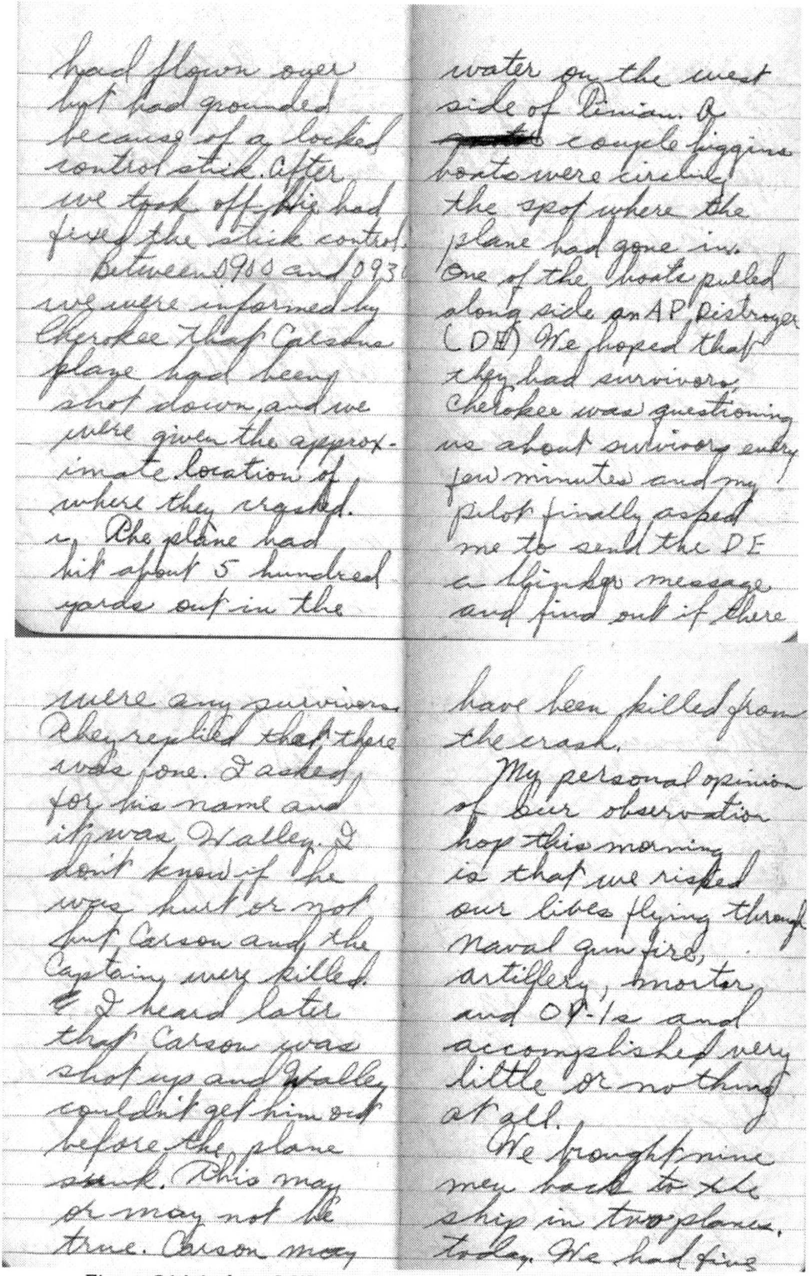

Between 0910 and 0930 we were informed by Cherokee that Carson's plane had been shot down, and we were given the approximate location of where they crashed. The plane had hit about 5 hundred yards out in the water on the west side of Tinian. A couple jiggins boats were circling the spot where the plane had gone in. One of the boats pulled along side an AP Distroyer (DE) We hoped that they had survivors. Cherokee was questioning us about survivors every few minutes and my pilot finally asked me to send the DE a blinker message and find out if there were any survivors. They replied that there was none. I asked for his name and it was Walley. I don't know if he was hurt or not but Carson and the Captain were killed & I heard later that Carson was shot up and Walley couldn't get him out before the plane sank. This may or may not be true. Carson may have been killed from the crash.

My personal opinion of our observation hop this morning is that we risked our lives flying through naval gun fire, artillery, mortar, and OP.1s and accomplished very little or nothing at all.

We brought nine men back to the ship in two planes today. We had five

Figure 214 Andrew J. Winnegar journal entry from August 1, 1944.

CHAPTER 27

POLLYWOGS AND SHELLBACKS - CROSSING THE EQUATOR - 16 AUGUST 1944

The Americans had secured Tinian and Saipan in the Marianas during the previous two months, and the men would soon be supporting the invasions of Peleliu, Anguar, and Ulithi. Thus, the stop at Espiritu Santo for resupplying was the perfect opportunity to pay homage to Neptune at the expense of the Pollywogs.

As the White Plains approached Espiritu Santo[82] in the New Hebrides on 18 August 1944, preparations for the delayed "Crossing the Line Ceremony" reached a fevered pitch. The age-old Navy tradition marking the transformation of a slimy Pollywog, one that has not yet crossed the equator, to a trusted Shellback or Son of Neptune, had been delayed three days by the demands of the Pacific war in 1944. Yet, the initiation rite commemorating one's first crossing of the equator could not be ignored nor further delayed.

"Preparations" for the Neptune Line Crossing Ceremony involved

---

[82] Espiritu Santo is 1680 miles southeast of New Guinea.

collecting all of the mess hall garbage for the past several days to create the disgusting 30-foot "tunnel" out of a canvas tow target that the Pollywogs had to crawl through before they ran the 300-foot gauntlet lined by hundreds of Shelaley-wielding Shellbacks. Every self-respecting Shellback had fine-tuned his canvas tubing Shelaley, filling it with water, soap, scraps of canvas, and the occasional nuts and bolts to give it some heft.

The one hundred men of VC-4 were almost exclusively Pollywogs in the upcoming Neptune ceremony. Only Lt. Fickenscher and a couple of the squadron Chiefs were experienced Shellbacks. Conversely, the ship's crew had crossed the equator several times in the White Plains' shakedown cruise and were all initiated Shellbacks.

The day before the initiation and hazing ceremony, Winnegar shaved his head.

"Hey, Chrome Dome! What's with the new look?" Hie asked.

"I don't want all that nasty grease in my hair. That stuff stinks, and you'll never be able to wash it out. So, a bald head is our only advantage," Andy replied, smiling.

"Crap! Maybe I better shave my head," Hie replied nervously.

Before lights out, half the compartment had shaved their head. "I hope you're right about this, Winnegar, Fournier said nervously.

"Being bald will be the least of your problems come morning," Andy replied.

Figure 215 Matt Bisenius ARM - radioman on Lt. Flateboe's TBM Avenger. US Navy Photograph.

The following day, the Shellback's fun began. Finally, the Pollywogs would pay the price for their inequities by standing trial before Neptune and his court.

Donald Crounse recalls, "At 1400, we had the Shellback initiation. While the initiation started in the form of a riot, they got things quieted down and went on with it. The Pollywogs got a thorough beating. Of course, we had a few injuries. One broken arm for sure, and a lot of sprained ankles and wrists." [83]

Figure 216 Captain D.J. Sullivan USN. USS White Plains. Public Domain.

The "riots" Crounse refers to had been going on for several days, to the displeasure of Captain Sullivan. Much like two rival fraternities, the Pollywogs and Shellbacks went at it in good fun with razors and electric cattle prods. Any Shellback caught alone by a mob of Pollywogs was guaranteed to depart the scene with half his mustache shaved off. Shellbacks "Sea-Dog" Mahlstedt, and Bosun Meske, two old-timers got their heads shaved for their enthusiasm. Two squadron Shellbacks, "Deacon" Fickenscher and "Big Hoss" Huser, likewise suffered this indignity. All in good fun, of course.

The electrified "cattle prod" rigged up in CIC was another matter entirely.

"Fuller, Hie, Walley, Matt Bisenius [84,] and Winnegar were exiting the second aircrew compartment across from CIC when they spotted Jones coming down the passageway. He was a big hairy guy sporting half a mustache.

"What's that prong thing he's threatening us with?" Andy asked,

---

[83] The Pollywog accounting of causalities was significantly different. Winnegar recorded one broken leg, several broken arms and fingers and a lot of bruised bottoms.

[84] Matt Bisenius was the radioman on Lt Flateboe's TBM Avenger.

backing up.

"Beats me, but it's got a long electrical cord going back into the CIC," Hie observed.

"I spent summers on a ranch. That thing's an electric "Pollywog Prod" plugged into the ship's circuits! That prick wants to electrocute us!" Fuller yelled.

"Hey, you, Pollywogs, don't run away. This will be fun!" the CIC radarman laughed as he thrust the electric prod towards them.

"Fun for you, maybe," Matt replied as he noticed a group of CIC men advancing behind their leader.

"Hold them off! I'll be right back!" Hie shouted as he bolted for the ladder to the hangar deck.

"Where the hell is Hie going?"

"He'll be back," Andy reassured Walley.

As they backed up towards the safety of their compartment, Fuller said, "Don't let them corner us in there. We'll be sitting ducks with no way out."

They heard running and panting from the hangar deck just before Hie reappeared, carrying a five-gallon blue cylinder of CO2.

"What are you going to do with laughing gas?" Matt asked.

"No! It's CO_2. Not NO_2 (Nitrous Oxide). Watch!" Hie explained

The threatening CIC crowd paused as they spotted Hie's cylinder.

Pointing the nozzle at the CIC ringleader with half a mustache, Hie turned the valve, opening the cylinder.

The cold blast of CO_2 froze Jones in his track.

"Ha! Ha!" Fuller laughed. "He's got icicles on his messed-up mustache!"

"Ouch! My face is frozen, you Pollywog scum!"

"Come on, guys. Let's get these Pollywog prodding pricks!" Hie yelled as they advanced down the corridor, pushing the CIC Shellbacks towards the CIC and the squadron ready room.

At that moment, the ship's intercom crackled to life, "All of the Pollywog and Shellback Hijinks will cease immediately! The White Plains is a US Navy warship and not a fraternity house. Do I make myself clear!"

A moment later, Captain Sullivan continued, "Don't test me, or you will end up in the brig!"

The CIC ringleader stepped forward, extending his right hand, "No hard feelings, Pollywogs! Here let me give you a parting..."

No sooner had the words left his mouth when Hie let loose with another cold blast of CO2, freezing Jones in mid-sentence.

"Take that, you Shellback scumbag!" Hie yelled, dropping the cylinder, which took off down the corridor with a jet blast of icy CO2 exiting its nozzle as it bounced off the walls.

"Catch that thing!" Andy yelled as they took off after the escaped CO2 cylinder.

At 1400 the Pollywogs and Shellbacks gathered on the flight deck in anticipation of the Crossing the Line Ceremony.

The grease came out by the bucketful, and every Pollywog got an unhealthy glob rubbed into his hair. When they got to Winnegar, the grease-wielding Shellback was clearly disappointed. "What's the meaning of your shaved head, Pollywog?"

"Easier to keep clean?" Andy replied.

"Smartass! No worries, get me that bucket of zinc chromate paint."

"Bend over, Pollywog! Perfect!" the Shellback proclaimed as he gave Andy's bald head a sloppy coat of yellow zinc chromate primer. "That's not washing off for a long time. Now go kiss the Royal Baby!"

Winnegar recalled the next phase of the Neptune ceremony, "Then we had to kiss the Royal Baby. He's the fattest guy they can find. They grease his disgusting belly and shove your head into his belly button."

The search for the "Royal Baby" was underway on the White Plains.

"Get Polanski out here. He's by far the fattest guy in the ship's crew."

Polanski came forward and took off his shirt, revealing a disgusting and grossly obese abdomen.

"Perfect! Now sit here, Polanski, and let me rub this grease all over your belly. The newly crowned Royal Baby took his place on the throne."

"Put more grease on the "Royal Baby," the Shellbacks encouraged.

In turn, each Pollywog was escorted to the Royal Baby's throne and had his face thrust into Polanski's disgusting, grease-laden gut. "Now kiss the Royal Baby's belly button, Pollywog!"

The raucous cheers from the surrounding Shellbacks filled the air as each Pollywog came up sputtering for air with his face smeared in grease.

Next, waiting for the Pollywogs standing trial, was the time-honored and wholly sadistic tradition of plunging into Davey Jones's pool.

Winnegar described the saltwater pool with a sardonic smile, "The pool was a canvas tank filled with saltwater. They put a chair on the tank that's hinged so it will tilt over backward. The back and bottom of the chair have copper metal plates with AC voltage connected to them. You're already wet when they sit you in the chair so you're a good electrical conductor. Then they

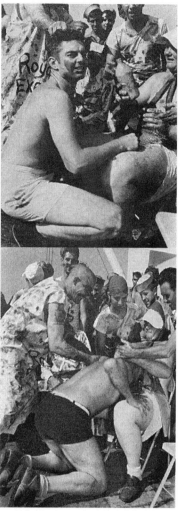

Figure 217 Lt jg Jack H. Osborne Kissing the Royal Baby. Over the Line Ceremony 18 August 1944. USS White Plains.

SHOCK YOU! Next, they tilt the chair backward, and you fall in the tank with a bunch of Shellbacks, who shove your head under the water. You have to fight to come up out of the water yelling, "SHELLBACK!"

285

Figure 218 USS White Plains 18 August 1944.Shellbacks pose with Shelaleys. Courtesy of Andy Winnegar

The final obstacle before the gauntlet is a gross garbage-filled 30-foot tunnel made from a canvas tow target. Each Pollywog crawls through the tunnel filled with chicken guts and garbage. Any portion of your anatomy that sticks out as you transit the tunnel is thoroughly whacked by the Shellbacks.

As the Pollywog exits the tunnel, he is at the start of the 300-foot "gauntlet from hell." The Pollywog runs the gauntlet wearing nothing but skivvies with hundreds of guys wailing on him with their Shelaley. Most of the ship's company lined up on both sides of the gauntlet, and they showed no mercy for the Pollywogs.

There is no particular order for the gauntlet run. But, by chance, Andy went through with Wildcat Pilot "Dunk" Maloney, a collegiate runner at Holy Cross.

Maloney had an idea how they could minimize the number of Shelaley blows. "When we start, you take the left line, and I'll take the right line," Maloney said, "Then we do the weave crossing back and forth. Hopefully, we can throw them off, so we don't get too many whacks from those Shelaleys.

"Maloney was fast. He got ahead of me pretty quick," Winnegar recalled.

"After I got through the gauntlet, I stopped running and started shaking myself off. A sailor at least 30 feet past the end of the line was standing out there holding something behind his back. I assumed he was one of us," Andy explained.

"When I got even with him, he whacked me across the back with his shelaley."

"Hie, who was two people behind me, saw the prick and came running up and cold-cocked him, using his momentum to knock the guy out cold!"

"I was turning around to go after the guy, but I was too late. He was out cold on the deck with Hie standing over him. Man, was that was sweet justice."

"After it was all over, we took a shower, but it was so crowded that the only shower you could get in was the saltwater shower. Sometimes they ran fresh water through the saltwater shower, but not often and not that day." [85]

That evening, Andy, Hie, and Fuller took the ladder down to the hangar deck on the way to dinner. As they came out onto the deck, they ran into a group of five shellbacks holding court over a recent Pollywog.

"Hold the pussy down while I paint his puny shaved head with yellow zinc chromate paint."

"Man, this doesn't look good. Those pricks are still picking on us!" Fuller yelled.

Just as Fuller broke into a run towards the shellbacks, Lts. Bear and Maloney came bounding down the ladder. In one slow-motion, choreographed dance, Maloney grabbed the paint bucket and dumped it onto the ringleader's head. Yellow paint streamed down over his neck and shoulders while his stunned coconspirators watched helplessly.

---

[85] The ship made some freshwater by evaporating saltwater.

"Isn't that a beautiful sight," Bear exclaimed as he and Maloney hooted and howled at the Shellback's expense.

"You look like a piece of modern art!"

"The next time you want to pick on someone, you come and find us first. We'd be happy to dump another bucket of paint on your worthless scumbag head!"

Andy, Hie, and Fuller had watched the scene unfold and now could not stop laughing.

"Don't mess with VC-4, boys. We stick together, and you don't stand a chance."

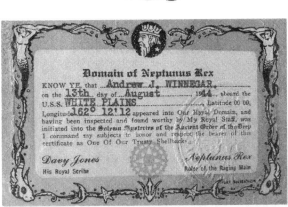

Figure 219 Andrew J. Winnegar. Domain of Neptunus Rex. Courtesy of Andy Winnegar

Eighty years after standing before King Neptune's Court, Andy Winnegar proudly shows his Domain of Neptunus Rex card.

While the "Crossing the Line" ceremony is practiced worldwide upon crossing the equator for the first time, I doubt that anyone can match the US Navy's WWII version for good-natured, blow-by-blow sadism. [86]

Espiritu Santo was also the site of another "all-for-one and "one-

---

[86] Most modern navies have instituted regulations that prohibit physical attacks on sailors undergoing the line-crossing ceremony.

for-all" Officers' Club brawl between the pilots of VC-4 and VC-10 of the USS Gambier Bay. The insult that precipitated this rumble involved one of the VC-4 TBM pilots. On the morning of 16 August 1944, Lt Huser on ASP sighted a surfaced submarine. Huser signaled it but got no return signal. Instead, the submarine crashed dived at this sign, so the TBM dropped its depth charges. Later, the submarine put its scope up and then surfaced again. It had been hit. Unfortunately, it turned out to be a U.S. submarine. It was heavily damaged and barely made it back to drydock

That evening, as Huser entered the Officers' Club at Espiritu Santo, he had a pit in the bottom of his stomach. I followed protocol. Stupid submarine captain should have identified his vessel as a friend. Besides, fat chance that anyone in here will know what happened out there today.

The club was packed, and all eyes were on Huser. Then, finally, a VC-10 pilot stood with his chair scraping the floor while the room turned silent. He shook his fist in Huser's direction and then sputtered, "You son of a bitch! You're the one who depth charged up my cousin's submarine!"

He charged Huser, a beer bottle in his right hand, with the intent to kill or at least maim the TBM pilot.

Huser tried to duck to his right but was held down by three other VC-10 pilots. "Take it like a man, you wimp! It's easy to shoot at your friends; now you're going to pay for your stupidity."

Figure 220 James Huser. VC-4 FM2-Wildcat pilot.

Figure 221 Officers Club on Espiritu Santo. 1944 South Pacific World War II Museum, Espiritu Santo.

The beer bottle came crashing down, striking the bar next to Huser's head. But unfortunately, he knew he wouldn't be so lucky with the next blow. Huser's arms were behind his back, and they had his face slammed down on the bar. *Oh shit! This is going to hurt.*

Suddenly, a rush of bodies and shouting came from the back of the room. All eyes turned towards the commotion.

Lts. Ferko, Bear, Wood, and Maloney were on the VC-10 pilots in a flash, pulling them off Huser and slamming them to the floor. Ferko threw the first clean punch, a right-handed jab to the nearest VC-10 pilot's chin. He dropped to the floor like a wet mop. Ferko's next wild swing missed its mark by a mile. The three remaining VC-10 pilots regrouped and charged Ferko with fists flying. Bear and Maloney tackled them to the ground, while Wood stepped in, pummeling the enemy with flying fists, elbows, and feet. Huser stood up at the bar, looked around, and spotted six more VC-10 pilots entering the Officer's Club.

"It's time to go, guys," Huser shouted, pulling his Wildcat pilots towards the back door.

Figure 222 Bar at the Espiritu Santo Officer's Club. South Pacific World War II Museum, Espiritu Santo.

Outside the Club, they heard the shouting from inside and ducked behind some crates. Huser pulled out five bottles of beer from his coat, passed them around to his bloodied but victorious friends, and made a toast. "All for One and One for All! Don't mess with VC-4!" The guys raised their bottles of beer in the moonlight. "Here! Here!"

While on Espiritu Santo, the VC-4 squadron took on new planes. With his seniority, Flight CMDR Owens received one of the new TBMs, while giving "27" to Lt. Dennis, a perk of having a higher rank.

Andy and Hie posed for one last photo with "27" before turning her over to Dennis' plane captain.

"She's a good plane, Hie. She got us through many battles without a scratch," Andy said, patting the old plane while inspecting some of the many bullet holes the metalsmiths had patched.

"Yeah. I hate to give her up. I fired a lot of rounds from her turret.

Figure 223 Andy Winnegar and Maurice Hie in front of their TBM Avenger.

Our new TBM had better not be a lemon!"

Andy and Hie spent the next couple of days outfitting their new plane, #20, which Pat dubbed "Spokane Chief II." Winnegar anticipated needing to install ready lamp, camera, 30 caliber machine gun, armor plate, depth charges, dye markers, bungee cords, etc. in the new plane.

"I should get at least one day's work out of this. I'm glad Hie and I have the ARM3/C helping us."

On 25 August 1944, Hie and Andy started work on their new plane. immediately after breakfast. First, they installed an Aldis Lamp, receiver remote tuner, first aid kit, two canteens, and radioman's safety belt and shoulder straps. Hie and Andy checked out the new life raft and equipped it with gear it lacked, including three mosquito head nets. This work kept them busy until about 1200.

"We secured the plane and started to wash up only to be informed that we had an ASP hop and that our pilot was in the plane ready to take off. We went up without chow. The only consolation we got was an exciting dog fight between us and the other ASP plane. It ended with us zooming a destroyer at water level going into a tight climbing turn and then zooming our ship which was all very well but didn't kill any Japs. We will have one more campaign then return to the states. We will see our next action around Yap."

"Looks like we got a good plane in Spokane Chief II, boys. No need for lemonade!" Owens reported from the cockpit.

CHAPTER 28

SHORE LEAVE ON ESPIRITU SANTO – BEER CHITS, JUNGLE VINES AND WILD BOAR – AUGUST 1944

Hey, Winnegar!" Hie hollered as he glided across the canyon, clutching a jungle vine.

Suddenly, the vine gave way, dropping three feet, with Maurice dangling precariously. Still moving forward, Hie let go and flew through the air, deftly grabbing the next vine and swinging across the canyon, finally releasing his grip for a perfect two-point landing on the far side.

"Piece of cake! Just like Tarzan!" Hie hollered. "Your turn, Andy!"

"You cashed in too many of

Figure 224 Jungle Vines. Wikimedia Commons. CC0 10 Universal Public Domain Dedication.

your beer chits, Hie! Let me enjoy my coke. It's the first coke I've had since we left the States."

"Come on, Winnegar. Hurry up, and bring your machete. We need you to climb up and fetch some coconuts for lunch and bring Edens and Fournier with you!"

Andy polished off his coke, took a deep breath, grabbed a thick vine, and let it rip as he glided over the canyon, flying through the coconut trees. Then, executing the mid-canyon vine exchange flawlessly, Andy let go and landed next to his friend.

"That was fun. Good thing we all watched those Tarzan movies," Andy laughed.

"You're a little shorter than Weissmuller, but you've got great form," Hie quipped.

"All right. You two are next, and I want to hear a Tarzan yell," Andy called out to Fournier and Edens.

The two radiomen came sailing across in tandem with their best Tarzan yells.

"Not bad! Now, who's hungry for lunch?" Hie asked.

Figure 225 Coconut Palm grove Espiritu Santo

"OK, Andy. It's your machete, so have at it!" Fournier smiled, gazing up at the 80-foot coconut palm trees. "Lunch is at the top!"

"I need to cash in more beer chits first!" Andy joked.

Halfway up the coconut palm, Andy's right foot lost its grip on the rough bark, leaving him dangling by his arms with his feet flailing fifty feet in the air. "Oh crap!"

"Don't wimp out on us now, Winnegar!" Edens yelled.

With his hands shaking, Andy cautiously shimmied the rest of the way to the top of the swaying tree and claimed his prize, a cluster of hairy brown coconuts. Then, pulling out his machete, he cut the coconuts off one by one.

"Look out below. Bombs away!" Andy yelled, sending twelve coconuts to the jungle floor.

"What a view! I can see the ocean and ships. There are rows and rows of bungalows on the island. They go on for miles!" Andy exclaimed from his swaying tree-top perch.

"Ouch! Who's biting me!" Andy hollered. "Crap there's red ants all over me and they BITE! Yikes! Get these suckers off me!"

Winnegar tried to quickly slide down the tree, but spurs covering the trunk tore into his skin.

"These damn ants give me the creeps," Andy yelled, running for the surf.

Jumping into the shallow water, Andy splashed around washing off the biting ants.

Laying in a shallow pool with the waves lapping at him Andy let out a sigh of relief, Ahh! That's better.

Inspecting his body for bites, Winnegar was horrified when he found leeches covering his legs.

"Oh Crap! Hie come over here and help me get these leeches off my back and legs!"

"Geez! You make a lot of noise, Winnegar. Are you afraid of a few leeches?" Hie laughed.

"Get these blood-sucking leeches off me!"

"No sweat. Come over here and hold still," Hie ordered as he held his glowing cigarette up to the nearest leech burrowing into Andy's leg. The air was filled with the sizzling sound and smell of frying leeches as one by one they dropped to the ground.

Figure 226 Banded Sea Krait. Wikimedia Commons. CCA Share Alike 2.0

"Thanks, Hie. Now, I'm glad you smoke like a chimney."

Edens and Fournier had gathered the coconuts into a pile. "OK! Now that Andy's excitement is over, who knows how to open these things?" Fournier asked, holding up the brown object of desire.

"It's easy," Andy replied still scratching his legs. "First, you have to remove this thick outer husk. Natives use their teeth and rip it off like this," Andy said biting and ripping the coconut husk.

"Or you can use a sharp stick to tear it off to get down to the hard shell. Next you poke out the eyes and drink the water. Then you whack the hard coconut shell with the butt end of this machete, giving it a turn between blows."

"Now crack it open and enjoy the coconut meat!"

Edens pulled out a bottle and guzzled warm beer while munching on the crisp white coconut. "Not bad!"

"I wish I had another coke," Andy lamented.

"If you were a Kraut, you'd be drinking their new Fanta. It's made from food scraps!" Hie added.[87]

"Fanta doesn't sound very German or American," Andy noted.

---

[87] Because of the War embargo, Coca Cola in Germany could not import the secret Coke syrup. In response, German businessman, Max Klein, invented Fanta in 1940, using left over produce materials. Fanta became a sensation in Germany and Europe. The current-day formulation of Fanta was developed in Italy in 1955.

Figure 227 Flowering Wonga Wonga Vine. John Tann. CC-BY-2.

"They probably make it out of leftover sauerkraut!"

After lunch of beer and coconuts, Andy was anxious to forget about the red ants and leeches and explore the surrounding jungle. "Hey, guys! I see some wild pig tracks! Let's follow 'em and have roast pork for dinner."

"Wild boars can weigh over 700 pounds and have really sharp tusks," Fournier warned. "You don't want to mess with them."

"No sweat! I grew up with pigs, and they don't scare me," Andy scoffed.

"I'm more worried about those green tree pythons," Edens added.

"No problem here!" Hie smiled as he pulled out his .38 caliber revolver. "We have plenty of firepower."

"It's that pretty striped sea snake you have to watch out for. It's poisonous and the natives claim it turns into a sexy woman to tempt young men and sailors," Andy added.

"You got my attention with sexy women, but first, it's bottoms up!"

Fournier said as he passed Andy the last beer.

"Coconut and warm beer. What could be more perfect?" Andy replied, throwing back another American Lager. "Hell of a lot better than Torpedo Juice."

With a little 3.2 percent alcohol fortification, the guys began their trek into the jungle with machete-wielding Winnegar in the lead, chopping a path through the dense vegetation. Hanging vines, and woody lianas twisting up from the forest floor made the going tough. Colorful pink and yellow flowering clusters hung from the Wonga Wonga vines as they encircled trees, reaching for the sunlight at the forest canopy.

After fifteen minutes of hacking, he paused with sweat dripping off his brow. Breathing hard with his hands on his knees, Andy looked up just in time to see a juvenile wild pig running across the path.

"There goes dinner!" Hie shouted.

"Quiet!" Andy hissed. "Mama boar is around here somewhere nearby, and she's gonna be pissed if we eat her baby."

The next instant, they heard grunting as the foliage parted, and they stood face to face with a growling 300-pound mean mama pig.

Figure 228 Wild boar juvenile. CC Attribution Share-Alike 4.0 International Charles Sharp.

Figure 229 Wild Boar. © Superbass / CC-BY-SA-3.0 via Wikimedia Commons

"Let's get the hell out of here!" Edens yelled.

The guys backed up slowly and then, in unison, spun around and started running for their lives, back towards the boat launch. Then back on the road, panting with an adrenaline rush that only a wild boar encounter can bring on, they collapsed to the ground.

"Is she still coming?" Edens asked, looking back at the jungle.

"No, but we aren't going to make it back in time" Andy panted, looking at his watch. "The powerboat is leaving at 1400. We've got 10 minutes to run a mile, and I'm pooped out."

Just then a jeep pulled up. "You fellas need a lift?"

"Hey, Crounse! Man, you're a lifesaver," Hie greeted their CIC shipmate.

"Hop in, fellas. I'm Lt. Kivett's chauffeur today so I'll have you at the Fleet launch in no time."

After Crounse dropped them off, Hie said, "I think we have time for

Figure 230 VC4 Airmen on shore leave Espiritu Santo / Azore Island Clifford
Richardson standing with Bill Lemon to his left. Courtesy of Christopher Dean,
Lemon's grandson.

another beer and there's Lemon and Richardson. So let's have one
more round! You got any more beer chits, Andy?"

"No. Get your own chits, but let me take the picture for you," Andy
grinned grabbing the camera.

As they waited for the open whaleboat back to the White Plains,
Fournier blurted out, "Man, that was one scary mama pig!"

"I guess we're not having roast pork for dinner," Andy laughed.

"Nope. It's shit on a shingle for your dining pleasure tonight!"
Maurice smiled.

"I've had this annoying stomachache since we had a warm beer and
green coconuts for lunch," Andy confessed. "I think I'll pass on the
SOS."

Figure 231 Espiritu Santo / Azore Island powered open-whaleboats transporting sailors to the Fleet Recreation Center. South Pacific World War II Museum, Espiritu Santo.

That night, aboard ship Andy, wrote his mother a short two-page letter. "Had a fun day of shore leave, but we're all a little sick of eating coconuts. Tomorrow we'll be shoving off for Guadalcanal, rumors say. We are taking on 150 bags of mail which is for Marines on Guadalcanal according to scuttlebutt. Thanks for all your letters, Mom. It's swell to hear from home."

By the time the scissor-wielding Navy censors got done with his letter, it had looked like swiss cheese.

Reaching into his pocket, Andy pulled out the shells and five cat eyes he'd picked up on the beach, souvenirs from his day of liberty on Espiritu Santo.

Figure 232 William F Draper. Espiritu Santo / Azore Island ships store with ice cream parlor and social headquarters for servicemen. USN. Public Domain

CHAPTER 29

DEALING WITH THE STRESSES OF WAR: BOOZE AND UPGRADED SLEEPING QUARTERS

The loss of the Skipper, Rocky Carson, Clyde Reams, and crewmen Albright and Lancaster brought the harsh realities of war front and center. Young men at war in the Pacific found ways of coping with the stress, the heat, and the humidity. While drinking alcohol was allowed for the officers, it was an offense worthy of a court-martial for any enlisted man on board. Ultimately, this threat wasn't much of a deterrent for these young boys thousands of miles from home, facing death every day.

"Hey, Winnegar! When are you going to share some of that pineapple juice you've been hoarding?" Coats asked for the hundredth time.

"What do you want with my 100% pure pineapple juice? 'PJ' boosts immunity, fights inflammation, promotes healthy digestion, improves vision, and makes you smell good. Anything I forgot, Coats?"

"Yeah! It cuts our "Torpedo Juice" and makes it almost palatable, if not Good Housekeeping safe."

Feigning shock, Andy replied, "You want to use my precious pineapple juice to flavor your illegal rot gut? If the Skipper catches you drinking that 180-proof grain alcohol, you'll end up in the brig, or worse!"

"Don't care. I need a drink, and Torpedo Juice hits the spot. "Bull" Durham, in ordinance, skims some from the cans of alcohol they use to fuel the torpedo motors. But we had to start filtering the torpedo alcohol. It turns out that someone is on to us and started adding stuff to it to make it unfit for drinking.[88]

Figure 233 Jimmy Bull Durham. USS White Plains.

"It was never fit for human consumption, but how are you filtering the alcohol?"

"Easy! We go to the ship's bakery, order up some loaves of French Bread, cut off the ends, and use the loaf to filter the torpedo alcohol. But we still need your pineapple juice to make it almost palatable! So, don't be a wus, Winnegar. I'll pay you double what you paid for the stuff."

"No way, Coats. It's worth five times that, and you know it! We're 4,000 miles from the nearest grocery store."

"Oh, alright, here's one hundred dollars for a case," Coats said,

---

[88] The US Navy began adding poisons to the torpedo motor 180-proof grain alcohol to render it undrinkable. In the first part of the Pacific War. U.S. torpedoes were powered by a miniature steam engine burning 180- or higher-proof ethyl alcohol as fuel. The ethyl alcohol was denatured by the addition of 5–10% "pink lady", a blend of dye, methanol and possibly other ingredients. Methanol causes blindness when ingested, and cannot be made non-poisonous. The methanol was said to be largely removed by filtering the fuel mix through a compressed loaf of bread.

Figure 234 Navy Sailors drinking. Public Domain.

pulling out a wad of money.

"I don't want your money, Coats. Here's one can, and only one can. Just promise me you won't go blind drinking this stuff. I want to be sure you can properly load our bombs and torpedoes on the Avenger.

"Thanks, Andy. How many cans do you have anyway?"

"Only one for you, Coats. So, use that juice sparingly," Andy replied, laughing as he closed and secured his locker.

There's no way I'm telling Coats that I have 48 cans of Dole Pineapple Juice in my locker!

Eighty-five degrees with 80% humidity was tolerable on the flight deck with a cool sea breeze. But, on the other hand, the same conditions in the sleeping compartments were stifling and oppressive with the men waking up drenched in sweat. After a full day of flying, the prospect of trying to get some shut-eye in the stale air of the compartment was enough to drive a sane man a little nut. Fortunately, fate intervened in the form of a 3/8" wrench and a four-foot metal plate leading to surreptitious air-conditioned sleeping quarters.

"Psst! Winnegar, wake up!"

Andy opened his eyes, wiping the beads of sweat from his forehead.

"What do you want, Bob?"

"You got to come with me. You're not going to believe what I found. Come on, Andy. Get a move on!"

"Oh, alright. But this better is good," Andy replied as he swung down from the top bunk. "Lead the way,"

Outside the compartment, Bob Fuller, who was half a head taller than Andy at 6'1", took a quick left and walked 30 feet to the end of the passageway.

"Here, look at this," Fuller said, pointing at a metal plate.

"Yeah! So, what? You brought me out here to look at a hunk of metal and a few bolts?"

"No. I brought you out here to show you this! "Fuller proclaimed as he swung the four-foot square plate, pivoting it on a single bolt.

"Where are the other bolts?"

Fuller pulled out a 3/8" wrench and a handful of one-and-a-half-inch long 3/8" bolts, grinning. "You mean these?"

"Look inside," Fuller instructed.

Andy poked his head inside and found himself in a room about 8x12 feet.

"Go on. Crawl in there!"

"Man! This is the coolest spot on the White Plains."

"Look down, Andy!"

"Woah! I can see the ocean down

Figure 235 Bob Fuller. TBM Avenger Radio operator on plane piloted by Lt. Huser. VC-4.

Figure 236 World War II aircraft carrier showing the air intake compartment for the ventilation system. US Navy photograph

there. I just hope no Jap subs decide to torpedo us while we're in here."

The men had stumbled onto one of the air intake rooms that supplied cool ocean air to the officers' quarters. The floor was a metal mesh through which Andy could see the ocean far below. They were essentially outside the ship. [89]

"How'd you find this place, Bob?"

"Just poking around, looking for a cool place to hang out.

"You know. We could sleep in here," Winnegar suggested. "Let's get a couple of cots and a food stash."

Within a minute, they had outfitted the room with cots, snacks, and two cans of Dole pineapple.

"Quick! Close the plate," Bob instructed as he pulled out two cigars.

"You can only smoke when the smoking light is lit," Winnegar said.

"Don't worry so much, Andy."

---

[89] The compartment outside the air craft carrier, located below the catwalk and the 40mm guns, is the air intake room for the officers' quarters air conditioning. This compartment also served as Andy Winnegar and George Fournier's secret air-conditioned sleeping quarters during the USS White Plain's engagement at Saipan in June 1944.

Just then, the smoking light announcement came over the ship's intercom.

"Saved by the bell!" Fuller grinned as he puffed on the stogie with smoke curling up into the air intake vents.

"This is heaven!" Andy said with his hands clasped behind his head, sipping on his pineapple juice.

The following day, Winnegar and Fuller left their air-conditioned sleeping quarters, carefully closing the metal plate, concealing their secret quarters.

At the end of the next day's hop, Andy smiled, imagining his cool air-conditioned sleeping quarters. He and Fuller had been living the cool life for seven days with no end in sight for their secret sleeping arrangement.

"Where do you go every night, Winnegar? George Fournier asked from the bunk across from Andy's.

"Too hot in here to sleep. I've been going up on the fantail. It's a lot cooler with a nice sea breeze," Andy replied as he hurried out the sleeping compartment hatch.

"We gotta be careful, Bob," Andy warned as he swung the metal plate back into place.

"You worry too much, Andy."

"Fournier's been asking me where I go every night."

"You didn't tell him about our secret, did you?" Fuller asked, laying on his cot with a worried expression.

"No, of course not. I made up some BS about going up on the fantail."

"Well, if we have to, we can tie George to the TBM propeller again," Bob laughed at the image of Fournier tied to the propeller, upside down, 12 feet above the deck."

"It wasn't too bad when we tied him to the bottom prop. But when we rotated the propeller to where he was on top, poor George was upside down, twelve feet above the deck! It was a hoot."

"We were mean. We didn't hurt George, but we sure did scare him," Andy added.

"Well, I'll smoke to that!" Bob proclaimed as he lit up a stogie and puffed smoke rings, immediately sucked up into the White Plain's ventilation system.

"Wait for the smoking light to go on, Bob!"

"Stop worrying, Andy. No way they can trace those smoke rings back to us. No one even knows about this room. It's our secret."

"Mark my word. There's going to be trouble, and your cigars will land us in hot water."

"No way, Andy," George mused as he puffed away on his cigar, absently flicking cigar ash into a tin can strategically situated between the two cots.

"Keep your ash off my cot, Fuller!" Andy grumbled.

Winnegar and Fuller enjoyed their air-conditioned sleeping quarters for several weeks, and we're growing accustomed to their luxurious berths. Captain Dennis J. Sullivan made a rare announcement on the White Plains' PA system the next day.

"Someone is smoking cigars and blowing their smoke into my quarters. When I find out which of you yoyo's is responsible, you will walk the plank and worse," Sullivan fumed.

Andy looked sideways at Fuller without uttering a word.

Outside the mess, Andy pulled Fuller aside. "You idiot! You've been blowing smoke rings into the Captain's quarters. I told you to cool it."

"Stop worrying, Winnegar. We're cool."

That evening Winnegar and Fuller arrived at the secret hatch ready for another refreshing night. Andy brought along another can of pineapple juice.

"Crap!" Fuller exclaimed.

"What's the problem? Where's your wrench?"

We're going to need a lot more than a wrench to get back in there,"

Upon inspecting the hatch more closely, Andy immediately saw the problem.

"It's been welded shut!"

"Duh! I guess those Navy guys are smarter than we gave them credit for."

"No way we can get back in there. Besides, they're probably waiting to see who shows up here. So, let's keep moving," Andy replied, heading back towards their compartment.

Captain Sullivan never did find the cigar-toting culprit, but that did little to dissuade him from eyeing every seaman and aircrew with suspicion.[90]

Heaven, help the idiot who's been fouling my air.

Figure 237 Captain D.J. Sullivan. USS White Plains. US Navy Photograph.

---

[90] Command of the White Plains changed in July 1944 with CMDR D J Sullivan replacing Captain Oscar Weller.

CHAPTER 30

PELELIU, ANGUAR, AND ULITHI ATOLL – SEPTEMBER 1944

The Peleliu invasion by the 1st Marine Division took place on 15 September 1944. Compared to Saipan, the terrain on Peleliu was much rougher, making it difficult to identify targets. Peleliu was rocky and chopped up, looking a lot like Bryce Canyon. Predictions that the island would be secured in four days underestimated the stiff resistance put up by the heavily outnumbered Japanese who often fought to the death in the name of the Emperor. The bloody ground battle for Peleliu dragged on for a full two months. Prior to Palau, Ens. Connors and Sheldon joined the VC-4 squadron.

On 16 September 1944 Lt Owens had a strike mission on

Figure 238 First wave of Marines invading Peleliu on 15 September 1944.

Figure 239 Men of the 5th Marine Regiment, US 1st Marine Division fighting their way up Beaches 'Orange' 1 and 2, Peleliu, Pacific. 15 Sep 1944. USMC 95256. Photographer PFC John Smith.

Peleliu. Naval gunfire had pulverized the southern end of the mountain range. The air space over Peleliu was thick with OS2Us, TBMs and Wildcats. Looking out the TBM tunnel windows, Andy couldn't help but think about their last midair misadventure over Saipan.

I hope we don't' have another mid-air collision.

"Leo 3, Torchy here. Target is a clump of trees, three miles out, hiding a Jap installation along your port side."

"You heard Torchy, men. Bombs and rockets ready," Owens called out already in his dive towards the target.

They unloaded five 100-pound bombs and eight five-inch rockets into the target with massive explosions as the hidden ammunition lit up the sky.

"Bulls-eye!" Owens yelled.

"Leo 3, Torchy here. Direct hit."

"Coming around for a strafing run," Owens instructed.

Andy and Hie unloaded their machine guns on the camouflaged buildings hidden in the trees. Long bursts from the turret .50 caliber gun and the .30 caliber stinger destroyed the buildings. There was no return fire.

"These strikes are not nearly as dangerous as on Saipan or Tinian," Andy observed.

"Heading back to the White Plains to rearm," Owens called out, surveying the damage of the smoking target on Peleliu. Far below they could make out the Marines slowly slogging inland from the hard-fought beachhead.

Figure 240 Bombardment of Anguar September 1944. US Navy Photograph

On 18 September 1944, three TBM Avengers from the USS White Plains led by Executive Officer Flateboe were sent out in formation with smoke tanks in the bomb bays. The mission was to lay smoke for the Marines invading Anguar. When they arrived at the drop site, they waited for orders instructing them where to drop the smoke.

Figure 241 Charlie M. Shields. TBM Avenger pilot. VC-4. Courtesy of Andy Winnegar.

"Where's the order for the smoke drop?" Shields called out to Flateboe.

"Yeah! We've been holding position and circling for over an hour. What gives?" Owens added.

"Patience, boys. No orders yet," Flateboe replied.

Ultimately, they called off the smoke drop out of concern that the smoke would be associated with poisonous gas and illegal warfare.

"Now, what are we going to do?" Owens asked Flateboe

"Yeah! We flew all the way out here to have our mission called off," Charles Shields complained. "Let's find a target and take it out."

Just then, an OS2U observation seaplane off one of the battleships or cruisers was flying across the island with little puffs of smoke right behind and ahead of it from Japanese anti-aircraft guns.

"Those AA guns have that OS2U on range and on target. The guy's toast!" Flateboe called out.

"Torchy, this is Leo 3. Request permission to strafe antiaircraft guns targeting our OS2U. They have him bracketed. Condition critical

. Over"

"Leo 3, Torchy here. Permission granted to engage the enemy. Over and Out."

"Let's go after the guns! Form on me." Flateboe yelled, immediately putting his Avenger into a forty-five-degree dive with Shields right behind him.

Puffs of smoke burst all around Flateboe's and Shields' planes as they went in with smoke and tracers pouring from their wing guns. Andy watched,

Figure 242 Lt WE Flateboe Executive Officer of Composite Squadron VC-4.

expecting them to be hit any second by the flashing AA batteries. They swept over the gun positions going into climbing turns as their turret and tunnel gunners opened up, Matt, McComas, Davis and Crawford were having a field day.

Meanwhile, Owens was still up above circling.

"Owens! Owens, what's your problem?" Flateboe called out.

"Don't have my gun sight installed."

"Quit stalling and engage! We're getting creamed by the ack-ack fire! Get down here!"

Owens was last in the lineup on the next run as they attacked the anti-aircraft guns.

"Oh no! Tail-end Charlie is the wrong place to be. We're gonna get whacked!" Hie exclaimed from the turret.

Puffs of smoke filled the sky, surrounding the three Avengers as they dove right into the mouth of the flaming Japanese anti-aircraft guns.

As they pulled out, Winnegar saw three anti-aircraft emplacements

Figure 243 Japanese 120mm antiaircraft gun defending Guam

surrounded by sandbags.

Man! I've got a direct shot into those gun emplacements. Sweet!

Winnegar struggled to get a bead on them while fighting to hold the .30 caliber up against the centrifugal force of the pull out.

"Here, take this!" Winnegar exclaimed, cutting loose with his .30 caliber stinger, filling the tunnel with smoke from a long burst. Hot spent .30 caliber cartridges littered the floor.

Hie was having a gunner's field day, in the TBM's turret, blazing away with his .50 caliber as Owens made a sweeping pull out to the right, following Shields and Flateboe. "Hooey! What rush! Let's do that again!"

"Crap! My gun's jammed!" Winnegar yelled into the intercom.

Andy cleared the jam, and on the next run, he let loose with an even longer burst from the .30 caliber machine gun. Smoke filled the tunnel as the hot spent cartridges clattered to the floor, piling up around his ankles.

"Jammed again! Ruptured cartridge's stuck in the barrel." Andy yelled as he took the gun apart to clear it and missed the next two runs. He could hear Hie firing away in the turret and yelling into the intercom.

"Jeez! Gotta get this gun cleared," Andy shouted into the intercom as he kicked the hot cartridges away from his feet.

"Andy! What the hell are you doing down there! Shoot your gun!" Owens yelled into the intercom.

Andy was disconnected from the intercom and could not hear Pat yelling. It was so loud inside the Avenger that without the intercom, you could yell directly into someone's ear, and they wouldn't be able to hear you.

"He can't shoot. His gun's jammed. He's trying to clear it, and you're throwing him all over the damn airplane!" Hie yelled into the intercom.

Andy finally cleared the jam and put the machine gun back together.

"Crap! Where's that bolt stud? I must have dropped it on the floor." Hundreds of spent cartridges covered the tunnel floor.

How am I going to find that bolt stud?

Andy was sifting through the spent .30 caliber cartridges, desperately trying to find the bolt stud while Owens was flying aerobatics to avoid the AA fire while throwing his crew around inside the Avenger.

"There you are!" Winnegar exclaimed as he reached down and retrieved the bolt stud. He put the machine gun back together and had it shooting on the last run. Then making up for the missed runs, Andy let it rip on the final pass, pouring lead into the target as his .30 caliber roared, and spit out cartridges, filling the tunnel with smoke and adrenaline coursing through his veins.

In the distance Flateboe could see the orange flashes of the Naval guns as they started to shell the enemy AA position, threatening to blow the three TBMs out of the sky.

"Let's get out of here. Return to base," Flateboe instructed.

The Japanese were still sending up flak as they departed, but the Avengers' job was done, and the target was a smoking mess.

After they emptied their smoke tanks and returned to the White Plains, Andy went to clean his .30 caliber gun in the ordinance room. He put the ramrod through the barrel and ran a rag through it but was surprised when he tried to look through the barrel.

What's going on here? I can't see through the barrel.

"Hie, take a look at this. It's the weirdest thing. I cleaned the gun, but I can't see through the barrel."

Hie smiled, took the barrel, placed it on a metal table, and rolled it. "Wop! Wop! Wop!"

"It's bent! You got it so hot, the barrel bent, Andy."

"Guess I'll need a new barrel."

"Next time, let your gun cool off, hotshot!" Hie laughed.

Figure 244 US Navy .30 caliber "stinger" machine gun.

That afternoon, Bob Fuller, Lt Flateboe, Ltjg Shields, Ens. Rox and Winnegar gathered on the fantail to fire their M1 rifles.

"We need something to shoot at," Rox said.

"Yeah! Like skeet shooting back home in Brave, Pennsylvania," Fuller added.

"Well, who has a clay pigeon throwing machine?" Shields inquired after firing his M1.

"Maybe the guys in the shop could make us one," Flateboe suggested.

"We don't need clay pigeons. Just shoot at the flying fish!" Andy said, pointing at the fish coming out of the high swells and sailing through the salt air to the bottom of the next swell.

"That just might work," Shields admired. "Let me take the first shot."

"I want the first shot," Rox said.

"Nope! I'm XO, so get in line behind me, Frank." Flateboe replied.

Flateboe tracked the next flying fish and fired his M1. The target instantaneously blew up into a hundred pieces.

"Wow! That was fun!"

"Let me try," Shields said.

"No, Fred is next, and then you can shoot," Flateboe instructed.

"This is a blast, but we need more of a challenge. Launch two fish at the same time," Shields ordered, laughing.

"OK, but you officers have to move over so we can shoot our guns," Andy replied. "Besides, I have a special gun made just for hunting a school of flying fish."

"What are you talking about, Winnegar?" Flateboe asked.

Pulling out his modified M1, Andy explained, "I filed the sear down, so now it's fully automatic! Here let me show you!"

Andy stepped up to the edge of the fantail, aimed his M1 at the swells, and waited. Then when the flying fish jumped out of the next swell, he let it rip. The gun exploded rapidly firing eight rounds in succession. The recoil pushed Winnegar back several feet. When the gun finally stopped firing, the barrel was pointed straight up and Andy was shoved up against the five-inch gun mount. Andy's face was white, but he was smiling.

"I guess I shouldn't have loaded a full clip."

"Man, I want one of those," Flateboe gushed. "It'll go with the .50 caliber machine gun I mounted on the ship's bow outside the wardroom. No way the Japs are catching me napping!"

No one else wanted to try Andy's modified M1, so he put his gun away and they returned to their competition.

Eventually, they all took turns. They kept score, and Hie was the winner, edging out Shields. Then, with the final fish flying through the salty ocean spray, Andy fired his M1, exploding the fish as cheers went up from the flight deck.

The fantail gunners turned around and looked up at the crowd of sailors and aircrew who had gathered to watch the fantail flying fish shooting competition.

Just then, Pat Owens came down the ladder carrying a box.

"If you let me shoot your gun, the Skipper says you can have a beer once you're done shooting!" Owens grinned.

"I'm done shooting!" Flateboe grinned.

"Me too!" Shields and Rox agreed.

"You enlisted guys will need to climb over onto that landing barge to drink your beer so you won't be breaking regulations about drinking aboard ship," Owens continued.

"But first, let me use your rifle, Andy. I'll even clean it for you."

"Here's a toast to the VC-4 fantail gunners May we be as successful hunting down the enemy!" Shields said as they raised their beer bottles to King Neptune and the Skipper.

Ulithi Atoll in the Caroline Islands is located 423 miles northeast of Peleliu. On 23 September 1944, seven TBM Avengers from the White Plains lined up wing tip to wing tip armed with 100-pound bombs and

Figure 245 237 Six TBM Avengers in formation. US Navy Photograph.

eight five-inch rockets. [91]

"Let's blow this place up!"

"Stay low over the beach and look out for the Japs. Let's clear out the enemy for our Marine brothers coming ashore behind us."

As they hit the beach, they were flying low.

"Nothing's moving down there," Flateboe reported.

The Avengers flew straight across the island with the Higgins boats coming in behind them, carrying Marines into the battle.

The Avengers did not bomb or shoot rockets that day. Instead, they flew straight across the island, turned around, and returned.

"Look at that! The Marines are coming out the other side!"

"I guess no one's home!" Shields called out, marveling at what later would be called the "Bloodless Invasion."

---

[91] Ulithi consists of 40 islets totaling 4.5 km² (1+³⁄₄ sq mi), surrounding a lagoon about 36 km (22 mi) long and up to 24 km (15 mi) wide—at 548 km² (212 sq mi) one of the largest in the world.

Ulithi was a natural harbor that the Navy began using that same night. Ulithi Atoll ultimately became the most extensive Naval base in WWII and the perfect location for staging its ultimate assault on the Japanese Empire. Ulithi was also Andy Winnegar's final mission for the VC-4 Squadron of the USS White Plains. [92]

Figure 246 Ulithi Atoll Naval harbor WWII. Public Domain. Wikimedia Commons

---

[92] Winnegar was put off ship on 11 October 1944 at Manus in the Admiralty Islands of Papua New Guinea with orders to report to Navy Flight School.

CHAPTER 31

WINNEGAR'S DEPARTURE – 11 OCTOBER 1944

In October 1944, after repairs at Manus in the Admiralty Islands, the USS White Plains headed for the invasion of the Philippines at Leyte. At Manus Island, they left behind one TBM Avenger Radio Operator.

Before hurriedly disembarking the White Plains, a yeoman took Andy to Lt Fickenscher's wardroom.

"Hello, sir, you wanted to see me?" Andy asked the skipper who was standing in his skivvies.

"Andy, you did one hell of a job for us. We'll miss your fast trigger finger on that .30 caliber stinger. Your rolls of film gave us a lot of

Figure 247 Lt CMDR ER Fickenscher. Commanding Officer of Composite Squadron VC-4.

good intelligence and kept the guys entertained."

"Thank you, sir," Andy replied, trying not to look at the Lt CMDR's underwear.

"You'll do great at flight school, Andy. So, hurry back, and I'll save you some gas if you can get back here in time."

Decades later, Winnegar recalled, "It all happened so fast. The skipper was almost the only one in the squadron that I got to say goodbye to."

As Andy was going down the gangplank, he heard a familiar call, "Psst! Hey Winnegar, up here!"

Andy stopped, turned with his duffle bag on his shoulder, looked back up at the White Plains and smiled.

"Good luck, Winnegar! Remember use your left jab followed by that right cross. Give 'em hell!" Willie smiled.

Andy waved and continued down the gang plank to his new life as a Navy Pilot Trainee.

A motor whaleboat took Andy from the White Plains to the shore. Andy looked out to sea on the dock with his duffle bag over his shoulder and orders in hand. The USS White Plains would soon weigh anchor and get under way, heading for the Philippines. [93]

"Man, was that was a pretty lonely feeling to get dumped off on an island. My home for the last year would sail off without me, and I didn't know a soul on this island.

Following his orders, Andy made his way to a Quonset hut and reported to the Master at Arms.

"I have to be in Liberty, Missouri by 17 November to start flight training."

The Master at Arms sneered and said, "Fat chance of that! Most of

---

[93] The USS White Plains left Manus at 0500 on 12 October 1944 headed for the Philippines in a convoy of 12 CVEs, 6 cruisers, 6 battleships.

Figure 248 Manus Island. 1945. US Navy Photograph.

my guys have been waiting for six or seven months."

"Well, three days later, my name was on a bulletin board, and I got on a troop transport, heading for Pearl Harbor," Andy recalled.

A brief stay on Manus was memorable for mountains of mud and military vehicles driving down muddy roads on the wrong side. With a tropical monsoon climate, it rains in Manus even during the driest months, with 68 inches of rainfall per year.

Andy recalled, "I never entered the chow line. From the Quonset hut barracks, I could see a long line over a hill with no beginning or end. Instead, I lived on candy bars from the hustlers that came around. At least the bunks were single, unlike the stacked bunks aboard ship."

The trip from Manus in the Admiralty Islands to Pearl Harbor was 14 days of absolute boredom on a "miserable troop transport". The USS General W.F. Hase was an unescorted Liberty Ship under constant threat of attack by Japanese submarines. Crowded with thousands of US soldiers going home from the War in the Pacific, her human cargo

Figure 249 USS General Hase launched 15 December 1943. US Navy Photograph

was exhausted. Even a casual observer could see that the men with glazed eyes were shell-shocked and in an overall general mess. Some came aboard tied down to stretchers while others came up the gangway on crutches. There were so many men that the 2500 American soldiers slept in crowded compartments with the bunks stacked five high.

"You couldn't even roll over without hitting your shoulder on the guy above you," Winnegar recalled. "I was on the bottom bunk, and it was claustrophobic."

A boxing ring on the deck with two black fighters putting on sparing exhibitions grabbed Andy's attention. When Andy inquired whether he could get involved and do some boxing, they asked what his position was aboard the ship.

"I'm a passenger," Andy replied.

"Well, then there is no way we can let you spar in the ring. Absolutely, no way!"

Going stir crazy with boredom, Winnegar went to the Master at Arms, asking what he needed to do to get a job aboard ship.

The Master at Arms replied with a smile, "I can handle that for you.

You'll eat in the regular crews' mess and eat regular meals three times a day. And you'll get to sit down instead of standing for meals twice a day with the passengers."

"Well, I thought this would be great! So, they put me in charge of seven 'heads.[94] I had the sorriest crew of ten men you've ever seen. They were Marines and sailors who were also passengers. All the men looked shell-shocked. To get those guys to work, you practically had to beat 'em up. No one wanted to work. They just wanted the three squares a day."

After three days of unsuccessfully cajoling and threatening his work crew, Winnegar went back to the Master at Arms and said, "I think I'll go back on regular passenger rations. I don't want any more of that crap. Scraping out urinals with your pocket knife and scrubbing sinks with steel wool and Bonomi is not much fun with that sorry work crew. I could do it faster by myself."

Andy spent every day pacing the deck in the bright sun.

"About the only entertainment, they offered the passengers was circumcision for those who needed it," Winnegar recalled slyly eight decades later.

After they reached Pearl Harbor, while still onboard the USS Hase, Andy picked up a newspaper to check out the latest news. The headlines made his jaw drop.

"When I got to Pearl Harbor and saw the headlines and Ens. Robinson's description of attacking "The Whole Jap Fleet,"

Figure 250 William Hugh Robinson FM-2 Wildcat Pilot VC-4 aboard the USS White Plains US Navy Photograph.

---

[94] "Head" is slang for a bathroom.

FIGHTERS DROPPED OUT OF CLOUD, SAW JAP FLEET BELOW

By MURLIN SPENCER

LEYTE, Philippine Islands, Oct. 25 (Delayed) (AP).—Eight fighter planes dropped through the clouds and discovered a Japanese fleet between U. S. Carriers and Leyte Island at 6:00 a. m. today, Ens. William Robinson, a Westfield (Mass.) pilot, said in describing ,the opening of one phase of the sea-air battles of the Philippines.

"There below us was what looked like the whole Japanese fleet and there were only eight of us, all fighters," said Robinson. "There must have been four or five battleships, as many cruisers and even more destroyers. They had slipped in during the night and got between our carriers and Leyte."

Figure 251 Battle off Samar Wm H Robinson FM-2 Wildcat Pilot VC_4 USS White Plains St Louis Post Dispatch 26 October 1944. Robinson's quote was printed in every major newspaper in the United States.

I could have kicked myself. Had I known this battle was coming, I would have skipped flight school," Winnegar confided. "It was the battle of a lifetime, and I missed it, sailing back to Pearl Harbor on that miserable troop transport."

The trip from Manus Island to Pearl Harbor was 8,900 km or 5050 miles (4822 nm). To avoid the Japanese submarines, they stayed away from the shipping lanes, sailing south around the tip of Tahiti. The continuing trip from Pearl Harbor to Treasure Island in San Francisco covered 13,100 km or 8,140 miles (7073 nm) from Manus to

California. The USS WF Hase docked at Treasure Island in San Francisco on 2 November 1944 after 20 miserable days at sea. Flight School beckoned, but for Andy Winnegar, the war was over.

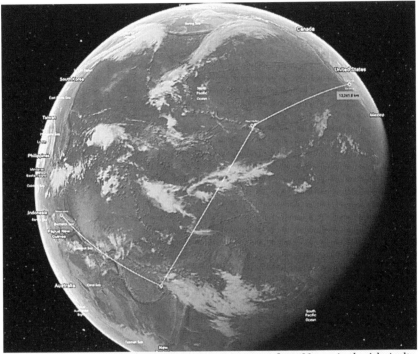

Figure 252 Google Earth. USS WF Hase troop transport from Manus in the Admiralty Islands to Pearl Harbor and San Francisco

CHAPTER 32

LEYTE AND THE BATTLE OFF SAMAR – 25 OCTOBER 1944

"In no engagement in its entire history has the United States Navy shown more gallantry, guts and gumption than in the two morning hours between 0730 and 0930 off Samar."

—Rear Admiral Samuel Eliot Morison

The Battle off Samar was the central confrontation in the larger Battle of Leyte from 23 October to 26 October 1944. Considered the largest naval warfare of all time, involving 200,000 American, Australian, and Japanese personnel, it aimed to support General Douglas MacArthur's invasion of the Philippine island Leyte

Historians have cited the Battle off Samar as one of the most

Figure 253 Japanese Vice Admiral Takeo Kurita. Wikimedia Commons.

remarkable last stands in
naval history; ultimately, the
vastly outnumbered and out
gunned Americans prevailed
over a massive armada; the
Japanese Imperial Navy's
Center Force under the
command of Vice Admiral
Takeo Kurita.

Admiral William Halsey Jr.
had been lured into taking his
powerful Third fleet after a
Japanese decoy fleet. Scouts
from Task Force 34 found Vice
Adm. Jisaburo Ozawa's four
carriers on the afternoon of
the twenty-fourth off the
northeast end of Luzon. Not
realizing that this was a

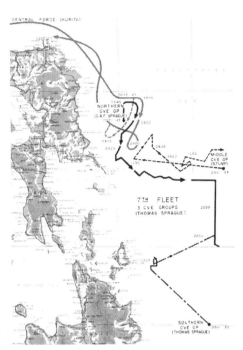

Figure 254 Battle off Samar. Wikipedia.

deliberate decoy, Halsey took the bait and pursued Ozawa Northward,
taking every ship in the area he had the power to command, including
four battleships and three fleet aircraft carrier groups

In addition, the heavy forces of the U.S. Seventh Fleet under Vice
Admiral Thomas C. Kinkaid's command were engaged to the south of
Leyte Gulf. This situation left only three Seventh Fleet's escort carrier
(CVE) task units (Taffy 1, Taffy 2, and Taffy 3) on the northern flank
of the Leyte operational area, where they had been providing close air
support and antisubmarine patrols for the amphibious landings.

Just after sunrise on 25 October, Rear Admiral Clifton A. F.
Sprague's "Taffy 3"—the northwesterly-most task unit was stunned
to confront a 23-ship Japanese convoy with four battleships including
the massive Yamato with her 18-inch main guns, six heavy cruisers,

two light cruisers, and 11 destroyers. Taffy 3 was severely overmatched with only three destroyers, four destroyer escorts, and six small jeep escort carriers, including the USS White Plains. The American ships' largest armament was five-inch guns, clearly no match against the powerful Japanese warships. The outcome seemed like a forgone conclusion, but the Americans had other ideas, attacking with their five-inch guns and torpedoes. U.S. planes from the escort carriers of Taffy 2 and 3, including FM-2 Wildcats, F6F Hellcats, and TBM Avenger torpedo bombers, took to the sky. The 400 American planes relentlessly strafed, bombed, torpedoed, rocketed, and depth-charged the enemy fleet. When they finally ran out of ammunition, they made "dry" runs at the enemy ships to confuse and harass them. Taffy 2 and Taffy 3 aircraft contributed to the sinking of the heavy Japanese cruisers Chokai, Chikuma, and Suzuya.

However, to tell this story, one must turn the calendar back to 12 October 1944, when the White Plains left Manus in the Admiralty Islands and headed for Leyte to support MacArthur's "promised return" to the Philippines. The Task Group included 12 CVEs, six cruisers, and six battleships with a total of 65 ships. Unfortunately, on 17 October, the fleet encountered a massive typhoon with heavy seas, low visibility, and 51 knot winds that threatened the ships and the aircraft on the six Taffy 3 escort carriers.

"Come on, Walley. Let's get to it!" Hie yelled as the wind and rain buffeted the men huddled on the flight deck, waiting for the storm to subside even briefly.

"We're gonna get blown overboard!"

"We gotta tie down our Avenger with these cables, or she's going to blow overboard, and then we'll be in the soup!" Hie yelled over the wind and rain.

Walley could hear the White Plains' plates buckling as they waited out of the rain.

"This is the worst storm I have ever been in," Walley yelled.

"Yeah, this is the storm of the century!" Hie agreed.

"OK! Let's make a run for the Avenger, now! Walley said during a brief lull in the 60 mph winds.

Both men ran towards their TBM Avenger, dodging other planes while being buffeted by the tremendous gusts of wind and rain.

"Here, take these steel cables and tie her down securely,"

It took 15 minutes to complete the job in the buffeting rain and wind, but at least No. "20" was secure.

Hie patted the Avenger's fuselage. "Take care, girl, we'll be needing you to shoot down more Japs for MacArthur real soon,"

"Man, that was even scarier than being in combat," Walley confessed after they were in the shelter of the hangar deck.

"Let's change clothes and get some coffee and hot cocoa in the mess room," Hie suggested.

"I'm with you, Maurice. Lead the way."

When the White Plains arrived at Leyte on 18 October 1944, they immediately began flight operations and antisubmarine patrols.

"Everyone realized that we had picked the middle of a Hornet's nest," Walley recalled.

Fighters from the ship took off and strafed runways on Tacloban and San Pablo airfields. They did not encounter any enemy aircraft. Later the White Plains launched six fighters and two bombers on strafing and bombing missions against gun positions South of Tacloban airfield.

Figure 255 Curtis D. McGaha. GM-2 Wildcat pilot. USS White Plains.

The Japanese at Leyte hid inside of caves. Lieutenant CD McGaha, and Ensign W. G. Schaufler, discovered Japanese emplacements in caves dug into a hillside. Flying within 50 yards, they were able to fire directly into the mouths of the caves destroying the Japanese artillery. Strafing, bombing and rocket firing continued, directed at enemy ammunition dumps, trucks, and buses.

Figure 256 William Schaufler FM-2 Wildcat Pilot. USS White Plains.

Two days later, on 20 October, the White Plains' fighters and torpedo bombers were launched at 0745. Suspected mortar positions at Leyte were heavily strafed and bombed in anticipation of MacArthur's return. Finally, in the early afternoon, General Douglas MacArthur came wading ashore through knee-deep water at Leyte in freshly-pressed Army khakis, sunglasses and marshal's cap, a historic event captured in the now-iconic photograph. In drenching rain, he strode ashore on the muddy beachhead near Palo.

MacArthur's triumphant words spoken into a microphone are recorded for history but gave no hint of the impending Naval battle that would be needed to preserve his victory:

"This is the voice of freedom. General MacArthur speaking. People of the Philippines! I have returned. By the grace of Almighty God, our forces stand again on Philippine soil. – soil consecrated by the blood of our two peoples.... Rally to me. Let the indomitable spirit of Bataan and Corregidor lead on. As the battle lines roll forward to bring you

Figure 257 General Douglas MacArthur comes ashore at Leyte Philippines 20 October 1944. Wikimedia Commons.

within the zone of operations, rise and strike.... The guidance of the divine God points the way. Follow in His Name to the Holy Grail of righteous victory!"

Meanwhile, the Japanese Fleet initiated their three-pronged attack through the Surigao and San Bernardino Straights, intent on catching MacArthur and shelling his rear flank from the sea at Leyte Gulf. First, Admiral Kurita would take his powerful Central Fleet through San Bernardino Straight above Samar Island and approach Leyte from the north. Simultaneously, Vice Adm., Shoji Nishimura's Southern Force would approach Leyte from the south through the Surigao Strait. Once these two Japanese forces rendezvoused off Leyte at 0900 on 25 October, they would turn their guns towards the Leyte beachhead and crush MacArthur's forces. The Japanese were willing to risk the loss of their entire Mobile Fleet to smash MacArthur's rear flank in a massive gamble. The successful decoy that had drawn Admiral Halsey's powerful Third Fleet northward, taking them out of the battle, set the stage for the Japanese Navy to shell MacArthur off the beaches at Leyte. There was little in the way of their success, other than escort carrier group Taffy 3 and the men who flew the fighters and torpedo bombers off the wooden flight decks of her six small escort carriers.

The ensuing naval and air battles pitted the aircraft of Taffy 1, 2, and 3 against Japanese land, sea, and air targets, making an ACE of one unlikely White Plains FM2-Wildcat pilot.

Leo Martin Ferko was born in Great Falls, Montana in 1915. His parents, Martin Ferko and Katie Starcevic, were born in Northern Croatia, immigrating to America in 1902. The family moved to South San Francisco where Leopold attended South San Francisco High School. His parents spoke Slavic and some German in the home while Leo and his brother Stephen usually answered them in English. Leo attended Stanford University where he starred on the football team as an All-American left guard on the defensive squad where he was listed as 5'11" weighing 188 pounds.

After graduating in 1937, Leo returned to South San Francisco High School teaching English and mathematics and coaching the football team. By

Figure 258 Lt Leo M Ferko,1915-1992, FM2 Wildcat pilot for VC-4 aboard the USS White Plains. US Navy Photograph.

Figure 259 Nakajima B6N2 "Jill" torpedo bomber. Public Domain.

1940, his father had passed away and Leo was living with his mom, and younger brother Stephen. Leo enlisted in the Navy on 3 February 1941, entered flight school, and became a flight instructor at Corpus Christi after which he was assigned to Composite Squadron VC-4 aboard the USS White Plains. While not the most aggressive or flamboyant Wildcat pilot, Ferko flew with precision and intelligence.

On 23 October 1944, following an attack of eight Zeros, Lt Leo Ferko tricked one Zeke into evasive tactics by firing a burst from out of range over the Jap's head. This opening allowed Ferko to close quickly. He opened fire at the fuselage and wing roots. The Zeke made a flat skid to the left and crashed full speed into the sea. "Nice shooting, Leo," wingman Ens. L.R. Pool congratulated Ferko. "Now you just need four more kills to become the squadron's first Ace!"

"Stow it, Pool,"

"Hey, Leo! My elevator got messed up in that dogfight. I'll have to land at Tacloban for repairs."[95]

"Roger, that. See you back on the White Plains."

On the way back to the White Plains, Ferko came upon a lone Japanese Nakajima B6N Jill torpedo bomber flying 1000 feet below him.

"Well, that's a sweet target."

---

95 Pool's landing at Tacloban airstrip was the first American landing in the Philippines since the Japanese invasion in 1942.

Figure 260 USS Kadashan Bay CVE 76. US Navy Photograph.

Ferko did a wing-over, made an overhead approach, leveled off, and opened fire at 1,000 feet. The Japanese fighter burst into flames, exploded with its flaming debris falling into the sea.

That makes two, but I'm running out of fuel. No way I can make it back to the White Plains.

Turning on his Z.B. radio receiver, Ferko picked up the homing signal from the Taffy 2's USS Kadashan Bay. After landing, he spent the night onboard the Kadashan Bay while plane crews fueled and rearmed his FM-2 Wildcat.

The next day on 24 October 1944, while on combat air patrol with VC-20 from the USS Kadashan Bay, they spotted a group of Nakajima Ki-43 tactical fighters code name Oscar flying far below them.

"We were flying tactical combat air patrol at about 17,000 feet when we spotted twelve Oscars headed for Tacloban airstrip." Ferko later recalled.

The Wildcats closed rapidly diving out of the sun, attacking the Japanese formation from above. Ferko picked out "Tail-End Charlie," blasting him out of the sky with his .50 caliber machine guns. The

Figure 261 Nakajima K-47 Oscar. A small and nimble single-seat fighter that was the mainstay of the Japanese army. Public Domain.

Japanese plane exploded and instantly disintegrated.[96]

"I then turned slightly to my left and hit a second Oscar. When I let him have it, I was so close on his tail, not more than 300 feet away,"

With cockpit cover and large pieces of fuselage and starboard wing flying off, the stricken Oscar crashed into the ocean in an uncontrolled spin.

An Oscar jumped on Ferko's tail during the dog fight and began shooting up the Wildcat.

Ferko's attempt to shake the enemy plane was unsuccessful, and his fate looked doomed when Wingman Pool dropped in behind the Oscar, shooting him out of the sky.

"Thanks for that, Pool," Ferko radioed.

Flight leader, Ens. Warren Kruk of VC-20, congratulated Ferko.[97]

"Nice shooting, Ferko."

"Lucky Pierre will look good with four Japanese flags on her fuselage," Ferko replied, referring to his Wildcat's nickname.

"Well, boys, it looks like we have an almost ACE in Lt Ferko. So, let's find Leo another Jap plane to seal the deal!"

On the same day, Navy CMDR. David McCampbell and his wingman,

---

[96] Leo M. Ferko VC-4 MN-2 Wildcat pilot and WWII Ace. Credited with shooting down five Japanese planes.
[97] Ens Warren Kruk of VC-20 based on the USS Kadashan Bay was awarded the Distinguished Flying Cross for heroism during the Battle Off Samar 25 October 1944.

Lt Roy Rushing, put on a remarkable show of dogfighting. Engaging 80 Japanese planes, Rushing shot down six aircraft while McCampbell brought down nine enemy planes, the single most victories ever recorded by an American pilot. [98]

Battle off Samar 25 October 1944

On Sunday, 25 October 1944, the day of the Battle off Samar, the White Plains launched fighters and TBM Avenger torpedo bombers at dawn just after 0600 for CAP missions off Leyte.

"They headed south from the White Plains. Had they headed north, they would have seen something to freeze them in their seats," Lt Russell Wood recalled.

"Just over the horizon, headed for Leyte Gulf, was a Japanese task force of four battleships, eight cruisers, and thirteen destroyers. Lying directly in their path was our group of six CVEs with their screen of

Figure 262 Kitkun Bay prepares to launch her Wildcat fighters while White Plains is straddled by 18-inch shells. Wikipedia. Public Domain

---

[98] LCDR McCampbell was awarded the Congressional Medal of Honor.

three destroyers and four destroyer escorts," recalled Ltjg Russell Wood, White Plains pilot and historian.[99]

At 0659, the battleship Yamato opened fire with her 18-inch guns at an estimated range of 17 nm, targeting the USS White Plain with her first four salvos. The first salvo landed a mere 300 yards off the ship's starboard beam. One shell from the third salvo at 0704 exploded beneath the turn of White Plains port bilge. While it was not a direct

Figure 263 18-inch shells dropping near USS White Plains as seen from Kitkun Bay CVE 7 during Battle of Samar. Public Domain.

---

[99] VC-4 White Plains' Memoirs and Scrapbook. Ltjg Russell Wood. US Navy Public Relations. 1943

hit, the salvo caused significant structural damage to the White Plains' hull, twisting the fantail, bending one drive shaft, and cracking a deck plate on the hangar deck damaging her starboard machinery. The blast knocked out all power to the White Plains.

"In CIC it was dark and so quiet you could hear a pin drop. In fact, we didn't know if we were underway or not. The White Plains was the closest carrier to the Jap Fleet,

Figure 264 Donald Crounse. CIC radar man USS White Plains. 1944. Courtesy of Don Crounse.

so we were really getting it. Everyone was preparing for going over the side," Donald Crounse wrote.

The room shook from the shells exploding along the port side of the White Plains.

"Oh my god, that was close! We're gonna have to swim to get out of this," Radarman Conly muttered.

The rumble of the low murmurs filled the room.

"All right, men. Settle down. We have a job to do here. Keep your eyes and ears open and call out the enemy ships and planes so we can keep these plotting boards up to date," Lt Kivett encouraged his men in CIC in his calm reassuring voice.

The Japanese fleet was running down the slower White Plains. Smoke screens helped, but few onboard had any hopes of getting out of this one without swimming for it.

Crounse stared at his surface-scanning radar scope filled with the blips of the Japanese Fleet and Taffy 3's ships. He regularly called out ship movements to Lt Kivett who plotted them on the horizontal plotting board.

Figure 265 CIC Combat Information Center US Navy. WWII. Public Domain.

"Good work, men. Keep calling out the radar indications and ship movements," Kivett said.

The radarmen on the air-scanning radar scopes tracked dozens of aircraft, calling out the rapidly changing positions to the plotter on the vertical plexiglass plotting board.

"Keep tracking those bogeys, men," Lt Slater, the FDO said.

"I can't tell the friendlies from the bogeys. Half our guys don't have their IFF lights on," grumbled CIC radarman, Lowell Dubose.

"If there is no IFF signature, then they're bogeys. So keep tracking them," Kivett instructed his men.

By now, twenty men, including all of the off-duty radarmen, packed the CIC, desperate to know how the battle was going. The CIC was a front row seat to the developing chaos. All Taffy 3's ship-to-ship and air-to-ship radio communications played over the CIC's speakers. The men were silent and spellbound, listening to reports of bombings, approaching Japanese cruisers and destroyers, shelling by the Japanese battleships, desperate counter attacks by the American ships, and the relentless strafing and dive bombing of the American planes.

At 07:35, Crounse reported, "Lt. Kivett, we have two enemy cruisers closing in along our port stern."

"What's the range, Crounse?

"27,000 yards, sir, and closing."

Kivett picked up the phone to the bridge, "Two Japanese cruisers on the port stern at 27,000 yards."

"Enemy cruisers on port stern at 27,000 yards. Fire at will!" the men in CIC overheard the instructions to the five-inch gun crew.

The White Plains gunners opened up with their five-inch gun scoring 8-20 direct hits on the Chōkai, exploding surface-mounted torpedoes and crippling the vessel. CIC continued to update the range from the surface radar scopes. By 0749 the enemy had closed to within 22,000 yards.

Crounse recalled, "I wanted to see for myself what the heck was going on out there, so on my next break I snuck out of the CIC and went up on deck. I got out there on the catwalk, looking out to sea. I saw these bright flashes and then more flashes in the distance. I recall my thoughts like it was yesterday."

Those lights must be ships signaling each other. They're sure sending a lot of messages.

"Suddenly, a shell hit 200 yards off our beam with a tremendous splash."

"Oh my God!! Those ships aren't sending messages, they're firing on us!"

"I could see the guns flash, and then the shells hit beside and over us. I watched the other carriers getting the same treatment with salvo after salvo straddling the ships," Donald Crounse recalled.

After five minutes, Crounse had seen enough. "To hell with this, I'm going back to the CIC."

Figure 266 The escort carrier Gambier Bay burning from earlier gunfire damage, is bracketed by a salvo from a Japanese cruiser (faintly visible in the background, center-right) shortly before sinking during the Battle off Samar. Wikimedia Commons.

By 0800 the Japanese destroyers made torpedo runs on the White Plains, coming within 9,600 yards. One Taffy 3 destroyer on the port beam was hit and sunk.[100] The Gambier Bay was hit and began dropping back. Two Japanese cruisers pounded her until she sank. [101]

The men in CIC sat and listened to the unfolding slaughter in stunned silence.

A few minutes after 0900, the Japanese cruisers on the port side were closing in.

"What's the range of those Jap ships, Kivett?" Captain Sullivan called down to CIC from the bridge.

"Crounse, we need a range," Kivett said.

"12,000 yards, sir," Crounse replied from his radar scope.

"They're at 12,000 yards," Kivett reported to the bridge.

---

[100] The first American destroyer sunk was the USS Hoel at 0855. The second destroyer lost; the USS Johnston sank just after 10:00.
[101] The escort carrier USS Gambier Bay sunk at 09:07

On the White Plains' stern, Chief Gunner WF Brisson, adjusted the range of his gun sight and poured his single five-inch gun into her while the destroyers fired their battery of five-inch guns into the attacking enemy. Overhead, the Taffy 3 aircraft strafed and bombed and did whatever they could to harass the enemy ships." [102]

Captain Sullivan ordered repeated course changes in a desperate attempt to avoid the enemy salvos. However, the situation looked grim for the White Plains and Taffy 3.

Meanwhile, the explosions from the enemy salvos and the return fire from the White Plains' five-inch gun shook the CIC walls where the lights flickered.

At the height of the battle, Lt. Kivett looked up and saw one of his men huddled in the corner with his head down. Walking over to the sailor, Kivett gently placed his hand on his shoulder.

"You're doing a fine job, son. We're all in this together and we will get through this together. Now come over here and give us a hand."

"It was a bloody mess out there," Don Crounse recalled.

With the first Japanese salvos, Admiral Sprague immediately ordered the Taffy 3 carriers to turn into the wind to launch every remaining available aircraft with whatever armament they happened to have onboard.

By 0731, the flight deck of the White Plains was chaotic as the VC-4 squadron's remaining planes were hustling to get airborne and into the battle. Pat Owens was the next TBM Avenger at the catapult on the port bow of the flight deck.

Owens looked to his right. The Flight Director was frantically waving at him, but could not be heard over the noise of the engines and battle. Owens looked out to sea at the splashes from the salvos.

---

[102] The White Plains five-inch guns continued firing nonstop for 36 minutes with a succession of three armored Japanese ships as targets. A total of 127 rounds were fired.

Figure 267 Men scramble to launch FM-2 Wildcats as the enemy surprises Kikun Bay off Samar 25 October 1944. Eighteen-inch Japanese shells splash around the USS White Plains in the distance.

"We got to go before the Japs sink this ship!" Owens hollered pointing forward towards the catapult and the end of the flight deck. "Let's get this show on the road!"

"Alright, Steve, you've got to fill Winnegar's shoes today as my radioman. Let's go hunt down the damn Jap fleet!" Owens greeted Steve Walley, his new radioman/bombardier.

"Whoa!" Maurice Hie yelled from the turret. "Winnegar's is going to be kicking himself once he hears about the battle he missed! This is going to be epic!" Hie yelled with gallons of adrenaline coursing through his veins.

"Settle down, Maurice. Just shoot straight and nail some Jap targets.

"Don't worry about me, Pat. I've been waiting for this day. Now, just find me something to shoot up."

After catapulting off the White Plaines at 07:40, flight leader Owens joined up with the three TBMs flown by Lt. Hearn, and Ensigns

Byrd, and Butcher as the flight of Avengers headed towards the Japanese fleet just over the horizon.

The remaining VC-4 Wildcats were also scrambling into the air as Yamato's salvos splashed into the waters around the White Plains. One of the waiting Wildcats had the tip of its port wing blown off by debris from the latest Japanese salvo.[103]

Lt Leo Ferko was one of the last FM-2 Wildcat to fly off the deck after his flight crew hurriedly reloaded ammunition for the .50 caliber wing guns. Looking down, Ferko observed the colorful geysers as the next salvo from the Yamato struck the waters just off the White Plains.[104]

The Japs are shooting at us in technicolor![105]

Ferko, the flight leader, radioed his men to form up around him.

Figure 268 Leo M Ferko in his FM-2 Wildcat nicknamed "Lucky Pierre."

---

[103] Maurice Hie journal entry October 25, 1944.

[104] The opening salvo of the Battle of Samar shells from the 18-inch guns of the Japanese battleship Yamato splash dangerously close to the USS White Plains at 0700 on 25 October 1944.

[105] Colored ranging shells were used to establish the correct range of a target.

Along with "Dunk" Maloney and "Wildman" Bear, Wingman Pool quickly dropped into formation.

"We didn't think you were coming to the party," Pool joked.

"Flight crew was still reloading ammo when the order to scramble came in. Wouldn't want to miss this fight or arrive with empty guns," Ferko replied.

"Roger that. Glad to have you along," Bear replied.

"Looks like we have the wild bunch here," Ferko replied, referring to their now-famous brawl with the P-47 pilots on Aslito.

We had a good day hunting Japs yesterday. Let's continue to add to that score today," Ferko said.

After launching the last plane, the flight deck was nearly empty. A lone seaman from the flight deck crew stood on the White Plains fantail gazing at the horizon with a sinking, hopeless feeling. The flames from the big guns of the Japanese battleships and cruisers lit up the sky in a spectacle of destruction as the enemy shells continued to straddle the Taffy 3 ships.

There's no way we're getting out of this alive.

The zig-zag course of the White Plains seemed like little defense against the enemy's 18-inch guns, and the Taffy 3 destroyers and cruisers had left to pursue the Japanese Fleet.

Figure 269 Lewis A Hunsaker. Seaman 1/c USS White Plains. Hunsaker Family Photograph.

"We're on our own out here," Hunsaker whispered.

"Hunsaker!"

Lewis turned around to find a group of four shipmates gathered behind him.

"Lew, we were thinking," the sailor paused, looking down at the wooden deck.

"Yes?"

"Well, we noticed that you're different than most of the guys. You don't smoke, and when on leave, you don't go to bars and drink, and you don't chase women."

"Yeah, so what do you want?"

"Well, we'd like to know, are you religious?"

"I guess you could say that."

"Well, the guys and I would like to know if you could say a prayer for us."

"What do you think I've been doing out here? But if you guys would

Figure 270 Lt Leo M Ferko flying number 5 FM-2 Wildcat "Lucky Pierre" off the USS White Plains 1944. Public Domain

like to come and join me, I'll say another for us all to hear."

At that moment, amidst the chaos, the five White Plains sailors took off their green caps and goggles and knelt on the deck as Lewis offered a prayer with his hands clasped. "Dear Heavenly Father. We are thankful for your blessings. We ask that you sustain life and guide us to find peace and understanding in these troubling times. On this day, please protect our shipmates and us. In the name of Jesus Christ, Amen."

That day, from the decks of Taffy 3's ships, there were many similar prayers offered to whatever divine being might be listening. [106]

"Let's go and find out who's shooting at us," Ferko radioed as his flight headed towards the Japanese fleet.

With a top speed of 332 miles per hour, the Wildcats were on the Japanese fleet within minutes.

"Look at the meatball on that battleship. She's the biggest warship I've ever seen," Pool said.

"The Yamato is the largest ship afloat. Let's give her a VC-4 greeting. Form on me." Ferko replied as he dove towards the battleship. [107]

The four Wildcats split up, attacking the Yamoto from different directions. Ferko and Pool from the port side and Bear and "Dunk" dove at the ship's bow. Their blazing .50 caliber wing machine guns ripped a path of destruction across the colossal ship, raking the deck and the bridge.

"Too much armor on that monster. Let's make another run with bombs and guns," Ferko yelled.

Between 09:06 and 09:17, Yamato received multiple strafing and

---

[106] Mark C. Hunsaker. Story of Lewis Alexander Hunsaker. https://taffy3modelships.weebly.com/lewis-hunsaker-uss-white-plains.html
[107] The massive Japanese battleship Yamato weighed more than all of Taffy 3's thirteen ships combined.

Figure 271 Leo M Ferko with his FM-2 Wildcat "Lucky Pierre" Public
Domain

torpedo attacks from U.S. aircraft, claiming one U.S. aircraft shot down
at 09:15. Next, wildcat fighter pilot Lt. Richard W. Roby from the USS
Gambier Bay raked the decks and then the bridge of the Yamato with
his .50 caliber machine guns, creating chaos on the Japanese flagship.

The Taffy 3 fighters and torpedo bombers relentlessly attacked the
Japanese fleet. They outnumbered the Japanese air power. Kurita's
Fleet only had thirty aircraft dedicated to kamikaze attacks on the
American fleet although they were supplemented by aircraft from
Japanese island garrisons.

The dawn TBM Avenger flight from the White Plains was diverted
to attack a Japanese Fleet battleship. Lt. CMDR. Fickenscher, who had
taken off from the White Plains at dawn, planted six bombs right on a
Japanese battleship of the Nagato class. Unfortunately, his wingman,
J. R. Connors, USNR., and his crew of Karl M. Wood, ARM3/C USN and
Clifford C. Richardson, AOM3/C USNR., were killed when their TBM
exploded in mid-air over the Japanese battleship.

"He was following me down," commented Lt. CMDR. Fickenscher
after the battle, "and he seemed to catch everything that went by me.
That was plenty, too."

Lt. W. E. Flateboe scored two direct hits with bombs on the starboard side aft of the stack on a Japanese battleship of the Nagato class. Unfortunately, his portside bombs failed to release. Lt. J. H. Osborne scored three direct hits with 500 pound and 250-pound bombs on a leading Nagato class battleship which was billowing smoke just forward of the bridge when the vessel was last seen.

Figure 272 James Conners TBM Avenger pilot. VC-4. Courtesy of Andy Winnegar.

Lt. Pat Owens dove his TBM Avenger at the Nagato class battleship, firing his .50 caliber wing guns and five-inch rockets into the bridge. Hie in the turret and Walley in the tunnel added to the destruction with their machine guns blazing away at the enemy ship. Smoke and hot cartridge shells filled the tunnel.

"Woah! Let's make another pass, Pat!" Hie shouted.

"Negative. We have three Jap Tone-class cruisers and five destroyers at 2 o'clock chasing down Taffy 3," Pat reported as they pulled ahead of the convoy. Get your guns

Figure 273 William Flateboe. VC-4. Courtesy of Andy Winnegar.

ready, and we'll strafe and drop our 500-pound bombs on them." [108]

"Sorry, Pat. We don't have any bombs onboard," Walley reported looking into the empty bomb bay.

Pat paused and then replied, "Well, now I understand what the deck officer was trying to tell me on the White Plains. I wanted to catapult off the flight deck before the Japs struck. I thought we felt awfully light in the air."

"Screw the bombs! We've got ammo," Maurice yelled, gripping his .50 caliber machine gun. "Let's go!"

Figure 274 Lt. Jack H. Osborne TBM Avenger pilot VC-4. Courtesy of Andy Winnegar.

"Byrd and Hearn, you're my wingmen. Butcher you're in the slot. Follow me!" Pat called out as he peeled off to the right in left echelon beginning an 18-degree glide at 200 knots from 8,000 feet, directing his empty TBM at the lead Japanese cruiser. The enemy anti-aircraft fire targeted the four-TBM formation with puffs of black smoke engulfing the planes. Owens flew a jinking course trying to avoid the deadly ack ack fire. At 6,000 feet Owens pushed over into a 50-degree dive headed straight for the cruiser.

The four TBMs dove at the lead cruiser, flying a straight path through the thick black anti-aircraft fire. At 2,500 feet they released their bombs at 300 knots while strafing the cruiser with machine guns and rockets. Ensign Byrd scored three direct hits with his 100-pound bombs on the enemy cruiser's bow. Meanwhile, Lt Hearn and Ensign Butcher straddled the cruiser's stern with depth charges, slowing its progress.

After releasing their bombs, the four-TBM formation dove sharply

---

108 The three heavy cruisers and five destroyers were closing to within 17,000 yards off the White Plains' port quarter.

Figure 275 VC-4 TBM Avenger flight. with Lt John Hearn and Bill Lemon in P15. Courtesy of Christopher Dean.

with evasive maneuvers avoiding the AA fire. Pat pulled out 10 feet above the water and executed a sharp break off to the right as they pulled out sharply, climbing into the clouds, joining up to the left of the enemy formation.

"Way to go boys!" Owens called out looking back at the smoking cruiser. "

"Don't know how we pulled that off," Hie marveled still gripping his .50 caliber gun. "That ack ack fire was thick as hell!"

"That was the worst ack ack fire I've ever seen," Lemon agreed.

"Next time, let's bring along some ordinance," Walley grumbled. [109]

"Permission to make another strafing run on the cruiser. My rockets didn't fire," Ensign Byrd requested.

"Permission granted," Owens replied. "But get your butt back up here. I'm running low on gas. I have to head back to the White Plains."

---

[109] Lt jg Pat Owens was awarded the Distinguished Flying cross for this mission. At a White Plains VC-4 reunion he confessed to Andy Winnegar that he was flying "empty" on that mission but led the strike anyway.

Byrd had already circled and started his solo strafing attack on the bridge of the tone class cruiser before pulling up and rejoining the formation.

Back on the White Plains in the CIC shack, Donald Crounse and the other Radarmen intently listened to the radio communications as the battle played out. That morning, Crounse's remarkable journal entries detail the events rapidly unfolding in the air and sea battles.

"We catapulted three TBMs with torpedoes. These TBMs put their fish into a cruiser, other TBMs off the White Plains scored hits with 100 and 500 lb. bombs on battleships and cruisers. One TBM was shot down, two others are missing from our ship. Our fighters made strafing runs on the Jap ships without loss to us. When planes got low on gas and ammo they went to the beach and gassed, there were no bombs ashore."[110]

Figure 276 Japanese Yokosuka P2Y "Frances" land-based bomber. Wikimedia Commons. Public Domain.

---

[110] Crounse's journal entry was made at 10:19 on 25 October 1944.

Air-to air-dogfights with land-based Japanese aircraft added to the chaos. Wildcat pilot,

Lieutenant Srsen cited a Japanese Frances land-based bomber, the port engine showing a light trail of smoke. Lieutenant Srsen made a rear approach with his wingman, Ensign Robinson, opened fire at 1200 feet, and closed fast. The Frances made an evasive turn which exposed the port engine. Another burst and the Frances was enveloped in flame, crashing to the ground immediately. [111]

Lieutenant Srsen added a Mitsubishi Sally heavy bomber to his bag shortly after this. Over the Leyte Valley, the group dived on the Japanese plane from a 200-foot altitude advantage. Lieutenant Srsen opened fire at 1200 feet. The Sally pulled up to the right, and Lieutenant Mudgett and Ensign Stamatis fired into Sally's starboard wing root and fuselage. The Sally continued to pull up to the right, did a high wing-over, burst into flames, and crashed to the ground.[112]

The pace of the fighting, refueling, and rearming the American fighters and torpedo bombers was chaotic, with planes landing on different escort carriers from Taffy 2. In addition, the White Plains and the other Taffy 3 escort carriers were engaged in direct surface warfare with the Japanese fleet and were often unable to receive the VC-4

Figure 277 Lt Frank C Srsen. FM-2 Wildcat pilot VC-4. Courtesy of Andy Winnegar.

---

[111] VC-4 White Plains' Memoirs and Scrapbook. Ltjg Russell Wood. US Navy Public Relations. 1943

[112] Lt Frank "Tiny Tim" Srsen. FM-2 Wildcat Pilot for VC-4 on USS White Plains.

aircraft. As a result, some of the VC-4 aircraft launched earlier were forced to land on the beach. Other pilots who had flown over the surface engagement informed them that there was no hope for any of the CVEs.

Nevertheless, they loaded up with all they could find on the beach and set out to do what they could do. Lt jg Salon N. Bales and Ensign W. G. Schaufler started by strafing the bridge of a Japanese battleship of the Fuso class. Lieutenant jg Bales commented upon his return to the ship, "I couldn't find anything else to do, so I made some strafing runs on a Jap battleship." [113] He later

Figure 278 Lt Solon N. Bales Wildcat Pilot for VC-4 on USS White Plains.

reported making five low-level strafing runs on two enemy battleships and one heavy cruiser with machine guns blazing away. Out of ammunition, Bales then landed on the American-won Dulag airstrip at Leyte, reloading his guns. Flying the fighter inland over Leyte, Bales attacked enemy ground troops, strafing trenches, pill boxes, gun emplacements, coastal barges, and Japanese snipers in the treetops.

Back on the USS White Plains, at 0932 Captain Sullivan ordered an emergency turn to avoid a torpedo launched by one of the enemy cruisers that seemed to be retiring to the northwest. Remarkably at 0944, the Japanese Fleet appeared to be retreating.

"They're now out to 26,000 yards and moving northward,"

---

[113] Lt jg Solon Bales and Ens. WG Schaufler were awarded the Distinguished Flying Cross for this action on 25 October 1944.

Crounse reported.[114]

"I don't understand why they're not pressing their clear advantage," Lt Kivett remarked. [115]

Crounse took a deep breath, "We can all breathe a little easier."

"Man, I don't get it! Why are they letting us get away? They must know they could sink us all if they moved in," Homer Roos, a radioman remarked in relieved disbelief.

"They must be afraid we have other ships close at hand," Crounse conjectured, shaking his head.

The crew was breathing easier and starting to relax, thankful to be alive. They had clearly dodged a very large bullet.

The adrenaline and bravado of the Taffy 3 ships' crew were not to be denied. The heavily damaged American force continued to press the battle. While observing the retreating Japanese Fleet, Admiral Sprague heard a nearby sailor exclaim: "Damn it, boys, they're getting away!"

After the Japanese fleet broke off the surface attacks, VC-4 continued the air attack, with parting salvos, launched by TBM torpedo bombers flown by Lt JA Huser and Ensign RJ Dennis. Starting a run on a Tone Class heavy cruiser, the two TBMs came roaring out of a cloud, dropping down to 200 feet above the water, at 200 knots. Flying straight and level, Huser had the cruiser in his gun sight dead ahead.

"Give me the range off your radar, Fuller," Huser yelled at his radioman.

"3000 yards and closing," Bob called out from the tunnel.

"2500 yards, 2000 yards! 1,000 yards! Now!"

---

[114] Almost 15 miles. Or 12.7 nautical miles.
[115] Captain Dennis J Sullivan out-smarted and out-maneuvered the enemy on every count His superb firing and maneuvering during this decisive battle won for him the Navy Cross and the grateful respect of the officers and men of his ship.

Figure 279 A U.S. Navy Grumman TBF-1 Avenger dropping a torpedo in late 1942 or early 1943. Wikimedia Commons.

Huser released the fish, which dropped into the water heading straight for the beam of the Japanese cruiser. On his wing, Dennis released his torpedo an instant later. Both 2,000-pound torpedos headed for the ship with their wake trailing behind.

The TBMs flew a jinking course as they climbed up and away from the Japanese fleet while a hail storm of anti-aircraft fire filled the sky around their Avengers.

Turning back to check the damage, Huser yelled, "Bull's eye! What a hit!" as one of their torpedos exploded directly beneath the cruiser's bridge.

"She's dead in the water!" Dennis shouted. "Way to go.
The Japanese cruiser was a sitting duck and soon aircraft of VC-75 from the USS Ommaney Bay (CVE-79) sunk her, sending the cruiser to the bottom of the Philippine Sea. [116]

---

[116] Lt. Russ Wood FM-2 Wildcat pilot and VC-4 historian. "Memoir of Battle." 1944.

Figure 280 Lt Richard Dennis and Lt James Huser TBM Avenger Pilots.
Courtesy of Andy Winnegar.

Lt. Owens' flight of four TBMs had been circling the Japanese fleet, searching for a place to land and rearm after strafing and bombing the Japanese cruiser.

"Fido Base (USS White Plains) can't take us. So, let's head for Banjo Base, (USS Manila Bay CVE-61)" Owens advised.

At 10:15, as they approached USS Manila Bay, she was turned out of the wind to avoid Japanese dive bombers and an enemy battleship whose salvos were bracketing the escort carrier.[117]

"We won't be landing on the Manila Bay anytime soon," Lt. Hearn observed. "Looks like Byrd is going to try to land on Manila Bay anyway."

"Tacloban Airfield is only landing emergencies and can't rearm us," Owens added.

"I'm flying on fumes, Pat. I'm heading for Tacloban," Ens. Butcher reported.

---

[117] Source is Maurice Hie's journal entry and Pat Owens' Distinguished Flying Cross citation.

At 10:30, after circling Tacloban for a few minutes Owens and Hearn watched Ens. Butcher land on the bombed-out air field. Owens knew he needed to be rearmed as much as he needed gas.

Won't find any bombs or ammo down there.

"We need bombs and rockets to get back into this fight," Hie yelled. "I'm getting tired of flying in circles.

At 1030, Owens heard that Taffy 3 was taking on planes. He had the ZB radio turned on, searching for the White Plains homing beacon. Low on fuel and armament, it was time to land his TBM Avenger.

Figure 281 Lt jg Walter P Owens. TBM Avenger pilot. VC-4. Courtesy of Andy Winnegar.

"OK, Hearn. Let's head for Fido Base," Owens called out.

Figure 282 Aerial view of Tacloban Airfield Public Domain

"Nice shooting today, Maurice," Steve Walley complimented their turret gunner.

"Piece of cake," Hie replied

Up in the cockpit, Owens approached the White Plains to enter his downwind leg. But, as he looked down on the flight deck, he saw the gunners at their stations.

"No, cables, barriers, or LSO down there. It looks like we're not landing on the White Plains. They're at General Quarters," Pat reported.

"The action must be pretty intense down there with the enemy in hot pursuit," Walley said.

"I see Zekes headed for the White Plains!" Hie yelled. "Let's find another escort carrier to land on before we run out of gas."

"We passed St Lo (Derby Base) on the way to the White Plains. Let's give her a try," Walley suggested.

"Heading for Derby Base," Owens called in as they set a course for the USS St. Lo with Lt. Hearn flying on his wing. [118]

Figure 283 USS St Lo CVE-63. Public Domain

---

[118] Derby Base was the radio code for the USS St. Lo.

The problems for the USS White Plains and the other Taffy 3 ships were far from over. Ninety minutes after the Japanese Central Fleet retreated, just before 1100 that morning, nine land-based Japanese kamikaze aircraft and pilots began an assault on the Taffy 3 escort carriers. Two of the kamikazes targeted the White Plains. The Kitkun Bay, Fanshaw Bay, and White Plains shot down or drove off their attackers. At 11:08 one kamikaze plane approached as if to land on the White Plains. Captain Sullivan ordered hard left rudder.

Lt. jg Gordon S. Husby and Gunner's Mate, Harold Williamson, in charge of the White Plains' port 20mm and twin 40-mm guns stood their ground as the kamikaze Zeke bore down on the escort carrier. Then as the White Plains swung around, the Zero came into view.

"Fire! Blow that bastard out of the sky!"

Figure 284 Twin Bofors 40-mm guns on USS Hoggatt Bay CVE 75 The 40-mm guns fired 120 rounds a minute and had an effective range of two miles. Public Domain.

On cue, the crews of the port ten 20mm and four 40mm guns opened fire as soon as the Zeke appeared in their sector, saving the White Plains from certain disaster. A hail of tracers and shells poured from their guns.

D.E Parker a veteran of Guadalcanal found the mark at point-blank range. The disabled kamikaze plane crashed and exploded just off the White Plains' port side, missing the ship by inches. The Zeke's 550-pound bomb exploded in midair below the flight deck level, showering pieces of the plane and the pilot over the White Plains' flight deck.[119]

The first Mitsubishi A6M Zero had attacked the White Plains a few minutes earlier, sustaining non-lethal damage from the escort carrier's antiaircraft guns before heading off in search of another victim. The USS St. Lo was dead ahead.

Figure 285 This kamikaze apparently "expected to land on the after end of the flight deck." CAPT Sullivan, White Plains commanding officer, avoided a direct hit by ordering a hard turn to starboard: the plane and its bomb exploded just off the port

---

[119] The next day, Harold Williamson picked the Japanese pilot's teeth out of the automatic loader on the forward starboard 40mm gun.

As Owens's TBM Avenger approached St Lo, things looked calmer for the time being.

"Looks like we're in luck," Pat called out. No GQ on St Lo."[120]

As Owens made his final approach and dropped toward St Lo's flight deck, the landing signal officer raised his flags above his shoulders.

Owens pushed the stick forward, trying to get the Avenger onto the glideslope, but it was too late. The LSO waved him off, aborting the landing.

Figure 286 Lt John Hearn. TBM Avenger Pilot VC-4. Courtesy of Andy Winnegar.

Pat opened the throttle and pulled back on the stick to go around and make another attempt at landing the Avenger on St. Lo. Lt Hearn's TBM Avenger was behind Owens and landed on the USS St Lo as Pat went around for another approach

Owens' second approach was perfection as the Avenger dropped onto the flight deck and caught the second arresting cable, bringing the plane to an abrupt stop at 10:45.

Owens, Walley, and Hie met outside the Avenger before heading off.

"I have to get a new turret microphone in the radio shack," Steve Walley said.

Figure 287 Bill Lemon Gunner on Lt Hearn's TBM. Courtesy of Chris Dean.

---

[120] GG is General Quarters.

"OK. You two should clean the guns while the crews are fueling and rearming the plane," Pat instructed.

"I'm famished. Let's eat first," Hie added as he caught up with Lemon and Edens from Hearn's crew and headed for the Ready Room.

Owens rode the aft elevator down to the hangar deck with "28," where she would have torpedos and bombs loaded. He reappeared on the flight deck a few minutes later when he met up with Lt Hearn.

Figure 288 Capt. Francis J. McKenna St. Lo. William F. Draper. Public Domain.

Meanwhile, Walley picked up the replacement turret microphone and took it back to the Avenger on the hangar deck where the deck apes were rearming her. He changed the battery, tested the microphone, and then went back onto the wing to throw the battery switch to the "Off" position when all hell broke loose. The explosion blew him off the wing onto the hangar deck.

"General Quarters! General Quarters! All hands, man your stations!"

At 10:51, a single Mitsubishi A6M Zero kamikaze damaged by the White Plains came streaking out of the squall, crashing into the St Lo's just forward of the aft elevator. Released seconds before, the Zero's 550-pound bomb crashed through the wooden flight deck, exploding on the hangar deck. It ignited a chain reaction as all the ordnance being loaded onto planes and aviation fuel exploded. The Zero's fire reached the torpedos being loaded onto planes on the hangar deck a few minutes later. This second massive explosion at 10:56 followed a few seconds later by a more massive explosion that raised the forward elevator about four or five feet.

At approximately 10:59, the third explosion went off, lifting the forward elevator in the air and flipping it wrong-side-up when it came down. Finally, when the torpedo bay blew, all was lost as the USS St. Lo blew herself up. Wounded men lay on the deck, engulfed by intense flames and choking black smoke as raging fires swept through the St. Lo. [121]

"Standby to abandon ship," Captain McKenna ordered at 1100.

"Which way should I go?" Walley yelled.

"Go to the starboard side of the hangar deck."

Walley looked out and saw 100 sailors already in the water at the ship's edge. He was 15 feet above the water.

He looked up and saw men coming down on ropes from the flight deck far above.

Looking down, Walley timed his jump to avoid men in the water.

OK. Let's go. Jump!

Walley hit the water, submerged, and then popped back up to the surface. He immediately pulled the cork handles opening the CO2 cartridges that inflated his Mae West.

Simultaneously Hie, Lemmon, and Edens were in the Ready Room eating sandwiches with a cup of Joe when the Japanese kamikaze struck the St. Lo. Running up to the Flight Deck, they saw the tail of the Japanese plane.

After the initial explosion, Lemon, Edens, and Hie went down onto the forecastle[122] where they saw their pilots, Owens and Hearn, coming down. In the chaos, it was the first time they had seen them since landing.[123]

"We have to get off this ship. The whole thing's going to blow!" Owens shouted over the noise and chaos.

---

[121] Source is Steve Walley's videotaped interview and Maurice Hie's written journal account of 25 October 1944.

[122] Forecastle - the forward part of a ship below the deck, traditionally used as the crew's living quarters.

[123] Source is Maurice Hie's written journal account of Battle off Samar.

Hie recalled, "Very shortly after that, we went over the side. We were all separated. As the ships went by me, I could see a lot of tracers coming out of the ship."

At 1108 Hie and Lemon in the water for five minutes looked out to sea and saw Zeros coming in from the northeast, heading for the crippled St. Lo.[124]

"Crap! They're coming back to finish us off!" Lemon shouted.

The Zeros dove on the USS St. Lo, strafing the flight deck while men were still going over the side.

"Bastards! Nail 'em!" Hie shouted as the St Lo's 20-mm and 40-mm guns continued firing at the relentless enemy with tracers and shells pouring out of their anti-aircraft guns.

Two of the Zekes burst into flames and a third plummeted into the ocean out of view of the cheering men.

A minute later, another violent explosion from the doomed ship refocused their attention as they swam towards the destroyer escorts.

Hie recalled, "The fire on the hangar deck must have set off more ammo and bombs. There were a few more explosions after I got off the ship. The St. Lo had all of its amidship blown away. At approximately 11:30, she began going under, stern first. A small fire was started on the water, but it didn't last very long." [125]

A minute later the concussive force of an underwater explosion slammed into the men in the water as the St. Low sunk 4,700 meters to the bottom of the Philippine Sea.

In the water a few minutes ahead of Hie, Lemon, and Edens, Walley, looked around at the chaotic scene. Hundreds of men were in the water. Many were injured. Walley helped a struggling mess cook and

---

124 Lt jg Carlson at 11:08 observing from the USS Dennis reported enemy planes diving on the USS St. Lo, bearing 240 degrees true North. Three planes were shot down.
125 On May 14, 2019 undersea explorers aboard Paul G. Allen's Research Vessel Petrel found the USS White Plains lying upright 4,376 meters beneath the surface of the Philippine Sea.

Figure 289 USS Dennis (DE-405) US Navy Photograph. Public Domain.

another sailor onto a cork floater net.

It's way too crowded around here.

Looking out to sea, Walley spotted a destroyer escort and started swimming for the USS Dennis (DE-405).

"You guys got room for one more?" Steve asked after a brief swim.

"Sure. We could use another pair of eyes to look out for torpedoes. Welcome aboard."[126]

At 11:45, a drenched but relieved Hie came aboard the USS Dennis. Fifteen minutes later, Lt Owens and Lt Hearn and his crew radioman Edens and gunner Lemon were also picked up as the two TBM crews were reunited aboard the destroyer escort.

"Man, I can't believe we all made it off the St. Lo!" Hie exclaimed, still dripping seawater onto the deck.

---

[126] The next day October 26th at 10:00 the USS Dennis was attacked by two torpedos. Evasive maneuvers avoided the torpedos. A periscope was spotted but the submarine was not located. At 14:00 another submarine contact resulted in depth charges being released. The ship and crew were on edge as the next day a school of porpoises set off another General Quarters alarm.

"There's still a lot of men in the water," Owens observed.

"I heard the Dennis is taking on water, but the captain has her right in the middle of the gas and oil fires burning on the water from the St. Lo's sinking," Hearn added.

That day the USS Dennis picked up 434 survivors from the USS St. Lo. About fifty of the men were wounded, some with severe burns.[127]

Figure 290 Radioman 287 Harold Edens TBM. VC-4. Courtesy of Andy Winnegar.

Lemon was shaking his wristwatch. "The darn thing's busted. It stopped at 11:03 the exact moment I hit the water."

"Glad it was just your watch that got busted. It could have been a lot worse for all of us," Hie commented. "I still have my .38 caliber revolver.

Owens, Hie, Walley and Hearn and his crew survived the sinking of USS St. Lo, occurring just eighteen minutes after they landed their TBM Avenger on its flight deck![128]

For now, they were happy and relieved to be alive as they enjoyed the hot soup and coffee offered to

Figure 291 Bill Lemon TBM gunner. VC-4. White Plains. Courtesy of Andy Winnegar.

---

[127] There were 746 survivors out of a crew of 889 men onboard the USS St. Lo.

[128] The kamikaze attack occurred at 10:52, just 7 minutes after Lt Owens landed his TBM Avenger on the St. Lo. The USS St. Lo was previously called USS Midway. As any old salt will tell you, changing a ship's name is a bad omen.

Figure 292 USS St Lo after kamikaze attack 25 October 1944

them by the crew of the USS Dennis.

After refueling on the Kadashan Bay, Ferko prepared to fly with squadron VC-20.

"Hey, boys! We have an almost ACE flying with us this afternoon," called out Warren Kruk.

"Let's find Ferko another Jap plane to seal the deal!"

At 1600 as the flight of Wildcats flew over central Leyte, they came across a squadron of Nakajima Type Ki-44 Tojo single-seat fighters – interceptors. Designed for climbing rate and speed, she had a top speed of 376 mph; all achieved at the expense of maneuverability,

"Looks like this is your lucky day, Ferko," Kruk called out. "Why don't you take the first crack at those Jap fighters?"

Ferko and the VC-20 pilots dove into the Tojos, who put up a better fight than the Jills from yesterday.

Figure 293 Nakajima Type Ki-44 Tojo single-seat fighter. Public Domain.

Ferko quickly closed in on the trailing Tojo, blazing away with his four .50 caliber wing guns.

"Burnt toast!" Kruk called out as the crippled Tojo plummeted into the sea in a blazing inferno. "Looks like we have a new ACE from the White Plains, boys."

"Five planes in three days! Not bad, Ferko."

By the end of a very long day during the Battle of Samar, Ferko had flown for seven hours.

"I have never been more tired in my life, not even after a football game," he later confided.

For the crew aboard the White Plains, the day felt even longer. Between the enemy salvos and the Kamikaze attacks, the White Plains' crew had been General Quarters for a mind-boggling 16 hours.

Losses for the American forces on 25 October 1944 were staggering, with 1161 killed and 913 wounded. Taffy 3 suffered the sinking of two escort carriers (St Lo CVE 63 and Gambier Bay CVE 73), two destroyers, one destroyer escort, and 23 aircraft. Damage to the other vessels was also significant. But the relentless and heroic fighting of the Taffy 3 surface vessels and the determined strafing and bombing of the escort carriers' fighters and torpedo bombers won the day. Moreover, the hectic, chaotic, and dogged fighting by Taffy 3 convinced Admiral Kurita that he was up against a much more extensive full-scale American fleet, leading to the early Japanese retreat by 0920 and a most unexpected American victory in this David and Goliath naval confrontation. Ultimately, little Taffy 3 was the only thing that kept MacArthur from getting shelled off the beach at Leyte by the Japanese Imperial Fleet.

CHAPTER 33

END OF THE WAR FOR VC-4 AND THE USS WHITE PLAINS

As the USS White Plains headed home from the Pacific War, for the men of VC-4 aboard the White Plains, the trip home from the Pacific War was full of long hours and anxious expectations. Yet, the slow-moving CVE brought them closer to home with each passing day.

Russ Wood recalls, "The ship crossed the international dateline in the morning on Tuesday, 14 November, causing us to repeat the day. As we counted the hours until our return to civilization--it was an undesirable outcome, but we were still drawing nearer and nearer to the US."

Following a seven-month alliance, VC-4 looked forward to detaching from the ship in San Diego with the men going ashore for rest and further training. However, before the streamlined squadron did so, the men reviewed their wartime deployment onboard White Plains and claimed to splash fourteen Japanese planes and sink Shoun Maru. In addition, they supported four amphibious landings and fought the enemy during the Battle of Leyte Gulf. Squadron VC-4 also mourned the loss of six pilots, three aircrewmen, and one Marine officer observer of VMO-4.

On 9 November Ensign W. G. Schaufler, USN., made the 3000 landing on the carrier. A Wildcat squadron flew the final CAP of the tour and returned to White Plains just before she entered Pearl Harbor, marking the ship's 3,058th landing. The carrier recorded six barrier crashes

Figure 294 USS White Plains record of Japanese planes shot down and ships sunk. Courtesy of Andy Winnegar

and eight planes lost while away from the ship. VC-4 came aboard the USS White Plains on 22 April 1944 and departed on 27 November 1944.

The White Plains departed Pearl Harbor on 19 November. Lt jg Marvin Cave, assistant navigator was on the bridge with Captain

Figure 295 USS White Plains. US Navy Photograph.

Sullivan, the Officer of the Deck and Chief Quarter Master. [129] "Plot a course to take us home, Lt. sCave. Keep your sextant handy, son. With everything this old gal has been through, we want to get her home in one piece," Sullivan remarked.

"Aye! Aye! Captain," Cave replied as he headed out to take his first sighting.

The USS White Plains finally arrived in San Diego at 0800 on 27 November 1944. This second cruise of the USS White Plains had covered 80,000 miles.

Home at last.

Figure 296 Marvin Cave 1944 US Navy. Public Domain

Figure 297 USS White Plains CVE-66 in San Diego 27 November 1944

Following the departure of VC-4, Donald Crounse set sail with the USS White Plains one final time on 19 January 1945, ferrying planes and Marines to Roi Island in the Marshall Islands. He was transferred

[129] Lt. CMDR. R.B Smith was the Navigator from December 1943 until July 1945.

off the White Plains on 11 February 1945 after 14 months aboard the CVE.

"My next assignment was serving aboard the U.S.S. Mississippi (BB41). The most significant operation I experienced on the "Missy" was the battle of Okinawa, considered to be the last major battle of World War II. We were primarily bombarding shore installations and giving support protection to ships.

Apart from being shelled from the beach ourselves and the near-miss of a kamikaze Jap plane, our part in the operation was somewhat routine. The battleship was a sturdier vessel, and I did not feel quite as vulnerable as we were on the CVE. However, I did miss not being involved with the squadron of fighters & TBM's. The climax of my serving aboard the Mississippi was being in Tokyo Harbor for the signing of the peace treaty on V.J. Day, 2 September 1945."

Beginning on 6 September 1945, USS White Plains took part in her final mission, Operation Magic Carpet, bringing thousands of American fighting men home from the Pacific War. For the USS White Plains and these men of the "Greatest Generation," the war was finally over.

These men eagerly returned to their civilian lives, to sweethearts and families, and to the task of rebuilding America. In their hearts, they carried the comrades they left behind in the

Figure 298 Lt. Walter Pat Owens receives Distinguished Flying Cross November 1944 in San Diego US Navy Photograph

Figure 299 USS White Plaines CVE-66 in San Diego 27 November 1944

Pacific, the real heroes who paid the ultimate price for our freedom. The men also silently carried the stories of their World War II experiences, locked away in their minds, or like Andy Winnegar, the last man standing of VC-4, stories stored safely in a metal box.

CHAPTER 34

PACIFIC WAR CONTINUES FOR STINSON OY-1 FEBRUARY-MARCH 1945

While VC-4 and the USS White Plains saw their last active combat in the Battle off Samar, the war was far from over. The Allies' relentless drive towards Japan continued with invasions of Iwo Jima and Okinawa in February and April 1945.[130] It is ironic that of all the planes that took off from the White Plains' flight deck, the little unarmed Stinson OY-1 of VMO-4 continued into battle long after the high-powered TBM Avengers and FM2 Wildcats of VC-4 had seen their last combat in the Philippines. Variously referred to as the "Grasshopper," "Maytag Messerschmitt," and the "Cricket Circuit," the tiny, fabric-covered Stinson OY-1 had one final battle to fight with the 4th Marine Division in early 1945. Men like Captain Grady Gatlin, and Lt. Thomas Rozga would once again put themselves in harm's way.

---

[130] The USS White Plains on 9 April 1945 did approach within 150 miles of Okinawa to launch 64 Marine planes which landed at Kadana Airfield. She did not engage in active combat during the ferrying mission.

Iwo Jima Campaign – 1945

After the campaign in the Marianas, during which VMO-4 flew 400 sorties while losing two pilots, they returned to Hawaii on 10 August 1944 to rest and refit. They were then deployed to Guam on 10 January 1945 with the squadron and six Stinson OY-1's aboard LST 776 equipped with an experimental Brodie launch and retrieval gear, also

Figure 300 Stinson OY-1 Tropics being loaded on USS Sargent Bay CVE 83 at Saipan on 13 February 1945 Courtesy of Mike O'Keefe.

known as the "Brodie Slingshot." While in Guam, they received 12 new Stinson OY-1 aircraft, which they flew to Saipan. They loaded the planes on six escort carriers, including the USS Bismarck Sea (CVE-95), USS Sargent Bay CVE 83, and USS Wake Island CVE 65, in preparation for their next mission, the Battle of Iwo Jima. After a rehearsal at Tinian on 13 February, the fleet of 450 ships departed for Iwo Jima on 16 February. They arrived at Iwo Jima during the early morning hours of 19 February 1945 with the VMO-4 squadron aboard multiple escort carriers.

Intelligence estimated that 12-14,000 deeply-entrenched Japanese soldiers defended Iwo Jima.[131] Unknown to the Americans, for nine months, the Japanese had dug a network of miles of underground tunnels linking caves, pillboxes, gun emplacements, and command posts. Months of bombardment by Marianas-based B-24s had begun in June 1944. The Marines requested ten days of Naval bombardment of Iwo Jima but got only three days of bombing,

---

[131] 20,000 Japanese defended Iwo Jima fighting from a network of caves and tunnels under command of Lt Gen Tadamichi Kuribayashi, Imperial Japanese Army.

preceding the Iwo Jima invasion that started at 0900 on 19 February 1945. The 4th and 5th Marines hit the Green, Red, Yellow and Blue beaches along the southeastern sector of the island. Five hundred landing craft in ten waves advanced on 3000 yards of beach.

The black volcanic sand covering the steep beaches was unlike anything the Marines had previously encountered. Each step was a struggle as the Marines' boots sunk a foot into the non-compacting black sand. As they attempted to climb up the steep beaches, they slid back down with each step. Once the Naval bombardment ceased to allow the Marines' advance, all hell broke loose as the Japanese began a heavy barrage against the invading forces from concealed caves and pillboxes. Fire from the looming Mount Suribachi pinned down the Marines on Green Beach. The Marines slowly advanced in small groups rather than a united front. Each cave and pillbox they encountered was a fight to the death. In the first 18 hours the American sustained

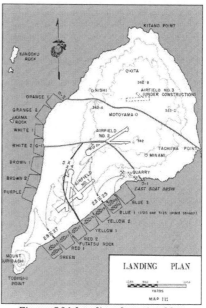

Figure 301 Iwo Jima Invasion Map February 1945 Wikipedia. Public Domain.

Figure 302 Iwo Jima Green Beach with Mount Suribachi in background. USMC Photograph Public Domain.

2300 casualties and the first night was described by Time-Life correspondent, Robert Sherrod, as a "nightmare in hell."

The Stinson OY-1 aircraft used the spotting techniques perfected in the Marianas to effectively direct naval and shore artillery fire o root out the concealed enemy. On Iwo Jima's D-Day, 19 February 1945, the small observer planes launched from escort carriers or LST 776's Brodie Slingshot "swooped low over the battlefield to pinpoint targets for naval ships that roamed back and forth along Iwo Jima shore." In spite of this, the Marines lost 566 men the first day. Later, VMO-4 and VMO-5 directed land-based artillery fire and carrier-based fighter-bombers against enemy targets hidden on reverse slopes, in ravines, or behind obstacles that would have been impossible to spot from the ground. This tactical observation and artillery spotting technique was so effective in neutralizing the enemy that the Japanese soon learned to cease fire and button-up whenever they spotted the small OY-1 "Grasshoppers, to avoid the inevitable retaliatory artillery strike." [132]

Figure 303 Stinson OY-1 (L5). CCA-2.0 SA. Wikimedia Commons

---

[132] Ronald J. Brown. A Brief History of the 14th Marines. Government Publications 1990.

Figure 304 First Iwo Jima Flag Raising 23 February 1945. SSgt Louis R. Lowery USMC Photograph Public Domain.

To extend the hours of their protective cover of Marines on the ground, the pilots flew risky predawn or dusk missions off unlit fields under constant enemy fire from adjacent hills.

On 21 February 1945 (D+2), the VMO-4 squadron was left homeless by the sinking of the USS Bismarck Sea (CVE-95) off Iwo Jima. Captain Grady Gatlin was aboard the escort carrier when she was attacked and sunk by two Japanese kamikaze pilots. At that time, there were onboard thirty-seven aircraft: 19 FM-2 fighters, 15 TBM-3 torpedo bombers, two OY-1 recon-naissance planes, and an F6F

Hellcat fighter. The attack started at 1845, and the USS Bismarck Sea sunk at 2115 with 318 men. Grady Gatlin was among the 605 men who survived the attack. The USS Bismarck Sea was the last American aircraft carrier sunk in World War II.

On 23 February 1945, the dramatic raising of the flag over Mount Suribachi recorded in iconic photographs on the island's southern tip, was only the beginning of the battle. There would be another 32 days of bloody fighting before Iwo Jima was secured.

VMO-4 transferred its operations to the USS Wake Island (CVE-65). On 26 February 1945, two Stinson OY-1 planes from the USS Wake Island, piloted by Lt Thomas Rozga with observer 2nd Lt Richard Dye and Lt. Harvey Olson with observer Captain Edwin Nevin Jr. of the 4th Division USMC, were the first American aircraft to land on the Japanese-held island. The Motoyama No 1 airfield, later called South Field, was still under heavy small arms and mortar fire. Nevertheless, aviation engineers and Seabees cheered the arrival of the Stinson Grasshoppers. By 5 March sixteen Stinson OY-1 observation planes had arrived, including seven for VMO-4 and nine for VMO-5 squadron, setting up an Air Operations bunker on the captured airfield.

Figure 305 First plane to land on Iwo Jima narrowly missed three.
Japanese mortar shells. VMO-4 Stinson OY-1 lands on 26 February 1945.

Figure 306 Marine Division Air Operations bunker on Iwo Jima 1945. Major Arthur O'Keefe in sunglasses, third from right. Courtesy of Mike O'Keefe.

One of the men who flew with VMO-4 on Iwo Jima was not officially a squadron member. Major Arthur O'Keefe was an experienced Marine pilot who had flown a Douglas SBD Dauntless on 29 hazardous missions with the 4th Marine Division at Guadalcanal in 1942. He was awarded a Distinguished Flying Cross for flying his SBD Dauntless unescorted more than 250 miles over enemy territory and successfully bombing a Zero floatplane base at Giza Harbor in the Solomon Islands. [133]

---

[133] On 6 September 1942, O'Keefe was one of eleven SBDs and six fighter escort planes leaving for a bombing mission to Giza Harbor. O'Keefe's plane became inoperative just prior to his takeoff and the other aircraft were

Figure 307 Maj. Arthur O'Keefe's Stinson OY-1 Pilot Iwo Jima 1945. Courtesy of Mike O'Keefe.

On Iwo Jima, Major O'Keefe was assigned to a non-flying staff position as Vice Assistant Division Air and Operations Officer. Despite his non-flying status, O'Keefe found opportunities to put himself into the thick of the battle.

O'Keefe's official responsibilities involved coordinating and directing close air support and day and night air observation activities. However, while off duty, he still managed to get into the fight, volunteering to fly ten observation missions with VMO-4 over hostile enemy territory, resulting in the enemy repeatedly shelling his unarmed Stinson OY-1. These low altitude flights were ideal for photographing enemy activity and direct artillery strikes, leaving the planes riddled with bullet holes. On 28 February 1945, O'Keefe piloted one of the first American planes to land on Iwo Jima. That was just the beginning.

O'Keefe's ability to handle the tiny Stinson was almost legendary,

---

forced to leave without him. O'Keefe obtained another aircraft and completed the four-and-a-half-hour mission, completely on his own, successfully bombing the Giza Harbor.

Figure 308 Captain Lyford Hutchins, Lt Col William Wendt, and Major Arthur O'Keefe in Iwo Jima sandbag bunker at Motoyama 1 Airfield, reviewing VMO-4 observation missions. Courtesy of Mike O'Keefe.

flying less than 300 feet over enemy lines, often dropping down to 50 feet to spot Japanese activity. His own artillery was exploding beneath his plane at times, tossing the little Stinson 20 feet higher into the air

On 5 March 1945, O'Keefe, flying with Captain Lyford Hutchins, discovered the location of a well-concealed enemy brigade headquarters.

"Hutch, what's that in the ravine on the port side?" O'Keefe asked as he dove the OY-1 lower to get a better look.

"Definitely looks man-made. The Japs will be shooting at us soon if we get any closer," Hutchins called out.

"It's not a Jap artillery emplacement. This is something else. Let me fly around the backside."

"I see it. It's hard to spot through the brush in that ravine, but it looks like a tent backed up to two caves!" Hutchins reported. "

"I see Japs looking over maps and another guy taking a bath!" Hutch

Figure 309 Aerial View of Iwo Jima from Stinson OY-1. Courtesy of Mike O'Keefe.

yelled as they passed over the enemy encampment at 50 feet.

"It looks like a Jap command post. They're trying to hide, not fight back with big guns," O'Keefe observed. "Call in their position for a Marine artillery strike."

Hutch tuned the VHF radio to 4500 kcs. "Gomez, this is Raffles One Zero. Can you handle a fire mission? Over."[134]

"Raffles One Zero, this is Gomez. Affirmative."

"This is Raffles One Zero, Grid 7 Delta. Test round. – Over."

"This is Gomez, Grid location 7 Delta. Test round fired – Over."[135]

"This is Raffles One Zero. Up 50, right 100.

"This is Gomez. Round fired, Over."

---

[134] Gomez was the radio call sign for the 4th Marine Division artillery. Raffles One Zero was the call sign for Captain Lyford Hutchins in Tactical Observation OY-1. 4500 kcs was the VHF frequency assigned to 4th Marine Division artillery spotting planes

[135] Sectional map of Iwo Jima is divided into locations by an alpha numeric grid. Each location is approximately 100 yards x 100 yards.

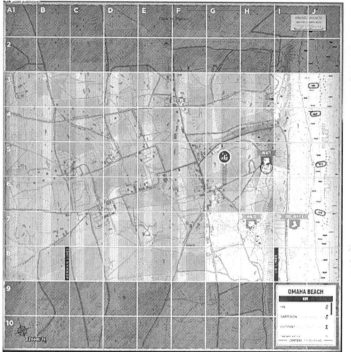

Figure 310 World War II Alphanumeric Sectional Map of Omaha Beach used for artillery spotting.

"This is Raffles One Zero. Fire for effect HE if possible. Over."

The incoming high explosive shell missed by a wide margin.

They're not even close," O'Keefe grumbled. "Redirect fire again, Hutch."

"This is Raffles One Zero, adjust fire, up 100, left 50".

"This is Gomez. Make up your mind. Damn it! Adjust fire, up 100, left 50."

The results of the redirected artillery strike were no better.

"Hutch, call for an airstrike. We'll mark it with phosphorous smoke grenades," O'Keefe ordered as he circled the enemy target.

"We have two carrier-based F4U Corsairs, in route. Let's drop some smoke."

As the Stinson OY-1 pulled out of its dive, Hutch dropped three smoke grenades marking the position of the enemy encampment.

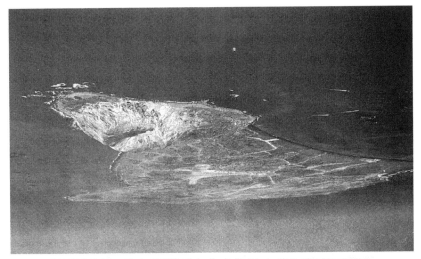

Figure 311 Aerial View of Iwo Jima 1945. Courtesy of Mike O'Keefe.

Hutch called out, "That should give our Corsair pilots something to shoot at!"

Several minutes later, O'Keefe asked, "Where are those guys?"

"They should have been here by now."

"Raffles One Zero, this is Charlie 2; where's the smoke? We've got two loaded Corsairs with no target, Over."

"You guys are late to the party, Over."

"Meet us over Mount Suribachi and lead us to your target, Over."

"Roger, that. ETA two minutes, Over and out," O'Keefe replied.

By the time they led the Corsairs back over the target, the smoke had cleared.

"Raffles One Zero, Charlie 2 here, Mark it again with lots of smoke, Over."

"Negative, Charlie 2. We only have one phosphorous grenade left, Over."

"Bring a photo back to South Field, and we'll come back to finish the job, Out."

"Screw this! Get your grenade bag out, Hutch! We'll take care of this ourselves."

Figure 312 Vought F4U Corsair, June 1945 firing rockets have attained paramount importance in World War. Official U.S. Navy Photograph. National Archives. Public Domain.

"Alright. Here are four grenades for you and four for me."

O'Keefe flew the Stinson in a slow, glide bombing run towards the enemy encampment with the cockpit nacelle retracted.

He dropped down to the treetops as they approached the cave, and looked down.

"There's the cave. I see the Japs!"

"Here, take this!" Hutch yelled as he and O'Keefe each hurled two fragmentation grenades out of the plane into the mouth of the cave.

The explosions were massive, and their aim was perfect as the tent went up in flames.

"Let me come around for another pass," O'Keefe called out. "Get ready, Hutch."

The second pass was met with machine-gun fire that ripped through the thin skin of the fabric-covered Stinson. The remaining fragmentation grenades scored a direct hit on the cave, silencing the gunfire. Hutch lobed the single phosphorous grenade into the ravine marking the spot.

"Bull's eye!" Hutch shouted. "Let's get out of here. That Jap camp is history."

"Raffles One Zero, Charlie 2 here, we see your smoke and are coming around. Out."

The two Corsairs dove into the ravine, firing five-inch rockets and dropping 500-pound bombs onto what was left of the Japanese encampment.

"Whoa! Will you look at that fireball!" Hutch called out as the massive explosions, and smoke filled the sky.

"Raffles One Zero, Charlie 2 here. Heading out. Strong work, Out."

For these missions on Iwo Jima, the United States Marine Corps awarded Major Arthur O'Keefe his second Distinguished Flying Cross. While he could have used his rank and non-flying billet to stay out of harm's way, Major Arthur O'Keefe was a Marine who flew towards. danger to remain in the fight

Figure 313 Major Arthur O'Keefe is awarded the Distinguished Flying Cross on Iwo Jima 1945. Courtesy of Michael O'Keefe.

Lt. Thomas Rozga, a self-proclaimed frustrated fighter pilot and the VMO-4 CMDR, decided he needed something more than his .45 caliber handgun to fight back. So to improve the odds in the Stinson OY-1, he added bazookas under each wing.

Figure 314 Lt Thomas Rozga with Lady Satan. Courtesy of Mike O'Keefe and Michael Polley.

"Do you think you can make it work?" Rozga asked.

"Well, sure. We'll get you some real firepower."

"What about the flames coming out the back of the bazooka tube? You don't want to ignite the plane in flight."

"And the plane's aerodynamics will be affected," Rozga added.

Figure 315 Bazookas being mounted under port wing of Lady Satan Iwo Jima 1945. USMC Photo. Low Family Collection.

"Well, I guess it's worth a try. Do you want me to try mounting one bazooka?"

"Hell no, if you going to do this right, you might as well go all out! Let's put three bazookas on each side. Now go find some bazookas!"

The test of the fortified "Lady Satan flown by engineering officer, Lt. Kelly," was an unqualified success. According to Rozga, six toggle switches installed on the instrument panel controlled the bazookas, allowing for "some great Marine Observation payback!". The initial concerns about fire coming out the back of the bazooka tubes causing an inflight fire turned out to be unfounded. Soon fights broke out amongst the VMO-4 pilots over who got to fly Lady Satan, the lone bazooka-armed OY-1.

"The procedure was to get up to altitude, select a target below and then push the nose over into a shallow dive. Most of the time I fired all six at once, and they zoomed towards their targets below.... as the Marines on the ground waved and cheered us on. They made one hell

Figure 316 Stinson OY-1 on Iwo Jima with three bazookas mounted under each wing. National Archives.

Figure 317 Stinson OY-1 landing on Iwo Jima March 1945. Public Domain. WWII Database.

of an explosion when they hit and it sure made us feel like fighter bomber pilots for a while," Rozga recalled. [136]

Even before the bazookas were installed, Rozga had ample opportunity to fly his Stinson into battle. On Iwo Jima, the Japanese artillery was shelling the US Marines mercilessly at night, pinning them down and inflicting casualties. The big enemy guns were hidden in caves and tunnels during the day and then brought out in the dark of night to shell the US Marines. The 4th Marine Division Commanding Officer ordered a dangerous night reconnaissance mission to locate the enemy artillery. Rozga refused to send his men into battle off the unlit Motoyama airfield No. 1. So, instead, Rozga, flying solo, took his observation plane, Lady Satan, up in total darkness to direct artillery fire, flying between 400 and 700 feet in between land-based artillery and shells fired from Navy ships.

That night, a cluster of campfires marked the front lines. Rozga circled, waiting for the enemy fire. The muzzle flash of the Japanese artillery on the starboard side of the OY-1 gave away their position. Looking at his grid map, Rozga estimated the position relative to a

---

[136] Thomas P. Busha. Wings of War. Great Combat Tales of Allied and Axis Pilots During World War II. Zenith Press 2015.

cluster of campfires and called in Marine and Navy artillery strikes.

"Gomez, this is Balkan 4. Can you handle a strike mission? – Over."

"Gomez here. Affirmative."

"Balkan 4 here. Grid location 4 Charlie. Fire for effect. HE if possible."

"Gomez here. Round fired."

"Balkan 4 here. Up 200, left 100. Coordinate Naval fire – Out."

The night sky lit up like the 4th of July as Marine and Naval artillery rounds annihilated the enemy target. Meanwhile, Rozga was tossed around as the little OY-1's wings rocked and the tail shook from the concussive force of the blasts.

"Balkan 4 here. Target destroyed! – Out."

After two hours of flying solo, locating enemy gun positions, it grew quiet as the Japanese withdrew into their caves. Rozga landed Lady Satan with the help of cheering fellow Marines, holding flashlights along the runway. [137]

The Navy awarded Rozga the first of three Distinguished Flying Crosses for this action. Lt. Rozga, flying Lady Satan ran towards the danger in a time of crisis with grit and a spark of gallantry to save his fellow Marines and to be a leader of men and a defender of freedom." [138]

On Iwo Jima, VMO-4 flew 204 sorties in just 19 days. Six of their seven Stinson OY-1s were so extensively damaged in combat that the Marines abandoned them for scrap. The crudely scrawled sign over the VMO-4 Squadron door proclaimed it best, "You name it, we'll aim it." [139]

---

[137] Thomas Rozga's observer was Captain Edwin Nevin Jr. with radio call sign "Balkan One."

[138] Thomas Rozga also flew TBM Avengers, the FU4 Corsair, Douglas SBD dauntless, and the PBY Catalina. He joined the Army Reserves following World War II, was sent to Korea and served during the Cuban missile crisis, finally retiring as a Major in 1969.

[139] The 36-day Iwo Jima campaigns was to that point the most costly and deadly in Marine Corps history with 6,821 Marines killed and 19,709 wounded out of 70,000 Marines who landed on the eight square mile volcanic island.

Figure 318 4th Division Marines on Iwo Jima 1945.
Courtesy of Mike O'Keefe.

CHAPTER 35

ANDREW J WINNEGAR POST
USS WHITE PLAINS

When Andy Winnegar first saw the headlines describing the Battle off Samar, he couldn't believe his bad luck. "I would have gladly given up Flight School to have been in this battle of a lifetime. Even when Donald Crounse later told him he would not have survived the battle and was lucky to have been transferred off the White Plains, Winnegar didn't believe him. But, with the spirit of a warrior, Andy Winnegar was not yet finished with the thrill of battle.

Contrary to the Manus Master at Arm's prediction that he would never make it to Flight School in Liberty, Missouri by 17 November, Winnegar arrived on time. "My first station in Flight School was at William Jewell College for four months for a refresher unit, studying physics, history, English, and math to develop study habits for Pre-Flight.

"My goal was to be a Chief Air Pilot – the top enlisted Navy rank rather than an Ensign, the bottom of the commissioned officer ranks.

Figure 319 William Jewell College in Liberty Missouri.

To be a Chief in the Navy is a much better job than being an Ensign, although you are promoted from Chief to Ensign. In my opinion, that promotion is really a downgrade. I talked to Grady and Pat about it. Pat said, 'The way to go is for you to stay as a Naval Student Air Pilot. Don't take the Cadet deal.'"

Ultimately, it was a financial decision. "If I entered as a cadet, you get $75 a month. But, if I entered at my 2nd Class Radioman rate, I got $96 a month plus fifty percent flight pay, plus three percent longevity pay. So, I wound up with something close to $200 a month compared with $75 a month. It doesn't sound like much, but I was from a poor family. My father had died, leaving my mother with a World War I Widow's Pension, about $40 a month. So, I needed extra money."

Andy's orders came through to go to Iowa Preflight training in Iowa City, studying aircraft and engines, and navigation – both celestial and dead reckoning with 1,000 other students. Andy's three roommates were all experienced ex aviation machinists' mates; like

Figure 320 Pliska Aeroplane 1911. Built by blacksmith John V. Pliska with Gray Coggin a chauffeur and auto mechanic in Midland Texas.

Winnegar, all three had seen combat. Ray Pliska was a gunner on a torpedo bomber.

The Pliska's who came from Austria, had a long history in Texas aviation. In 1911 Ray's uncle John V. Pliska, a blacksmith, and Gray Coggin, a chauffeur and auto mechanic, built the first airplane in Texas, which now hangs in the lobby of the Midland Odessa International Airport.

Preflight focused equally on academics and athletics. Both Winnegar and Pliska were trained boxers. Ray Pliska was an exceptional boxer and was the Oregon State High School Boxing Champion and national AAA finalist as a left-handed middleweight. Andy and Ray enjoyed sparing in Preflight. The daily schedule was highly structured from

Figure 321 Iowa Pre-Flight Spindrift Boxing. Public Domain.

Figure 322 Iowa Pre-Flight John Glenn (left). 1940s Public Domain

0600 until taps at 2100.

Classroom instruction at the University of Iowa College of Engineering included courses in communication, theory of flight, gunnery, celestial navigation, aerology, aircraft recognition, engines, and Naval history, traditions, and regulations.

With an emphasis on intense physical conditioning, they required each student to participate in one of the school's teams. Andy Winnegar represented Company H in boxing and wrestling.

Pre-Flight was followed by Primary Flight Training in Memphis, with 100 students flying Stearman PT-17 biplanes. The program lasted for six months, ending 8 March 1946. As the end of the war approached, many students used points from Flight School to be discharged back to their civilian lives. Both Ray and Don left just before the end of Primary Training. Only ten percent of the Primary Flight Training students finished the program.

On Andy's final flight in Primary, he took Calvin Piece, a friend from back home, on a solo cross-country flight. They planned a slight detour to buzz Thomasville but couldn't do the town justice as with the detour, the flight exceeded the maximum range of the Stearman. They did manage to buzz the gas station where all the men hung out to listen to the afternoon ballgames.

Figure 323 Andrew J. Winnegar. VC-4 USS White Plains.

"Look! There's Uncle Lanty waving at us!" Andy exclaimed as the Stearman buzzed the station at tree-top level, blowing Lanty's hat off his head.

With the detour, the flight exceeded the maximum range of the Stearman. When they returned to Jonesborough, long overdue with an empty gas tank, instructors were waiting for them in SNJ planes.

Man! I'm in a heap of trouble.

"Where have you been? You're 90 minutes overdue. We figured you ran out of gas and crashed!"

"Yes, sir. I got lost and had to keep circling until I picked up a landmark I recognized and then flew right back here to Jonesborough," Winnegar explained. "The float gas gauge is hitting empty."

The relieved instructors accepted Andy's explanation without

Figure 324 PT-17 Stearman with Air Cadet and Flight Instructor. Public Domain. Wikimedia Commons.

further questions.

Towards the end of Primary Training, the course introduced night flying. Four kerosene-burning flare pots marked the runway on each side. The solo night flight was at 2000 feet. The student pilots circled the airport in the dark while the new pilots did touch and go approaches with their instructors in the dark. Since there were no radios in the Stearman, instructors shined a searchlight on each plane when it was the student's turn to land solo.

"I was following the white tail light of the Stearman ahead of me. It was otherwise pitch black."

Deciding to do a snap roll, Andy proceeded to execute the maneuver. When he came out of the roll, he picked up the white light of the plane ahead of him and followed the Stearman through the dark Tennessee night.

Figure 325 Rankin Field Primary Training Cadets Approaching PT-17s.

I wonder why that idiot ahead of me isn't turning?

After several more minutes of straight flying, Andy felt a pit in his stomach and an awareness that something was terribly wrong.

Looking more closely at the Stearman's white light, Andy shouted, "Ah crap! That light's not a Stearman. It's a farmhouse!"

Winnegar looked around and saw that all the lights were gone. There were no landmarks and no planes. He was lost and had no idea where the airfield was.

"I was out there in the country all by myself! That got awful lonely in a hurry!"

"I started looking around, and I spotted the beacon for Memphis Municipal Airport in the distance!"

Well, that's what I'm going to have to do. There's no way I can find those four flare pots in the night. I have a choice. Either I bailout or I fly to the Municipal Airport, save the plane and washout.

So, Winnegar headed for the Memphis Municipal Airport about 20 miles away.

"I was cruising along, cursing my bad luck, when suddenly there were airplanes all over the place. I was right in the middle of them! So,

Figure 326 Waco Biplane. Public Domain. Adrian Pingstone. Wikimedia Commons.

I slid back into the circle, and after a few more passes, we came in and landed between the flare pots."

When we went into the debriefing room, the Officer of the Day standing at the podium said, "We know that one of you gentlemen took off and toured the country during the flight. We know who it is, and we expect him to stay in the room when everyone else leaves."

"Well, he dismissed the class, and we all stood and left. He was bluffing, trying to smoke out the wayward student pilot! I never heard another word about it!"

"I completed Primary Flight Training which gave me 126 hours of flight time in a Stearman. "

Even in Primary Training, Andy was also flying on the weekends at a small airport in West Memphis, Arkansas, directly across the Mississippi River. "I was flying over there with an old guy who had a converted WACO biplane in which he gave aerobatic lessons. I got there by accident. I was tooling around there one day and got to

Figure 327 Albany Air Field. PT-17 Stearman Primary Trainer Biplanes.

talking with him. I think he charged three dollars an hour. So, I took a flight with him. It was a WACO biplane with less power than the Stearman, but it's lighter and more maneuverable. It did neater aerobatics."

Winnegar was in Naval Pilot Training from November 1944 through March 1946. At that point, the war was over, and Winnegar saw little reason to stay in the Navy for Intermediate and Advanced Pilot Training. Fortunately, fate intervened.

After an aerobatic flight in the WACO the old guy said, "How did you learn to fly like that?"

"Well, they teach aerobatics in Primary in a Stearman. I do snap rolls, split S's, Squirrel Cages, Immelmann's, and a little stuff I made up myself."

"I'm going to talk to a friend of mine about you."

"Well, his friend was a guy in Cincinnati named Clem Honerkamp, who had just gotten out of the Army Air Corps and was forming a

Figure 328 North American SN-5. Wikimedia Commons. Courtesy of Jon Sullivan.

traveling Air Show. So, Clem came down on the weekend, interviewed me, and took a ride with me in the WACO."

After the ride, Clem said, "You'll have to buy your own airplane."

"I think he saw that I was a ready customer for an airplane he wanted to sell. He had a Navy SNJ with my name already written on the $1200 "Bill of Sale."

Clem offered, "You could go on to Intermediate Flight Training and get acquainted with the Navy SNJ."

"Well, you have one. Why can't I get acquainted with it right here?"

"Well, that's another way," Clem smiled.

"So, instead of going to Corpus Christi and having the Navy teach me how to fly the SNJ, I let Clem teach me. But, of course, his SNJ didn't have two cockpits. It had a smoke tank in the back. So, I didn't get any dual instruction. My first flight in an SNJ was from the front seat by myself. Man, that sunburst paint job was sweet!"

"There wasn't that much difference from a Stearman. However, it did have retractable gear and a controllable prop that the Stearman

Figure 329 A U.S. Navy North American SNJ-5 Texan (BuNo 91084) based at Naval Air Station Oakland, California (USA), in 1950. William Rockwell USN. Wikimedia Commons

didn't have. For two years, I was in the National Air Show based in Columbus, Ohio. I could have stayed another year, but unfortunately, I got married."

Winnegar was honorably discharged from the Navy in November 1946 when he was 21 years old. After his Navy flight training, Andy continued his more advanced training in the private sector as a pilot in the National Air Shows, in which he flew the Navy SNJ. The four regular Air Show pilots, Clem Honerkamp, EV Avery, Ray Miller, and Andy Winnegar, split the gate, which on a busy Sunday, could net Andy $600.

By 1949 Andy was a student at the University of Cincinnati, flying air shows in the summer. He was in a used car business with his uncle, Leo Ottinger. They opened A & L Auto Sales in Cincinnati, Ohio. Everything was going great and Andy was living the dream.

Figure 330 Andy Winnegar in front of A&L Auto Sales in Cincinnati, Ohio. Courtesy of Andy Winnegar.

Andy found a place to rent in Cincinnati, not far from the University and within driving distance from the weekend National Air Shows. When Andy invited his mom and sister, Wanda, to join him they jumped at the chance to live in the Big City. In truth, most cities were big compared to little Thomasville in Missouri. In Cincinnati, Andy was prospering in the automobile business with Uncle Leo. Andy's natural gift for gab kept the customers returning and the cars rolling out the A & L Auto Sales doors. Thomasville, only 500 miles west from Cincinnati, felt like it was a million miles away, until Uncle Lanty came visiting.

The knock at the front door was loud and persistent, but at the same time friendly and familiar.

"I got it," Andy called out as he jumped up from the easy chair in the front room and ran to the front door.

411

Opening the door, Andy beamed, "Uncle Lanty! Why didn't you call. I would have picked you up at the bus station!"

"No worries, Andrew. Besides, I didn't take the bus. I rode the rails for old times' sake," Lanty grinned.

"I should have known. You've got your hobo overalls on. Just like the old days. You never did take me along for a ride on the rails, Uncle Lanty."

"You were too busy flying fast planes and shooting big guns, Andy!"

"Well, it's great to see you."

"Here give this to your mother, Andy," Lanty said handing Andy a package wrapped in white paper. "It's a little something from my cousin's meat packing shed."

"Great! Steaks for dinner! Come on in Uncle Lanty."

"It's venison."

"Mom! Wanda! Uncle Lanty's here and he brought venison steaks!"

"Lanty! You are a sight for sore eyes!" Ellen exclaimed, hugging her brother-in-law, "You're making me miss Thomasville," she whispered.

"Here Wanda, help me get these steaks marinating and, on the grill," Andy said.

In the kitchen, Andy unwrapped the package, revealing bright red steaks. *Uncle Lanty! What did you bring us?*

Andy quickly threw the steaks on the grill as Wanda walked into the kitchen.

"Here, let me cook the steaks, Andy. Go visit with Uncle Lanty"

"Lanty! These steaks are delicious," Ellen proclaimed. "They are so flavorful!"

"Yes, thanks Uncle Lanty!" Wanda added.

"Well, your biscuits and gravy were perfect, Ellen," Lanty smiled.

After dinner, Andy joined his uncle on the porch where Lanty was smoking his pipe.

Figure 331 Uncle Lanty's steaks.

"Uncle Lanty," Andy whispered. "Was that bear meat?"

Lanty continued to puff away before answering, "No. Why do you ask?"

"Those steaks were bright red just like bear meat. It certainly wasn't venison!"

Lanty paused before replying. Puffing on his pipe he looked away, "Well, don't ever tell your mom or Wanda, but we had horse for dinner!"

Ellen and Wanda came out onto the porch as Lanty winked at his favorite nephew.

"Perfect evening, Lanty," Ellen cooed.

"Well, thanks for the meal and the company, Ellen. I'd travel 500 miles for your biscuits and gravy any day," Lanty laughed.

The next morning, Lanty relented and let Andrew buy him a bus ticket back to Thomasville.

"It's good to have you around, Uncle Lanty, but you still owe me a ride on the rails," Andy laughed.

"Anytime, Andrew. Anytime."

"I never forgot your advice, Uncle Lanty. Remember what you told me? Never be afraid of explosions, danger, bullies or bullets!"

"That advice kept me in the fight when others were ducking for cover. Thanks, Uncle Lanty."

"No thanks are necessary, Andrew. Those are just words. The real spirit is in your heart."

Later that afternoon there was a commotion in the Winnegar home, "What do you mean Lanty fed us horse?" Ellen said with her face turning white. "Why didn't you warn us?"

"I swear I didn't know until later!" Andy said.

'Well, when Lanty comes back for my biscuits and gravy, he's going to get a healthy dose of sautéed cat!"

"Then the marriage deal came up with a 'shotgun wedding.' At the time, I felt I couldn't get out of it. That absolutely blew the life that I was living before," Andy reminisced.

"To make matters worse, she was against my flying, the one thing that gave me joy and a sense of freedom. In fact, she was against everything. I spent 20 years enduring that."

Andy Winnegar, who had faced down the enemy in the Pacific with a .30 caliber machine gun, was done in by an unhappy marriage.

The attacks and nightmares began in the early 1950s. The attacks were not frequent, lasting a few seconds, but the effect of each episode continued for days.

"I had trouble getting a breath. I thought I was going to die. I was uncoordinated. I couldn't dial the phone. Sometimes there was ringing and popping in my ears."

Witnesses to these panic attacks described Andy's, turning white, looking like he was about to pass out. Not knowing when the next attack might strike made these episodes debilitating. Winnegar saw boatloads of doctors who consistently misdiagnosed the episodes as a form of cardiac angina. The prescriptions for nitroglycerin flowed freely without any clinical improvement.

Recurring nightmares began about the same time. In the dream, walking down a railroad track, Andy encounters another person coming from the opposite direction. They are going to shoot it out. Andy has a shotgun, and the other person has a handgun.

"The other guy doesn't have a chance. So it's going to be super easy."

So, Andy waits until the other guy is in range, raises the shotgun, and pulls the trigger. But unfortunately, the trigger goes limp, and the gun doesn't fire.

"Now, I know I'm gonna get shot. Then I wake up in a cold sweat. "

"I believe it was PTSD." Although, I never heard that term until decades later."

"I trace that dream back to Peleliu when I had the jammed cartridge and couldn't shoot back at those anti-aircraft guns.

The "PTSD" continued until the 1970s, finally ending when he divorced his wife.

"I moved my family from Albuquerque to Lubbock, Texas, hoping to get the kids out of a drug environment. I opened a stereo business in Lubbock. I had one final attack, and the doctors as always assumed it was a heart problem, putting me on medications that made me sleep for about three days."

Once again, the doctors gave him nitroglycerin.

In September 1977, Andy married Dolores Adame, and the panic attacks never returned.

And whatever happened to Uncle Lanty? Well, red-headed, occasional hard drinking Lanty, with a propensity for blowing stuff up, out lived all five of his siblings. [140] When he was 82 years old, he took the bus to Springfield, Missouri for a doctor's appointment. Later, Lanty stopped to visit Andy's mother and sister, Ellen and Wanda, living in Springfield.

"Hello, Uncle Lanty. You're just in time for lunch," Wanda greeted her favorite uncle.

"Well, I did plan this trip with your mother's Vinegar Dumplings and Biscuits and Gravy in mind," Landy replied laughing.

"As long as you didn't bring us any more horse meat disguised as venison," Ellen said. "When Andrew told us what you made us eat, I was fit to be tied! We were going to fix you up some sautéed cat next time you visited."

"I don't have any idea what you're talking about. But I guess I'll have to inspect your dumplings a little more carefully," Lanty smiled. "Here's a jar of pickled pigs' feet as a peace offering."

As they sat around the table enjoying the special lunch and each other's company, Lanty reminisced, "Do you remember that time I blew up all the stumps in the front yard with little Andrew?"

"Do I remember? I was furious with you, Lanty! Andrew was only six years old."

"Well, I never told you, but little Andrew was ready to jump in there and light the fuse. I think he takes after his Uncle Lanty. No fear of explosions, danger, or bullies," Lanty recited.

"That's not quite how he tells the story or recites the mantra, but I'm glad you both survived."

Lanty took the bus back to West Plains and was walking to catch his ride to Thomasville when he keeled over and died. Lanty was 82 years old, independent and fearless until the end. In his pocket they found an unopened pint of Mexican home-brewed Mescal, and a .30 caliber shell, both gifts of his favorite nephew, Andrew.

---

[140] Although Lanty only rarely drank, he bragged to this blacksmith drinking buddies, that when drunk he could "squat lower, jump higher, and spit further than anyone in Oregon County.

Figure 332 Andy Winnegar and Uncle Lanty. Courtesy of Andy Winnegar.

CHAPTER 36

EPILOGUE - 1988

The twelve men with graying hair covered by their blue caps shuffled into the room, each clutching an invitation from the Judge. A few used canes to hold themselves upright. Most were slightly stooped, the price of decades of living. Yet, in their mind's eye, they were the young, confident, and ramrod erect warriors that had taken to the seas and skies over the Pacific to protect each other and a fragile ideal.

Almost half a century before, their country had molded them into fighting men, each similar to the next. Since then, their lives had taken them in vastly different directions. Now, they were an airline pilot, an architect, salesmen, a fishing boat captain, airplane mechanic, lawyers, engineers, telecom workers, and a judge. Yet, what they had in common was an experience they shared a lifetime ago.

When they spotted one another from across the hall, they stood erect, grinned, and extended a hand or slapped comrade's back. They openly and silently missed those who should have been there but

Figure 333 White Plains and VC-4 Reunion.

were not; those shipmates left behind, buried at sea, and the many of their ranks who died much too young. Their stories could fill volumes.

Andy grasped Pat's hand and pulled him close, giving a bear hug to the man who had been his pilot and big brother on their TBM Avenger #27. Their eyes were moist for reasons that only men who have gone to battle together can fully understand.

"Good to see you, Andy. How are you coming on your 1st Class Rating?" Pat joked.

"Always nagging! I'm on top of it, Pat."

They laughed, shared another hug, and then looked around for old friends.

"Where's Fickenscher?" Andy asked.

"We lost the "Deacon" a few years ago," Pat replied. "He was a good CO."

"I remember how stoked we were when he sank that ship off Rota with his torpedo," Andy reminisced.

The ship's crew and officers and the aircrew and pilots all mixed easily. Their worlds had been so different on the USS White Plains, but now with their dwindling ranks, they had a lot more in common.

Don Crounse, the CIC Radarman 1st Class, came over and introduced his wife, Pat.

"Don, are you still climbing those poles for Pacific Bell?" Pat asked Crounse.

"No, I moved into sales and then retired. Nowadays, we're traveling all the time."

"Do you remember that electric cattle prod the Shellbacks were using on us Pollywogs?" Andy asked. "Who was that guy anyway?"

"Don't have any idea what you're talking about, Andy," Crounse replied smiling.

"Hey! ACE! Over here!" Pat called out to Leo Ferko.

Leo looked up and smiled, "Hello, Owens. Not an ACE anymore. You'll just have to call me Mr. Mayor," Ferko laughed.

The guys greeted old friends, Wildcat and Avenger pilots, aircrew and ship's crew; men who were bound together by their shared past and survival of a bloody war.

"Hey, Russ Wood! Over here," Ferko called out to his fellow Wildcat pilot.

"Hi, Leo! Are you still living in the Bay Area? I remember when we buzzed your mom's house in '44," Wood laughed.

"Yes, I'm still in South San Francisco. Some of the old-timers still remember that day."

"Who else was on our flight that day?" Ferko asked, thinking back over the decades.

"Bear Pool, and McGaha I think," Wood replied. "We lost track of Pool, and you know that "Wildman" Bear left us too early and that CMDR McGaha was a career Navy man."

"Same with "Red" McLean, "Tiny Tim" Srsen, and Stamatis. This group is loaded with Lt Commanders and Commanders. We even had a Navy Captain in the Deacon," Ferko replied.

"Looks like CMDR Johnson wants to address the group," Pat said, looking at the podium.

"Maybe the Judge will dismiss my speeding ticket," Ferko laughed. "Welcome to this VC-4 White Plains Reunion," Bob Johnson began. "Marion and I have prepared a little tribute to each of our fellow crewmen based on the questionnaires we sent you. It's a work in progress, and we'll update them every year. So, enjoy your stories, and let's remember and respect our friends who are no longer with us."

Walter Patrick Owens (1921-2014) was awarded the Distinguished Flying Cross, presented aboard the USS White Plains when she returned to San Diego in November 1944. Following the War, Pat Owens returned to Spokane, Washington, in the Pacific Northwest, where he married Cecile Phillipay Harper in 1952. They raised a family of five sons and a daughter in Spokane. Pat spent nearly six decades in the automobile sales industry, winning numerous awards. Pat Owens flew with the Air National Guard out of Fairchild Airbase for a time but ended that assignment when

Figure 334 Walter Pat Owens Courtesy of Owens family.

he felt that the aircraft were not maintained to his satisfaction. Pat weighed his responsibilities as a father against his love of flying and chose his family. A life-long avid sports fan Pat was gregarious and a civic leader who enjoyed friendly poker games. The bonds of brotherhood forged by their wartime experiences in a TBM Avenger resulted in a life-long close friendship with Andy Winnegar and other Navy veterans with whom Pat loved to socialize.

Figure 335 Pat Owens and Andy Winnegar at White Plains / VC-4 Reunion.

Maurice Hie (1924-1990), the TBM Avenger gunner, disembarked the USS White Plains on November 27, 1944, and was honorably discharged in January 1946. Maurice returned to San Diego, settling in Spring Valley in East San Diego County. He married Bianca Brunetta Mora, with whom he raised a family of five children. Maurice worked as an aircraft mechanic and later as a supervisor at North Island Naval Air Station. Fred Hie recalls that his dad flew in the Naval Reserves for 20 years out of Los Alamitos retiring in the 1960s.

Figure 336 Maurice Hie. Courtesy of Hie family.

Maurice and Bianca created a wonderful life together. They built their home, which is still in the Hie family. They enjoyed hunting, shooting, and fishing while introducing their children and grandchildren to the outdoors. Granddaughter Chrissy fondly recalls catching her first halibut with her grandpa. "There was a fish biting, and I caught my first halibut. Well, my Poppa said, 'Chrissy, please hold this so I can grab a beer.' He was the most amazing grandpa. He had a way of speaking and saying things that could calm and fix anything." His daughter Magda Lynn remembers her father as the wisest person she ever met. If she ever had a problem, Pop's reply was, "Don't worry, baby doll, it will be OK, and then he'd make it OK."

"If our friend's cars broke down in the middle of the night, they didn't call their own parents. They called Pop. He'd go get them with a tow bar. He'd bring them back to the house, and he'd work on their car the next day. When he got tired of working on my car," Maggie recalled, "he'd sit in the front yard in a lawn chair with a can of beer and tell me how to change the starter, or change the oil, or whatever else I needed. Which prompted me to be the first female in my high school to take auto shop and auto mechanics so I could work on my own car and Pop wouldn't have to."

Chrissy added, "When I was ten years old, I told him I wanted to be a fighter pilot, and he got very serious and said he hoped I never saw a war; that he didn't want that for me. I never heard him speak much on the war." In fact, Maurice Hie did not mention any of the details of his battles or his surviving the St Lo's sinking on October 25, 1944. This part of his life remained unknown to his family until after Maurice's death when they found a journal with a scrawled hand-written account of the events of the Battle off Samar.

Maurice enjoyed doing fun things like tumbling rocks and agates and making jewelry for Bianca and belt buckles. Photography was another of Maurice's interests and passions.

His daughter Maggie recalls that "Pop was a character. After he retired, he let his hair and beard grow long. He wore nothing but blue jeans and flannel shirts. He said he wanted nothing more than to walk back onto the base and flip off the Admiral."

Fred Hie recalls that Maurice had the gift of gab and could talk to anyone. Ultimately, Maurice Hie believed that being happy in life is a choice, that we should learn and grow from our experiences, and that love of his wife, children, and grandchildren is eternal and unconditional

Andrew J. Winnegar (1924-), the young airman who read a book a day onboard the USS White Plains, assumed the role of squadron historian. Keeping the flame alive for his squadron and now for future generations is a noble undertaking. Now that the squadron roll call has been reduced to one, Winnegar's role in preserving and sharing the courage and ideals of his generation is no less important. Andy maintains the Facebook page for VC-4 and

Figure 337 Andrew J. Winnegar

the USS White Plains. USS White Plains Facebook, and a webpage USS White Plains. The "Market Street Geezers" group is a tongue-in-cheek salute to these American warriors' bravery and advanced age.

Andy raised two sons and two daughters in Albuquerque, New Mexico, and Lubbock, Texas. Never one to let moss grow under his feet, he moved to Colorado Springs, towing gliders for Black Forrest Glider Company, Springfield MO, and Wichita Falls, Texas. Then, in 1972, seeking cooler weather, he headed to Corpus Christi and a Lincoln Mercury Dealership. Finally, it was back to Lubbock in 1973 where he worked in auto sales and married Dolores in 1976.

Because Andy Winnegar left the USS White Plains on October 11,

1944, to become a Navy pilot, he missed out on the pomp and circumstance that awaited the crew upon their return to San Diego in the Fall of 1944. As the squadron stood in review, the presentations of well-deserved medals occurred without Winnegar, who was in Flight School. It took over seven decades until the United States Navy finally corrected this oversight, honoring one of their own for heroism in combat. At the Silent Wings Museum in Lubbock, Texas, the delayed presentation of Distinguished Flying Cross and seven Air Medals to 92-year-old Andrew j Winnegar took place on August 27, 2017.

Figure 338 Andrew J. Winnegar Receives Distinguished Flying Cross and Seven Air Medals on August 27, 2017.

Lt Colonel Henry Grady Gatlin Jr (1921-1999) was awarded the Distinguished Flying Cross. On February 21, 1945, Gatlin was aboard the escort carrier USS Bismarck Sea off Iwo Jima when she was attacked and sunk by two Japanese kamikaze pilots. Gatlin reunited with his wife Jane Elizabeth after the war, whom he had married in October 1942 while in training. They raised one daughter. Gatlin attended flight school, becoming a US Naval Aviator. He continued flying in the Marine Corps Reserves until retiring in 1963 with the rank of lieutenant colonel.

Figure 339 Henry Grady Gatlin, Jr. Vanderbilt University Yearbook 1942.

Grady Gatlin received his undergraduate and law degrees from Vanderbilt University in Nashville, Tennessee. Gatlin had a long and distinguished career as an aviation lawyer, working for the Air Transport Association of America.

Steve Walley (1924-2013), after four- and one-half years in the US Navy, was discharged on April 4, 1946, receiving the Air Medal for his service in VC-4. He returned to Albany, New York, where the Walley family had lived for six generations. Jan "John" Walley, born in 1742, migrated from France settled in Albany before the Revolutionary War. Steve returned to his Albany roots, and in 1947 he married Norma Gay Vadney in November of that

Figure 340 Steve Walley.

year. They raised a family of four daughters and two sons in Albany, where Steve worked for a telecommunications company building communications towers. Living in upper-state New York, Steve and Norma enjoyed snowmobiling in the winter and picking blueberries in the summer, from which Norma made her famous jams later sold at White Plains VC-4 reunions.

Figure 341 Steve Walley and Andy Winnegar at Tucson Reunion 20

Dennis Eugene Durick (1917-2007), the FM-2 Wildcat pilot, was born in White Butte, South Dakota. His grandfather John Durick immigrated from Ireland in 1840, settling in Wisconsin and later moving to South Dakota in the 1880s. After the war, Dennis Durick married Maxine Smith in 1947. They raised three children, including two sons and a daughter.

Lt. Comdr. Leo Ferko (1915-1992) returned to his wife Frances in South San Francisco after the war, where they raised a family of three children. Ferko worked in educational sales and consulting and served on the South San Francisco City Council and as the mayor of South San Francisco in 1947-1948. He was an active leader in the Elks Lodge of San Mateo, serving as the Exalted Ruler. Ferko retired from the US Navy with the rank of Lt. CMDR. Leo M Ferko, the White Plains Ace, awarded the Distinguished Flying Cross, passed away in 1992 and is buried at the Golden Gate National Cemetery in San Bruno.

Figure 342 Leo Ferko. US Navy Photograph. Public Domain.

CMDR John Hollis Bear (1918-1957), born in Fredonia, Pennsylvania, remained in the US Navy after World War II, serving from 1941 until his untimely death due to a motor vehicle accident in 1957. During his Naval career, Bear served in World War II in the Pacific Theater and later in the Korean Conflict. CMDR Bear was awarded the Distinguished Flying Cross with three stars, the Air Medal with four stars, and the Presidential Unit Citation. After World War II, Bear attended General Line School for one year in Newport, Rhode Island, and became an instructor at Notre Dame until June 1950. He attended the Naval War

Figure 343 Comdr. John H. Bear. US Navy Photograph

College in Newport, RI, in 1952-53 and then served in the Bureau of Aeronautics in Washington DC from 1953-1955. In July 1955, Bear was assigned to Composite Squadron 8 (VC-8), later designated Heavy Attack Squadron VAH-11. Bear was initially executive officer and then, on April 1, 1957, assumed command of the Heavy Attack Squadron VAH-11 based at Sanford Naval Air Station 20 miles north of Orlando, Florida. Bear married Anne Rebecca Burhans and raised a family of three daughters.

Captain Edward Robinson Fickenscher (1918-1984) was a Baltimore native. Edward came from a long line of German American Fickenschers. They first migrated from Bavaria in Southern Germany to Baltimore in the 1850s with great grandfather Johann Heinrich Fickenscher (1816-1881).

Edward R. Fickenscher was a 1940 graduate of the U.S. Naval Academy. Fickenscher was the commanding officer of Composite Squadron Four aboard the USS White Plains in World War II, assuming command after Lt Comdr. Robert Evins was lost at sea on June 17, 1944.

Figure 344 Captain Edward R. Fickenscher. US Navy Photograph

After World War II, Edward R. Fickenscher continued to serve with a distinguished career in the US Navy. Fickenscher commanded the USS ALSTEDE (AF-48) and the USS WASP (CVS-18). He was later detached from duty as Chief of Staff and Aide to CMDR Anti=Submarine Warfare Force Atlantic in June 1964. In September 1965 was assigned duty in the Office of the Chief of Naval Operations, Navy Department. Fickenscher retired from the Navy in 1968. His awards included the Legion of Merit, the Air Medal, and the Distinguished Flying Cross (DFC).

In 1942, Fickenscher married Jan Anne Schule, who passed away in 1959. A second marriage was to Julio Anderson Riggs. Fickenscher raised a family of two sons and two daughters in Baltimore. After retiring from the Navy in 1968, he worked as an executive for Loral Corporation, an electronics company In New York City. He retired in 1983 and passed away the following year when he was 65 years old.

LCDR. William E. Flateboe (1920-1949)

After the war, Flateboe returned to his home state of Washington, where he rejoined his wife, Virginia. They had one daughter born in 1947. Flateboe worked as Assistant Manager of the Sumner Iron Works.

Flateboe realized his dream of being a fighter pilot after joining the US Naval Reserve. He was promoted to Lt. CMDR and assumed command of the Naval Reserve squadron 73A of NAS Seattle, flying F4U Corsairs. Flateboe was described as the best fighter pilot in the local Naval Reserves.

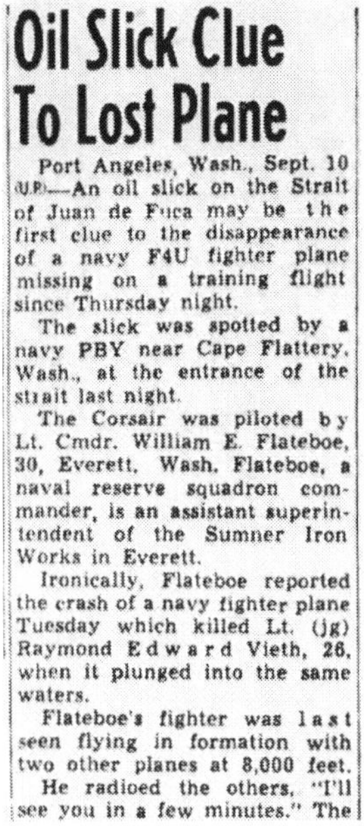

On Thursday, September 8, 1949, Flateboe was returning from a night training flight with two other Corsairs flying from Sand Point NAS to Tatoosh Island at 8,000 feet. He departed Sand Point at 2100 on a VFR flight plan to join up on a two-plane flight that had left ten minutes earlier on the 170-mile flight to Tatoosh Island. After joining up, the three Corsairs flew in formation for several minutes. Flateboe then advised Ltjg Miller

Figure 345 Lt William Flateboe 1948.

Oil Slick Clue To Lost Plane

Port Angeles, Wash., Sept. 10 (UP)—An oil slick on the Strait of Juan de Fuca may be the first clue to the disappearance of a navy F4U fighter plane missing on a training flight since Thursday night.

The slick was spotted by a navy PBY near Cape Flattery, Wash., at the entrance of the strait last night.

The Corsair was piloted by Lt. Cmdr. William E. Flateboe, 30, Everett, Wash. Flateboe, a naval reserve squadron commander, is an assistant superintendent of the Sumner Iron Works in Everett.

Ironically, Flateboe reported the crash of a navy fighter plane Tuesday which killed Lt. (jg) Raymond E d w a r d Vieth, 26, when it plunged into the same waters.

Flateboe's fighter was l a s t seen flying in formation with two other planes at 8,000 feet.

He radioed the others, "I'll see you in a few minutes." The

Figure 346 Capital Journal Sept 10, 1949

that he was leaving the formation and would see them in a few minutes. Flateboe was seen flying near the formation for the next few minutes, and after making a pass under the formation, LT jg Miller saw Flateboe's lights revolve violently to the left and go out. The violence at which the plane rolled led witnesses to believe some form of structural failure had happened to FG- 1D BuNo 88 178. Flateboe's plane disappeared over the Straight Juan de Fuca and was never seen again. A moonlight air and sea search failed to find any trace of the missing aircraft. After several days of fruitless searching, the search was called off. William E. Flateboe was 29 years old.[141][142]

Lewis Alexander Hunsaker (1924-2016), the White Plains seaman who prayed for his shipmates, after he was discharged in December 1945, he returned to Utah and his wife, Betty Lou with whom he raised a family of five children. After his wife passed away, Lew remarried Sharilyn Kroll when he was 83 years old in the Jordan River Temple. Described as a renaissance man, Hunsaker was a Roman rider, mechanic, Navy seaman (WWII), pilot, long-haul trucker and long-time member of the Beehive Statesmen Barbershop Chorus.

Figure 347 Lewis A. Hunsaker. Hunsaker Family Photograph.

---

[141] David Grant, Colt Denfeld, Randall Schalk. US Navy Shipwrecks and Submerged Naval Aircraft in Washington: An Overview. International Archeological Research Institute. Dec 1996.

[142] Flateboe the previous week had reported the crash of a navy fighter plane which killed Lt jg Raymond Edward Vieth (26) in the same waters.

CMDR Frank Charles Srsen (1917-1989), the FM-2 Wildcat fighter pilot and the Little All-American football star, was born in Fremont, Nebraska but grew up in Tacoma, Washington. Srsen was highly decorated with a Distinguished Flying Cross and other awards. After the war, Frank returned to Tacoma, where he and his wife Helen raised a family of three daughters and a son. He retired from the Navy with the rank of CMDR. For 32 years, Srsen was Commandant of the Marymount Military Academy, where he also taught 9th grade and coached.

Figure 348 Frank Charles Srsen.

Russell Jerome Wood (1920-2000), the FM2 Wildcat pilot and author of "Memoirs of Battle," was born in Baxter Springs, Kansas but spent most of this life growing up in Missouri. When Russ Wood enlisted in the Navy in 1942, he worked as a draftsman in Detroit, Michigan, previewing his post-war career. After the war, he enrolled at the University of Southern California, graduating cum laude with an architecture degree. Wood had a distinguished international career as an architect and inventor. He was licensed to practice as an architect in California, Massachusetts, and New York. Choosing to practice in the Boston area, he moved to Sudbury. He married Elizabeth Little and raised five children, including two sons and three daughters.

Figure 349 Russell J. Wood

Wood had an international career as an architect, living with his family in India for two years while collaborating with noted Indian architect Achyut Kanvinde on the design of the Indian Institute of Technology in Kanpur, India. Upon returning to the United States, Wood joined V.V. Starr & Co. Inc in New York City, serving as vice president and corporate architect. Wood oversaw the design and construction of the firm's worldwide corporate offices and commercial properties.

In 1974 Wood changed his focus to managing Spiroll International Corporation, a company he founded in the 1950s as a manufacturer of architectural drafting products. Wood invented the Spiroll drawing protractor used by architects and designers worldwide. Wood also held other patents for ergonomic drafting products. Wood remained CEO and chairman of Spiroll International Corp until his death.

CMDR Curtis Dee McGaha (1919-2019) was born in Roosevelt County, New Mexico; McGaha attended Eastern New Mexico University and New Mexico State before enlisting in the Navy in 1941. As a VC-4 FM-2 Wildcat fighter pilot, he was awarded the Distinguished Flying Cross, three Air Medals, and two Presidential Unit Citations. After the war, McGaha continued to serve in

Figure 350 Curtis D. McGaha US Navy. Courtesy of the McGaha Family.

the US Navy with a 28-year career, retiring as a CMDR. McGaha then worked as an Employment Officer with the Colorado Division of Employment for ten years. He lived in Colorado Springs from 1963 until 2012 and later in Fort Collins, Colorado. Curtis Dee McGaha was married to Edith Janet McGaha for 61 years. They raised a family of three children. Curtis D. McGaha lived to be 100 years old.

CMDR Robert Pine (1920-2008) the White Plains' Landing Signal Officer and later the Assistant Air Officer aboard the USS White Plains, was born in Kansas. He married Dorothy May in San Diego in 1942. They raised two sons and a daughter. After the war, Robert remained in the Navy as an aviator and retired as a CMDR after 22 years. They then settled in Boulder Colorado, where Robert worked for the University of Colorado as the Housing Administrator for 25 years. He and Dorothy traveled extensively, visiting all of the world's 192 recognized countries and 123 territories and island groups. In 2006, Colorado recognized them as the world's most traveled couple.

Figure 351 Robert Eugene Pine. Courtesy of Pine Family.

CMDR Coll H. McLean (1919-1987), the first American pilot to land on Saipan and Tinian, was from Evansville, WI, and later lived in Coos Bay, Oregon. He married Doris Ann Boswell of Pensacola, Florida, in September 1942. They raised three daughters in Pensacola. McLean served in World War II and the Korean Conflict. His nickname was "Red." He was the owner of "Captain Reds Charter Boat Business and Fishing Center" and was a member of the Pensacola Beach Elk's Club. He retired from the US Navy in 1962 with the rank of CMDR.

In 1978 McLean was selected to play a grizzled deckhand on the police boat in the movie Jaws II filming in Pensacola. In his fifties at the time, Coll said he was selected for the part because of his appearance that fit a "rugged old sea dog." As a result, he grew a beard with traces of the red coloring that earned him his nickname. McLean appeared in six scenes in Jaws II, released in 1979. Not letting the experience go to his head, McLean said, "Making movies is exciting, and it sure opens a new door of experience, but as soon as I get back

Figure 352 Lt Coll McLean on wing of his TMB Avenger. US Navy Photograph

from Hollywood, I'm going to start getting my charter boat business in shape and prepare for the summer season. Fishing is the only thing I'm depending on doing."

Lt. John Barrett Hearn (1921-1952), born in Darlington, South Carolina, attended the University of North Carolina at Chapel Hill for two years before enlisting in the Navy. He played on the UNC intercollegiate baseball team with his father, Bunn Hearn, serving as the coach. In the Pacific War, Hearn, a TBM Avenger pilot, landed on the doomed USS St Lo with Lt jg Pat Owens minutes before she sank. Hearn and his two crew members Lemon and Edens, survived after being picked up by the USS Dennis. After the war, Hearn returned to North Carolina. In February 1952, Hearn enrolled in a six-week

Figure 353 John B. Hearn UNC Chapel Hill 1941

Figure 354 T-6 Texan Air Force Trainer used in 1952 at Stallings Air Base in North Carolina. Air Force Photograph.

USAF pilot instructor course at Graig Air Force Base in Alabama.

Upon completing the pilot instructor course, the Navy assigned them to teach new aviation cadets at a civilian contract flying school for the Air Training Command. Hearn was assigned to Stallings Air Base in North Carolina. In Primary Flight Training, they flew T-34 Mentor, T-6 Texan, and T-28 Trojan aircraft. At 7:47 am on June 4, 1952, John Barrett Hearn was killed in an Air Force training accident in rural North Carolina one-one half miles WNW of Stallings Air Base in Kinston, North Carolina. The accident involved two T-6 training planes flying over the airbase. Cadets John Schroeder or Minneapolis and William Vann of Arbuckle, California, were also killed. Hearn never married and was 31-year-old.

Lt Colonel Arthur Francis O'Keefe (1921-1913) the Stinson OY-1 pilot on Iwo Jima, continued to serve his country in the US Marine Corps as Commanding Officer of multiple squadrons. In 1959-60, his last squadron, VMCJ-2, was stationed at Marine Corps Air Station Cherry Point in North Carolina. The squadron flew the F-8U Crusader with a top speed of

Figure 355 Arthur F. O'Keefe.

1,225 miles per hour, certainly a far cry from the Stinson OY-1 he flew in Iwo Jima with its top speed of 105 miles per hour. Ultimately, O'Keefe flew thirty-six different types of military aircraft. Arthur O'Keefe retired from the Marine Corps in 1963 and returned to Southern California.

Art made his home in Coronado, where he had grown up, raising four sons and a daughter with Patricia Wiltsie, whom he married after flight training in 1942. O'Keefe enrolled at San Diego State College in

Figure 356 Arthur O'Keefe and family at Marine Corps Air Station Cherry Point North Carolina, July 20, 1959. CMDR of VMCJ-2 – F8-U Crusader. Courtesy of Mike O'Keefe (center)

1964 to complete his undergraduate degree.143 According to his son, Mike, Art O'Keefe excelled academically. O'Keefe then spent more than fifteen years working as a San Diego County tax assessor. Art loved sailing, a passion that began as a teenager at the San Diego Yacht Club in his leisure time. He was an active member of the Coronado Yacht Club for over 40-years, serving as Commodore in 1969. He raced his Pacific Class boat, "Even Odds," and his Catalina 31, "Gray Eagle," winning more than one hundred trophies. His son, Mike, recalls that "In his day, my dad was easily recognized by his signature "bucket hat" and powder blue Karmann Ghia convertible."

Remarkably Arthur O'Keefe never mentioned his wartime experiences to his children. Instead, they uncovered the stories and photographs after he passed away, documenting their father's heroic actions that led to his being awarded Distinguished Flying Crosses on Guadalcanal and Iwo Jima.

Figure 357 Lt. Col Arthur O'Keefe in FU-8 Crusader. Courtesy of Mike O'Keefe

---

143 In the early 1870s San Diego State College became San Diego State University.

Donald J. Crounse (1925 -), the White Plains CIC Radarman 1st Class, was born in Tacoma, Washington. He attended Radar School at Point Loma, San Diego. After serving on the USS White Plains and the USS Mississippi, he was discharged from the Navy in May 1946. After discharge, Don returned to Tacoma, Washington. He was employed by ç Telephone Company, splicing massive lead-covered cables composed of hundreds of pairs of wires. He used heated lead to splice the wires and then placed a lead sleeve over the spliced cable. The job required Don to climb up on telephone poles and work under the streets. He recalls, "it took days to make one cable splice." Don worked as a splicer for 12 years and later worked in sales and service for the same company. Crounse retired from Pacific Northwest Bell after a 38-year career

Figure 358 Donald J. Crouse.

In 1949, Don married Patricia Jane, the girl across the street, a librarian and school teacher. They raised two sons in Tacoma. Don and Pat enjoyed traveling extensively in the United States and Europe, including England, Scotland, and Ireland. Pat was instrumental in planning their travels which were often centered around Patricia's love of literature.

Don was the "repair guy" throughout his life wherever they went. They bought and sold twelve homes which he repaired and maintained. They had homes in Tacoma, Seattle, Long Branch, Day Island, Normandy Park, and later in Tucson, where they went to retire. Don started playing golf when he was 45 years old and thoroughly enjoyed the game. They bought and sold three homes in Tucson. "It was so damn much work." Fortunately, Crounse kept their family

Figure 359 Don and Pat Crounse at 2006 VC-4 White Plains Reunion in San Diego

home in Long Branch, Washington, so for 18 years, they spent summers in Washington and winters in Tucson, Arizona.

Don is now 96 years old, living in Puyallup, Washington, 10 miles southeast of Tacoma. Pat, the love of his life, passed away three years ago after an almost seven-decade marriage. The White Plains CIC Radarman, Donald Crounse, continues to live independently, requiring little assistance other than a prepared dinner. His days are busy, and he enjoys the company of his friends and sharing his memories of the War in the Pacific.

Matt I. Bisenius (1921-2018) the Radioman in Lt. Flateboe's TBM Avenger, was born in Cascade, Iowa. Matt was named after his great grandfather Mathias Bisenius (1812-1876) who immigrated from Alsace a region in Northeastern France near the border with Germany. The area is a combination of French and German culture and people. By 1926 the family had moved west to Mount Angel, Oregon, 18 miles northeast of Salem. Mount Angel was founded in the 1800s by German settlers, even today maintaining its German roots. The Bisenius family moved to Portland by 1935.

Figure 360 Matt I. Bisenius.

Matt Bisenius enlisted in July, 1942. On 25 October 1944, Bisenius was the radioman / bombardier in Lt Flateboe's TBM Avenger when they engaged a Nagato-class Japanese battleship in the Battle off Samar, scoring two direct hits. Matt recalled, "Never before had I ever experienced such G-pressure while entering the dive on the battleship then on the pullout with evasive maneuvers.

Figure 361 Matt I. Bisenius Courtesy of Andy Winnegar.

Lt Flateboe was one of the very best bomber pilots who knew how to get maximum speed and efficiency to gain an advantage over the enemy." After the war, Matt married Nancy Jean Lind in January 1947. They raised a son and daughter in Portland, Oregon. Matt Bisenius worked in the Portland Oregon Department of Public Safety for thirty years.

James Eugene Straughn (1921-2008), the VC-4 FM-2 Wildcat pilot, was born in Vaughn, New Mexico. Before the war, he attended the University of New Mexico, majoring in engineering. In December 1944, he married Virginia Louise Wilds. After the war, Eugene returned to New Mexico, where he and Virginia raised a family of four daughters. Straughn flew for Delta Airlines for more than 35 years. Eugene loved to travel, loved family, and was blessed with a wonderful sense of humor. Eugene later moved to Fort Worth, Texas..

Figure 362 James Straughn

Edward Morris Billinghurst (1922-2015), the FM-2 Wildcat pilot, was born in Indianapolis, Indiana, and grew up in Jackson, Michigan. After the war, he married Christine Maynard in San Diego, California, where he earned a degree in Electrical Engineering. Billinghurst lived in Southern California, later moving to Orange County.

Figure 363 Edward M. Billinghurst

Charles Franklin Selig (1920-2002), the VC-4 Radio Technician whose bunk was right below Andy Winnegar's, was born in Baltimore, Maryland. His family had long-standing roots in Baltimore. John Michael Selig migrated from Bavaria in Southern Germany to Baltimore in 1844. After World War II Charles married Pauline Rita Wailaver. They raised a family of five children, including three sons and two daughters in Norfolk, Virginia.

Figure 364 Charles F. Selig

CMDR Robert Basil Stamatis (1921-2006), the FM-2 Wildcat pilot, was from San Francisco, born to Greek immigrant parents. In the Pacific war, Stamatis flew more than 60 missions off the USS White Plains. After the war, Stamatis studied at Golden Gate College and worked for the California State Income Tax office. He remained in the Navy following World War II. In 1953 Lt Stamatis flew for the Navy aboard the USS Philippine Sea in the Korean conflict. In March 1953, Stamatis was forced to ditch his jet fighter in the Sea of Japan 50 miles from his carrier. The lieutenant, who sustained a back injury, was fished

Figure 365 Robert B Stamatis FM-2 Wildcat Pilot VC-4 Courtesy of Andy Winnegar

from the icy waters by the Canadian destroyer Athabaskan which transferred him to the carrier USS Valley Forge. Stamatis was sent home to his wife Irene and two children, Jimmie, 4-1/2, and Billy, 6-1/2 years old, in San Francisco. CMDR Stamatis spent 28 years as a Naval aviator. He was also a certified public accountant and auditor for the California Board of Equalization for fourteen years. He and Irene Davis Stamatis were long-time residents of Orinda in Contra Costa Country, California.

LCDR. Solon Norris Bales (1920-1993), the FM-2 Wildcat pilot, was born in Clovis New Mexico, the fifth of six sons of Homer Bales, a carpenter. The Bales family moved to Northern California where they lived in Marysville. Bales was a student at UC Berkeley when he enlisted in 1942. Lt jg Solon N Bales was awarded the Distinguished Flying Cross for his five strafing runs on two Japanese Battleships and a heavy cruiser along with Ens. William G Schaufler during the Battle off Samar. After the war, Bales returned to Northern California, living in Oakland, Marysville and Auburn, California. He stayed in the Naval Reserves based at the Oakland Naval Air Station, flying the F8F "Bearcat" and later serving in the Korean Conflict. Bales earned a degree in Business Administration from UC Berkeley. By the mid 1960s Bales was a bachelor doing odd jobs in Soda Springs, California. Solon N. Bales the "Demon's Deacons" Wildcat Warrior, is buried in Auburn, California.

Figure 366 Solon N. Bales Courtesy of A. Winnegar

Robert W. Egan, (1920-2010), the Radioman on Ens. Frank Rox's TBM Avenger, was from Plattsburgh, New York. On 21 October 1944, while over the Philippines, Rox's TBM was struck by shrapnel, injuring his radioman, Bob Egan, who received a Purple Heart. His brother Thomas Egan, also an aviation radioman, died the following June 16 1945 in the Philippines. After the war, Bob Egan returned to Plattsburgh, New York where in June 1948 he married Pauline Decelle. They raised a family of three daughters and two sons in Plattsburgh.

Figure 367 Robert W. Egan

Bob was a member of the Veterans of Foreign Wars Post 125, the American Legion Post 20, a life member of the Benevolent and Protective Order of Elks Plattsburgh Lodge 621, the Knights of Columbus Council 255, a very active member of Telephone Pioneers of America, member and a trustee of St. John's Church and a faithful bingo worker for 30-plus years. He was also one of the founders of St. John's Athletic Association. In addition, he enjoyed reading, dancing and taking his grandchildren to the candy store after Mass.

C. Marvin Cave (1925-), the Assistant Navigator served for three years aboard the USS White Plains. Born in French Lick, Indiana, Cave is a member of the Indiana Basketball Hall of Fame. After the War, Cave attended Indiana State University and Berea College earning a BS degree in 1948 and a Master's degree in 1951. He married Pat

Figure 368 Marvin Cave. Courtesy of Julie Dereschuk

Moore and raised a son and daughter. For eight years, Cave taught math and PE at Frankfort and Decatur Central High Schools. He then joined Eli Lilly and Company as Director of company personnel for marketing and administration, retiring in 1988 as Vice President of Human Resources. Marvin's favorite pastimes included golfing and flying his Beech A-36 airplane.

Lt. William G Schaufler (1920-1953), the FM2-Wildcat pilot was born in New Jersey to German immigrant parents. In World War II he was awarded the Distinguished Flying Cross in 1944 for strafing attacks against two Japanese battleships and a heavy cruiser along with Lt Solon Bales. In 1945 Schaufler rescued a Navy pilot whose plane crashed while attempting a carrier landing in the Caribbean area. After the war, he married Doris Wheatley in Keansburg, New Jersey, and had two children, William Jr. and Sandra. Schaufler remained in the Naval Reserves and was

Figure 369 William G. Schaufler.

killed in a routine cross county Navy training flight in a Beechcraft plane flying back from St Louis to Atlantic City. Two others were also killed in the accident in which the twin-engine Navy plane crashed into a mountainside sixteen miles west of Bedford, PA.

George Fournier (1921-2001), the TBM Avenger Radioman, was born in Westbrook, Maine, to French Canadian parents initially from Quebec, who migrated to the United States in 1902. The family roots in Quebec go back generations to Guillaume Fournier, who immigrated from France to Quebec in 1651. The Fournier family spoke French, and George's father worked in the local mills. After the war, George returned to

Figure 370 George Fournier.

Westbrook, where he worked as a "Cutterman" in a local paper mill. In 1947 he married Marguerite Perron, a graduate nurse from Somersworth, New Hampshire.

Robert J. Dings (1922-1992), the 2nd Marine Division Navy Corpsman on Saipan, Guadalcanal, and Tarawa, was born in Modesto, California, into a family with four sisters. He and his sisters invented a secret language they all used in public, inserting the code words into conversa-tions to see if anyone

Figure 371 Robert J. Dings at Sierra Clinical Laboratories. Courtesy of Karen Low

would notice. As a result, the sisters gave their brother the nickname, Schmirrll, long before the Marines gave him the name "Onion Head."

In WWII, Robert Dings was awarded a Bronze Star for his participation in five major campaigns and was eligible for a Purple Heart. Dings was also a musician and played the piccolo in military bands when not serving as a corpsman.

After the war, Bob returned to California, earning a Bachelor's Degree at UC Berkeley and certification as a Bacteriologist, Bioanalyst, and Clinical Laboratory Technician. He worked at the Dewitt State Hospital in Auburn, where he was in charge of the laboratory. He was also the owner and director of the Sierra Clinical Laboratories.

Bob was active in civic organizations, including the Auburn Kiwanis Club, of which he was a charter member and District Lt Governor. Dings was also very active in the Pioneer Methodist Church. In addition, he was a member of the Auburn Civic Symphony, in which he played cello.

In 1968, Bob was the Auburn Community Concert Association president, bringing internationally famous musicians to Auburn.

On a personal side, Bob Dings was a cartoonist, vocal impressionist, and prankster who more than anything loved an excellent practical joke. In addition, he is remembered as a caring husband, father, employer, and community leader.

Frank Fitzgerald Rox (1923-2001), the TBM Avenger pilot, was born in Augusta, Georgia. After returning from the Pacific, Rox attended Emory University, obtaining an undergraduate degree followed by a law degree. Frank Rox practiced Aviation Law and was counsel for the legal division of Delta Airlines for decades. In 1974 Delta Airlines elected Frank F Rox Senior Vice President of law and public affairs. His successful career took him to California where he made his home in the exclusive Belvedere Tiburon in Marin Country north of San Francisco.

Figure 372 Frank F. Rox. Courtesy of Andy Winnegar.

LCDR. James A Huser (1917-1948), the TBM Avenger pilot, was born in Antlers, Oklahoma. Huser was the band instructor at Webster Junior High School in Oklahoma City. He married Elizabeth King Erwin in August 1943. Huser served for 19 months on combat duty, flying a TBM for VC-4 off the USS White Plains and was awarded the Distinguished Flying Cross. James Huser's daughter was born one month after the Battle of Samar in November 1944. Huser remained in the Navy after World War II. On February 7, 1948, LCDR. James Huser was one of six TBM Avengers engaging in amphibious maneuvers at San Clemente off the Southern California coast. The Navy torpedo bomber was carrying 1,000 pounds of high explosives when it exploded in midair, bursting into flames and partially disintegrating before it crashed into San Clemente Island, killing Huser and aviation radioman 1/c Norman C. Benson. Huser was 30 years old. Elizabeth remained in Coronado, California, where she was a school teacher.

Figure 373 James A. Huser.

Captain Martin Donelson Jr. (1917-2005), the VC-4 Flight Surgeon, was born in Norfolk, Virginia. His father, CMDR Martin Donelson, served in the US Navy, taking his family to postings worldwide. In 1942 Martin Donelson Jr. graduated from the University of Virginia Medical School. He served in WWII as a flight surgeon aboard the USS White Plains, where Donelson flew along in Pat Owens' TBM Avenger, an experience that developed into a life-long love of flying.

Figure 374 Martin Donelson Jr.

After WWII, Donelson continued in the Naval Reserves Medical Corps, retiring as a Captain in 1968. He served twice in Vietnam. In 1962 he worked as a surgeon for one month at the Schweitzer Hospital in Haiti and in 1967 was a volunteer surgeon for MEDICO at Santa Rosa de Copan, Honduras. He moved from Seattle to Dallas to Philadelphia before settling in Danville, Virginia, where the small-town atmosphere suited him. Dr. Donelson was described in 1971 as a gray-haired physician with bow tie and sparkling eyes, sitting slumped in the chair in his home office with his feet propped up on his deck. Martin Donelson was constantly in motion on his motorcycle, bicycle, or piloting his plane. He was twice married and raised five children and six stepchildren.

Richard J Dennis (1919-2001), the TBM Avenger pilot, was born in Little Rock Arkansas. On 25 October 1944 in the Battle off Samar, the USS White Plains rearmed the TBM's flown by Lt jg Dennis and Lt. Huser at about 10:20. The two TBM Avengers launched their 2,000-pound torpedos at a Japanese Tone-class cruiser, stopping the cruiser which was then sunk by aircraft from VC-75. Dennis and Huser were each awarded the Distinguished Flying Cross. After the War Dick Dennis returned to Little Rock, Arkansas where he married Caroline Marie Kern in November 1945. They raised a family of six daughters and one son in Little Rock and later moved to Richardson, Texas.

Figure 375 Richard J. Dennis. Dennis Family Collection Ancestry.com

LCDR. William Alan Mudgett (1916-1989), the FM2 Wildcat pilot and Lt. CMDR. Evins' wingman on his final flight, was born in Wilbarger County Texas. He graduated from the University of Texas in Austin. After the war, Mudgett returned to Bryan Texas and ran for the office of State Representative of the 26th District. In 1947 William married Geraldine Ray Jones with whom he raised a family of five children, including three sons and two daughters. In 1949 Lt CMDR Mudgett was the commanding officer of the newly activated the Naval Reserve Unit VC 8-10 in Dallas Texas. In 1947, Mudgett was a board member of the

Figure 376 William A. Mudgett. Courtesy of Andy Winnegar.

Bryan Texas Junior Chamber of Commerce and in 1960 was a member of the East Texas Chamber of Commerce Labor Relations Board.

Charles Malcolm Shields (1921-2016), the TBM Avenger pilot, was born in San Jose, California and grew up in Fresno in the California Central Valley. Malcolm had a younger sister, Beverly, born in 1923. He attended Roosevelt High School followed by Fresno State College where he was a 13 foot plus intercollegiate pole vaulter. Shields was employed as a draughtsman for Pacific Gas and Electric. In October 1943, Ensign Shields married Mildred Dye of Glendale while at NAS Arlington as a Naval aviator in

Figure 377 Charles M Shields. Yearbook photograph.

training. He had met Mildred at Roosevelt High School in Fresno. Shields was awarded the Air Medal for his action in the Battle off Samar scoring a near miss on a Japanese ship. After the war, Shields returned to Fresno and later found employment in Saudi Arabia, working for Standard Oil Company. In 1980 at the time of his father's death, Shields was in Saudi Arabia. He later moved to Colorado Springs and returned to Fresno in California's Central Valley.

CMDR. Austin W. Kivett (1898-1993), the CIC Air Information Officer, was born in Stilesville, Indiana. Kivett served in the Navy in World War I. He then attended law school at the University of Chicago earning, PhD and J.D. degrees. In May 1942, when he was 43 years old, he left his practice, Kivett and Kasdorf in Milwaukee, to enlist as a lieutenant in the US Navy in World War II. A remarkably calm and steady figure aboard the USS White

Figure 378 Austin W. Kivett. Low Family Collection.

Plains, Kivett formed bonds with young men that lasted a life time. After the war, he lived in Wauwatosa, WI with his wife, Mae, whom he married in Chicago in 1932. Professionally, Kivett was described as a "Legal Lion" and the "Great Trial Attorney, Austin Kivett." He retired from his law practice in 1983. Although, Kivett was a "father figure" for his men in CIC, he never had his own children. Active in fraternal and professional organization, Kivett was a member of the Masons, Shriners, American Legion, Sons of the American Revolution, and American College of Trial Lawyers.

Figure 379 WWII Command Information Center.

Ira H. Goldberg (1924-2013), Andy Winnegar's boxing sparring partner and shipmate was born in Davenport, Iowa. He returned to the Chicago, Illinois area following the war where in May, 1945 he married Phyllis Lurie. They raised a daughter and two sons in Buffalo, Illinois. He initially found work with the Chicago and Northwestern Railroad as a trucker.

Figure 380 Ira H. Goldberg.

Everett "Bill" Lemon (1920-1972), the gunner on John Hearn's TBM was from Hillsboro, Oregon, west of Portland. Bill was a descendant of an Oregon pioneer family. His maternal grandmother Augusta Berry, traveled from Arkansas by covered wagon in 1885. Bill grew up on a hog farm in Hillsboro, at one time offering a job on the pig farm to his shipmates after the war. Bill's sense of humor and ever-present good nature is reflected in his nickname, "Smiley." All his shipmates universally liked him. After the war, Bill returned to Oregon where he married Betty Jane Jacobson in 1949. They raised two daughters with Bill remembered as a

Figure 381 Everett "Bill" Lemon. Courtesy of Christopher Dean.

fun-loving parent. Bill loved history and reading which is reflected in his hand-written World War II journal. He worked for Pacific Bell in Oregon as a plant inspector. Bill passed away in the prime of his life from brain cancer.

CMDR. Robert F. Johnson (1920-2000) was born in St. Paul, Minnesota, completing two years of college before enlisting. The White Plains' Arresting Gear Officer loved being a part of the Navy. After the war, Bob stayed in the Navy Reserves and became a Naval Aviator, retiring as a CMDR. After the war, he married Marion Lidstad on August 15, 1945, the day after the Japanese surrender. Bob and Marion raised a family of three daughters in St Paul. Bob completed his undergraduate degree and then attended law school in the 1950s later serving as a District Court Judge in Ramsey County, Minnesota.

With his amiable personality, Bob Johnson loved people and could strike up a conversation with anyone. His list of friends seemed endless. Bob remained close with his Navy shipmates, and it was only natural that Bob was the organizing force behind the White Plains / VC-4 reunions. Reuniting and reminiscing for a few days each year brought back memories and rekindled old relationships undimmed by the decades that had passed since their days aboard ship.

Figure 382 Robert F. Johnson. Courtesy of Johnson Family.

Figure 383 Bob and Marion Johnson on their wedding day. Courtesy of the Johnson Family.

Figure 384 Bob and Marion Johnson organizers of VC-4 White Plains Reunions. Courtesy of the Johnson family.

Bob's wife, Marion, was instrumental in organizing and running the reunion group. For over fifteen years, they served as President and Secretary/Treasurer of the White Plains/VC4 Reunion Group. The guys spent hours reliving the battle scenes, with each man adding a piece to the puzzle of what really happened all those decades past.

Figure 385 USS White Plains / VC-4 Reunion 1999 St Louis Missouri. Courtesy of the Johnson Family.

APPENDIX

Crew of Composite Squadron Four (VC-4)

Albright, Roger R AMM3/c

Atkinson, Fredrick LTJG

Axt, Robert Lee

Baker, Henry ENS

Baker, Jake R.

Bales, Solon LTJG

Barnes, Cyral K.

Bear, John H. LT

Bentoglio, Lloyd ENS

Billinghurst, Edward ENS

Byrd, Harold E. ENS

Bisenius, Matt ARM1/c

Borcher, Richard ARM2/c

Bowman, Ant ARM3/c

Briggs, A. J. AOM2/c

Bruce, F. J.

Burge, R. B. ACOM

Butcher, Paul ENS

Carson, Harold H. LTJG

Cash, Bob

Chasten, E. "Doc"

Clark, Paul AMM2/c

Clever, Gordon E.

Cody, Larry T. ARM2/c

Conners, James ENS

Cook, Kenneth D

Cooper, Robert R. AMM2/c

Crawford, G. E. AMM2/c

Davis, Howard W. ARM2/c

Dennis, Richard J. ENS

Donelson Jr, Martin LCDR

Durham, Jimmy AOM2/c

Durick, Dennis E. ENS

Dyer, Lance ENS

Edens, H. B. ARM2/c

Edwards, Michael

Egan, Robert W. ARM2/c

England, Bill

Evins, Robert C. LCDR

Ferko, Leo M. LT

Fickenscher, Edward R. LCDR

Fincher, Sam

Flateboe, William E. LT

Fonger, Bob

Fournier, George F. ARM2/c

French, Joseph LTJG LSO

Fries, G. E. ARM3/c

Fuller, Bob ARM2/c

G. A. Sembritzky ACRT

Gowan, Eugene

Hatterman, Bernard A.

Hearn, John B. LTJG

Hie, Maurice AMM2/c

Hooper, George E. Capt. USMCR

Huser, James LT

Johnson, Calvin ARM3/c.

Johnson, J. R.

Kidman, Delbert ARM3/c

Kurz, Fred E. LT

Laudenslager, George H. ENS

Lechleiter, Tom AMM1/c

Lemon, Bill

Ludwig, Curtis

Maloney, Francis J. LTJG

Mayher, John R. LTJG

McComis, C. W.

McGaha, Curtis D. LTJG

McLean, Coll LT

Merrin, George ARM2/c

Metcalf, Billy L. AMM2/c

Miller, Earl Kenny

Mudgett, William ENS

Nichols, John S. Sgt. USMCR

Osborne, Jack H. LTJG

Ott, L. A. ARM1/c

Owens, Walter P. LTJG

Palmer, Henry C. LT

Patterson, Wesley F.LTJG

Pine, Robert E. Lt LSO

Pool, Lee Ross ENS

Reams, Clyde F. ENS

Richardson, Clifford AOM3/c

Robinson, William Hugh ENS

Rox, Frank F. LTJG

Schaeffer, Joseph AMM1/c

Schaufler, William G. ENS

Scott, William R.

Selig, Charles F. ART1/c

Sheldon, Wilford ENS

Sherouse, Shorty

Shields, Charles H. LTJG

Srsen, Frank C. LT

Stamatis, Robert ENS

Stewart, Leonard L. ENS

Straughn, Eugene LT

Tigner, Melvin L. ARM1/c

Walley, Steven R. ARM2/c

Weber, Dewey ARM2/c

Weniger, Mike

Wiley Jr, Albert LT

Winnegar, Andrew J. ARM2/c

Wood Karl M. ARM3/c

Wood, Russell LTJG

Figure 386 TBM Avengers and FM2 Wildcats on flight deck of USS Coral Sea.
April 1944

TBM Avenger Crews VC-4

Radio Operator   **Pilot**   **Gunner**

TBM Avenger Crews VC-4

Radio Operator	Pilot	Gunner

TBM Avenger Crews VC-4

Radio Operator　　　　**Pilot**　　　　**Gunner**

TBM Avenger Crews VC-4

Radio Operator   **Pilot**   **Gunner**

TBM Avenger Crews VC-4

Radio Operator **Pilot** **Gunner**

TBM Avenger Crews VC-4

Radio Operator	Pilot	Gunner

Dewey Weber — Harold E. Byrd — Michael Edwards

Calvin Johnson — Wilford Sheldon — Jake R. Baker

TBM Avenger Crews VC-4

Radio Operator   **Pilot**   **Gunner**

Matt Bisenius   William E. Flatebve   C. W. McComis

Art Bowman   Paul Butcher   Bob Fonger

TBM Avenger Crews VC-4

Radio Operator   **Pilot**   **Gunner**

TBM Avenger Crews VC-4

Radio Operator **Pilot** **Gunner**

Larry T. Cody   Richard G. Dennis   Robert Lee Art

Figure 387 Memorial to VC-4 Members Killed During World War II.

Lance Dyer   Harold H. Carson   James Conners   Karl M. Wood   Leonard L. Stewart

George H. Laudenslager   Clifford Richardson   Robert C. Evins   George E. Hooper

Selected Entries from Journals of Andrew J. Winnegar VC-4 TBM Avenger Radio Operator

Difficult return in White Plains due to malfunctioning ZB radio.

June 22, 1944: We took off at 0615 this morning with orders to land on the USS Sangamon, a converted tanker, and to operate from there until our carrier was refueled at sea.

Figure 388 Andy Winnegar

Before we were catapulted, Selig our Radio Technician gave me a list of frequencies and asked me to see that our ZB (homing radio) was set on them when we landed on the Sangamon. We landed on the Sangamon a little after 0630 and I took the ZB straight to the Radio Shack. While the Chief RT worked on our ZB Hie and I went to the mess hall for breakfast. The Sangamon mess deck is about fifteen feet above the water line and open, allowing the sea to occasionally come across the deck. When we got the timing down, of raising our feet and taking bites, it was very pleasant, much cooler than our mess on the White Plains.

Back at the Radio Shack the Chief said our ZB was beyond repair and with only two spares they couldn't give us one. With Gatlin in the turret and Hie in the center cockpit we launch without radio navigation and are on station to relieve Leo 1 at 0900. Most of the hop is spent looking for Jap artillery. We report our troop positions in Shackle Code to Paymaster and try to find out if they are being fired on. We see some enemy shells hitting behind our lines but we do not have troops in that location and can't spot their guns.

We were relieved by Leo 1 at 12:10 and ordered to help another TBM with a Jap emplacement in the side of a gorge. We strafed and fired our eight rockets. We saw Army P47s landing at Aslito, too bad we couldn't call them in on our target with their eight wing .50 cals.

We landed on Sangamon at 12:45 and had late chow with some of their Anti-Sub Patrol crewmen then relieved Leo 1 at 1445. We were directing Pittsburgh's fire on troops gathering for a counter attack in and around a farm house. Hie in the center cockpit noticed artillery rounds a little too close as we cruised back and forth inside the arch of the shells. That is one of the hazards of observation over a small island, you have naval gun fire underneath, artillery over the top and other "friendly" aircraft in the center; then there's the bad guys shooting at you. Having no rockets or bombs we directed a final volley from Pittsburgh and at 1800 headed back to sea to find our ship.

Clouds were building up with several rain storms limiting our vision and when we dead reckoned to where we thought our ship should be it wasn't there. I couldn't pick up anything on radar and it was getting dark. I set the frequency for Convict Base and Owens called in. They asked for emergency lights and I turned on the IFF and got a bearing of 050 30 miles. After holding this course for a few minutes, we spotted a plane off our starboard. Convict Base said they had the plane identified as a bogey and would like us to investigate. We went into a dive to build up speed and the bogey took off. When we reported this, they said it had now been identified as friendly and gave us a new course of 070 at 12 miles. Owens made visual contact at 3 miles and made a night approach and landing.

Crossing the Line Ceremony – Pollywogs and Shellbacks

16 August 1944

We ate breakfast with a knife this morning. We sighted the New Hebrides at about 000. We are supposed to anchor at 1230. I believe we are supposed to anchor off Espiritu Santo Island. The islands look swell. I would like to go hunting here. Some of the islands are very mountainous. The Shell Backs have constructed a tank on the flight deck. It is about 10' by 10' square and 5' deep. They have a chair one side of it hinged so that it will flip over into the tank. There are two copper plates on the chair. I see where us Pollywogs are going to get a ducking and shocking at almost the same time.

They have just informed us that the initiation will be today. We finally cut Pot Ashes mustache. He came up near our compartment and we jumped him. I used a razor on one side of it without benefit of shaving cream.

The line we must go through starts off with the greasy belly of the fattest Shell Back on the ship. They had some kind of grease on him. Next was a drink of some kind of hot spice then we were laid on a table had our mouth sprayed with powdered quinine while receiving a shot of electric current. Next on the program was a box with a gate at one end and filled with garbage. We had to crawl out of the garbage and through two tow sleeves while Shell Backs beat us with shillalas. When we stood up after crawling through the tow sleeves a salt water hose was turned on us. Next came the tank. We were told to sit in the seat on the side of the tank. The juice was turned on us and we were dumped over backwards.

When we came up to the top. We had to shout "Shell Back" before the men in the tank could duck us. I was not ducked. Last but not least was the shillalas line which we had to run.

I believe all the casualties occurred in it and there were several. One broken leg several broken arms and fingers. I got through with a very bruised bottom. Next to the pilots we got the roughest treatment on the ship. The deck apes made it pretty tough on us in the shillalas line. Their pride was hurt when we shaved a few of their heads Then just before the initiation we rouged them up a little and threw a few of their shillelaghs over the side. We could have thrown them all over had we so desired. They had no taste for blood while we were resisting. I threw two over myself but if I had it to do over, I'd make it twenty. The captain has ordered that there will be no more Shell Back initiations on the U.S.S. White plains. Metal was found in some of the shillelaghs and the regular service men who never had what could really be called an initiation were not such good sports. In fact, one of our men had to punch one of them to take the fight out of him before the initiation.

Maurice Hie's Journal Entry Describing the Battle off Samar 25 October 1944

At approximately 07:00 on the morning of October 25, 1944, General Quarters was sounded aboard the USS White Plains. A few minutes after it was sounded, we heard shells hitting all around us from Jap battleships, cruises, and light cruisers. Two shells hit along portside aft. One of our fighter planes that was preparing to take off, had his wing tip blowed off from the explosions. The shelling continued for approximately three hours.

Figure 389 Maurice Hie

At 07:40, we manned our TBM's and took off. Four planes left the deck. They were piloted by Mr. Hearn. Mr. Owens, Mr. Byrd, and Mr. Butcher. We joined up over the Jap formation, all of us except Mr. Byrd who joined us sometime later. Jap power consisted of five cruisers CA, one light cruiser CL, three battleships BB and an unknown number of destroyers DD. One light cruiser wa leading a group of destroyers, three cruisers and began closing in on our carrier force (Taffy 3).

Seeing this, we made our bombing attack on the leading cruiser. Two of us went down. They were Mr. Owens and Mr. Hearn. Mr. Hearn was loaded with three depth charges and we had two 250 pound and two 500-pound general-purpose bombs. The anti-aircraft was thick as hell. I still don't see how we got out. We had no fighter protection. I did not see our bombs but think we got at least one or two hits on the cruiser. She seemed to slow up after we dove. Mr. Butcher did not dive with us and I never saw him anymore after that.

When pulling out of the dive, Walley took pictures of the whole force but the camera was lost later. After the dive, we circled the Jap force again. At this time, Mr. Byrd joined up on us. I don't think Mr. Byrd or Mr. Butcher had any bombs.

After circling the Jap force, a while, we called for permission to land and get rearmed. Fido Base could not take us so we went to Banjo Base. Just as we were about to land the Jap force began firing on them so they could not take us aboard. We then went to Tacloban. They would only take emergency landings and they would not rearm us anyway. After circling Tacloban for a while, we heard that Taffy 3 was taking on planes. After this we continued to Taffy 3. After arriving there, we received instructions to land on Derby Base (USS St Lo).

We landed on Derby Base at approximately 10:45. Our planes were taken below to be loaded with fish. Our plane was in good condition except for the microphone in the turret of "28" which was out. After landing, the ACI officer talked to Mr. Hearn. Mr. Owens went down the elevator with the plane and returned to the flight deck. Mr. Hearn remained on the flight deck. Lemon, Edens and I went below to the ready room. Wally went to the Radio Shack and got a new mic.

At approximately, 10:50 General Quarters was sounded and a couple of minutes later at 10:52 a Jap plane made a crash dive at the carrier. The Jap plane was a Frances. The plane hit a little forward of the aft elevator A fire was started in the hangar deck. After we felt the plane hit, Lemon Edens and I left the ready room and went to the forward end of the flight deck where we saw the tail of the Jap plane. Wally was on the wing of "28" when the lane hit and was thrown off. He remained on the #1 sparrow until the third blast, then he went over the side.

A few minutes later the plane hit the fish that were being loaded in our planes and exploded, raising the forward elevator about four or five feet. There were a good many wounded men on deck by this time.

At approximately 10:59, the third explosion went off. I do not know what caused it unless it was gas. This explosion lifted the forward elevator way up in the air and it came back down wrong side up. After the explosion, Lemon, Edens and I went down on the forecastle. Just as we got on the forecastle, we saw Mr. Owens and Mr. Hearn coming down. That was the first time we had seen them since we landed.

Very shortly after that, we went over the side. Lemon's watch stopped at 11:03 which was the time he hit the water. We were all separated here. As the ships went by me, I could see a lot of tracer coming out of the ship. The fire on the hangar deck had set off the ammo and bombs. Threw were a few more explosions after I got off the ship. The ship had all of its amidship blown away at approximately 11:30. She began going under stern first. A small fire was started on the water but it didn't last very long.

At approximately 11:45, I was taken aboard the USS Dennis (DE-405). She was the nearest ship to the carrier. As a matter of fact, she was too close for her own safety. Wally was already aboard when I was taken on. About ten or fifteen minutes later we saw Mr. Owens and Mr. Hearn, Lemon and Edens got aboard.144

The DE-405 was taking on water but she continued picking up men while all around her there was oil and gas on the water. She had a

---

144 Lt jg John Hearn was a TBM Avenger pilot. Bill Lemon was his gunner and HB Edens was his radioman.

total of 434 survivors and about 50 of them were wounded or burnt pretty bad. Not much more happened that day.

At approximately 10:00 on the 26th the lookout sighted two torpedos coming at us. We got away from them and began looking for the sub. At approximately 10:20 a periscope was sighted off our port aft. After looking for the sub awhile, we continued on our way to Kassel Passage. Somewhere around 14:00 to 15:00 we made another sub contact. The DE fired a salvo of hedge hogs (depth charges) but did not hit anything. A little while later General Quarters was secured. Everything was OK after that until about 20:30 that night when some planes were overhead. Although they were friendly, some of the cans began firing. After that, we got very little sleep.

Figure 390 "Bill" Lemon – Courtesy of Christopher Dean.

Bill Lemon's Journal-
June 15-17, 1944 Saipan Invasion

June 15, 1944

This Is The Day And What A Day It Was.

First The Marines Started Their Attack At Eight Thirty After Our Fighters With Forty Others Strafed The Beach. The Japs Let The First Two Waves Get Inside The Reef And Then Stopped Them Cold. The Third Wave Got Ashore Okay And Part Of Them Reached Their Objectives. They Continued Their Landings All Day And Although They Didn't Come Up To Expectations The Marines Did Damn Well In Face Of The Resistance.

We Have Planes Flying Marine Observers Over The Island Spotting Gun Emplacements And The First Couple Of Times They Ran Into Some AA Fire. One Shell passed Thru The Radio Compartment And Grazed The Radio-Man's Head. Another One Came Thru The Bottom And Tore His Back Pack Off. Later In The Day When He Was Up Again A Shell Tore A Huge Hole In The Rudder. He Must Have A Charmed Life.

We Went On Our Usual Patrols

And The Only Excitement We Had Was
Seeing An Oil Slick Where A Sub Had
Been Bombed And Seeing A Destroyer
Pick Up Some Jap Survivors One Of
Whom Commited Hari-Kari In The
Water.

Late In The Evening While We Were
Waiting For The Last Hop To Come
In G.Q. Was Sounded And Word
Was Passed That Some Jap Dive Bomb-
ers Were On The Way. All Hands
Stayed On The Flight Deck To See The
Action. We Watched Our Own Fighters
Knock Down Four Out Or Five While
The Fifth Went To A Destroyer.
Lt. Kurz, Lt. Straughn, Lt.(Jg.) Durrick,
And Ensign Wood Each Got One Of Them.
The Japs Never Knew What Hit Them
Hardly. They Certainly Had Plenty Of
Nerve To Try It Tho. The Planes
Were A New TB Called Jill.

When The Fighters Were Coming
In One Tore His Tail Assembly Off
And Went Over The Side. He Got
Out O.K. Tho And Was Picked Up By
A.OD.

A Good Day For A Beginning.

June 16, 1944

They Rolled Me Out Of Bed This Morning And Told Me I Had A Hop. I Dove Into My Clothes And Hurried To The Ready Room And Found We Were Going On A Bombing Attack. We Finally Took Off At Eight-Thirty, Two Of Us, And Joined Up On Ten Planes From The Other Carriers.

We Flew Around For About Forty-Five Minutes Until An Observer Spotted Some Targets For Us. Then We Went In And Made Some Rocket Runs On Some Artillery Batteries And Some Barracks. We Got Three Batteries And The Barracks. After We Had Polished Off These They Told Us To Pick Our Own Targets And Bomb Them. We Laid A Stick Of Four, One Hundred Pounders In A Barracks And As We Pulled Out I Strafed Another One. There Were A Couple Of Other Positions That Looked Like Artillery So We Bombed Them Just To Make Sure They Were Knocked Out.

This Afternoon We Recieved
Word That Tigner, The Radioman In
One Of The Observer Planes Had Been
Hit In The Arm And The Plane Shot
Up Pretty Badly. They Landed At
Charan Kanoa Airfield Which The Mar-
ines Had Taken About A Half Hour Be-
For. Evidently The Jap Lines Were Very
Close. We Recieved Word That All
All Of Them Were O.K. Tho.

This Evening The Japs Came Over
Again And Really Came In Force. The
Anti-Aircraft Fire Was Terrific. Hon-
estly It Didn't Seem Possible That A
Plane Could Fly Thru It But They
Did. Two Planes Made Dive Bombing
Run On Us But Pulled Out Too High
To Drop. At About The Same Time
A Plane Made A Run On The Fanshaw
Bay And Scored A Bomb Hit On The
After Elevator. It Exploded On
The Hangar Deck Killing About Ten
And Injuring Quite A Few. It Def-
initely Put The 'Fanny B' Out Of
Commission. I Saw Three Enemy
Planes Go Down During This Attack.

A Destroyer Took A torpedo, And When It Shot Down The Plane, It Crashed Into The DD. The DD Sank Shortly After.

After It Really Began to Get Dark Everything Got Fouled Up. The AA Boy Were Shooting At Every thing. All Of Our Planes Were Ordered to Turn On Their Lights. Evidently Some Of Them Didn't Recieve The message Because They Attempted to Join The Landing Circle With Out Them. Although Their Was No Excuse For It A Lot Of them Were Fired On And Some Of Them Shot Down. I Watched One Of The Carriers Shoot Down One. It Looked As If It Made A Good Water Landing But It Was Getting Too Dark too Really tell.

When the planes Started to Come In To Land It Was too Dark To Tell Which Carrier Was Which So All Hands Just Sat Down Where They Could. We Had One TBF Up And It Got Back OK. One Fighter Landed OK But When The Next One Came In It's Guns Went Off And

483

When We Had Expended Our
Rockets And Bombs We Headed For
Home. On The Way The Flight Leader
Asked For Permission To Strafe An
Air Strip And Were Told To Go Ahead.
As We Went Down The AA Really
Started To Come Up So We Pulled
Up Plenty High, For Which I Was
Very Thankful. We Didn't Pick Up
Any Holes But Our Other Plane Did.
A Twenty M.M. Hole In The Wing Stub.

Later That Day We Had Another
Anti-Sub Hop With The Usual Results.

The Colonel Told Us Tonight that
The Landing Was Proceeding Much
Better But Still Wasn't Up To Ex-
pectations. From What He Said
The Marines Will Really Attack Tomorr-
ow.

June 17, 1944

This Morning Was Pretty Uneventful
Except That The Marines Launched
Their Attack And Did Very Well. They Att-
ained All Of Their Objectives.

Right There The Youngest Lemon Boy Left The Flight Deck.

Everything Went OK Until A Fighter Tried To Come In Without Flaps. He Didn't Make It. He Hit The Last Barrier But It Didn't Stop Him. He Piled Into The Planes Ahead Of The Barrier And Made A Mess. Two Fighters Went Over The Bow. Two TBFs Were Wrecked, One Completely. The Worst Part Was That Several Men Were Caught In The Wreckage. The Pilot That Crashed Recieved A Pretty Bad Head Wound But Will Be OK. Two Other Men Were Banged Up Some And One Was Knocked Overboard, He Wasn't Recovered. The Worst Part Was That One Of The Crewman Was Severely Injured And Died Later. He Was Rojer Allbright And A Swell Kid.

The Latest Report Accounts For All Of The Pilots Except Our Skipper. I Certainly Hope He's OK.

The Japs Probably Don't Know It But They Did OK. One Carrier, One Destroyer, And At Least Ten Planes.

Figure 391 Donald Crounse

Selected Entries of Journal - White Plains CIC Radarman Donald Crounse

"MY NAVY LIFE ABOARD THE WHITE PLAINS"
1943-1945

May 30th: We left Pearl for Eniwetok in the Marshal islands. We escorted 21 transports, 35 ships in all.

June 1st: Our convoy was fired on by an enemy sub. Two torpedoes were fired, no ships were hit.

June 2nd: We lost one pilot and two fighters (FM2). These planes were going up for ASP. Just crashed in the water. No explanation given.

June 9th: Arrived Eniwetok, dropped anchor 0800.

June 11th: We started for Saipan on our way to Saipan. We have been given talks about the coming invasion of Saipan. We are to furnish air support.

June 13th: Picked up a bogey, vectored CAP to intercept. Reported they saw Jap 'Betty'. Another carrier reported a second one as a 'Sally'.

"D-Day" June 15th, 1944: The invasion started on Saipan. We sent planes to support ground forces. 1750 we picked up a bogey, CAP investigated. Reported five jap 'Kates.' Shot down 2 at 29 miles. The fourth at 5 miles. The fifth was damaged but got away, it was seen from the ship. In landing our CAP, one fighter (Lt SN Bales) went over the port side.

June 16th: We lost another fighter in the water. Operations continue on Saipan. This evening a destroyer depth charged a sub and picked up six survivors.

June 17th: Usual morning and evening air strikes by our planes on Saipan. At 1800 we picked up bogey at 124 miles, the raid split into three groups. The ship went into GQ. We tracked raids coming in, sent our fighters to intercept, made some interceptions at 30 miles. Pilot reported 20 bombers, 15 fighters in one group. Undetermined how many in all. Main group that broke through attacked west side. About 8 to 12 torpedo and dive bombers came to us on the east side. We commenced firing. About four to six different times, we opened fire. Our ships AA fire downed one torpedo plane and one dive bomber. The Fanshaw Bay got a 500 lb. bomb hit on aft elevator, it exploded in elevator pit. Split seams they took on some water. Killed thirteen outright and two died next day. She started back for Pearl. A destroyer and tanker were hit a few miles from us. In bringing our planes on board two fighters went over the side. Another fighter hopped over the barrier and crashed into five other planes, started fire. Fire was put out. One man was reported knocked overboard with a plane. Another man was hit and severely injured. He died before morning.

June 20th: Back at island but nothing to report, just usual day of operations.

June 22nd: It is officially known that 353 Jap planes were destroyed by our fleet off Guam, and also when they came to land on Saipan. Our fleet also sank one of their large carriers, put another one in flames, scored other hits on many ships.

June 23rd: Enemy planes flew within 9-13 miles of our task group 0200. At 1200 we went to GQ. 5 Jap planes were coming in, we vectored out the Midway planes (CVE63). They shot down two for sure and two probables. At 1600 we sent out 8 F6Fs with 500 lb bombs. They attacked a troop or cargo ship of about 5000 tons. This ship was in the harbor at Rota Island about 110 miles from us, bearing 230o. The planes attacked the cargo ship and two destroyers scored only one hit.

June 25th: Usual air strikes on Saipan. About 1000, two of our own TBMs and 4 FM2s with2 F6Fs off another carrier went to Rota to finish the job. It took only one TBM with one torpedo. The ship sank within three minutes. The F6F's dropped their bombs on the air fields and city of Rota.

June 26th: 1830 I picked up bogey at 83 miles. We tracked him in, tried to intercept but missed. At 2330 I was aroused by GQ, three enemy planes came in, one made three sweeps over us, we heard some bombs. Destroyer shot one down. Terrific explosion that shook ship, determined to be the depth charges and torpedoes in plane shot down.

June 27th: 1900, bogies appeared, three raids, small. Night fighters tried to intercept. One plane got within 17 miles but did not come over. We secured from GQ, a couple of planes came over but didn't drop anything. Several of the destroyers opened fire, but no report of hitting any planes.

June 29th: 0100 They came over again, only two or three, we went to GQ. Secured at 0200, but to no avail, for a short while later a couple more came over, and we went to GQ again. The night of the 29th, as I was sleeping outside under a 20-millimeter gun, six torpedoes were fired at us, forcing us to make emergency turns. One or two of the torpedo wakes were seen from our ship. No damage was done to our task group, which was five CVEs and seven Destroyers.

June 30th: We dropped anchor seven miles off Saipan and Tinian on the west side. The purpose was to take on bombs, which we did. I looked the islands over with glasses. I could see cultivated fields on

Tinian and homes on them, also a small village. All day cruisers and planes were bombarding both Saipan and Tinian. We pulled away from Saipan at 1600 and rejoined task group.

July 1st: Usual day, from reports, they are making good progress on Saipan. Task group was notified to be on alert for air attack because Japs were massing some 300 planes at Yap and Palau. Yap is 552 miles from Saipan.

July 6th: We had GQ at 1900 and 2000 and again at 0230 in the morning. They were coming to get some high Jap officials off the doomed Island. One plane was shot down in flames, those topside could see it.

July 7th: The day was quiet, at 1930 we had bogies, we went to GQ. The planes headed for the island; night fighters tried to intercept. The Japs were using windows to jam our radar.

July 8th: Usual day and no bogies at night. A fighter was shot down over the island today, (CVE 68)

July 9th: The island of Saipan is now in the United States hands. We started back to Eniwetok about 1900. (3DDs and Kalinin Bay).

July 10th: We were 200 miles out when the Kalinin Bay lost another fighter and pilot in the drink. We are having our first movie tonight since June 7th.

July 12th: 1400 we arrived Eniwetok, anchored. There were enough ships here to give the appearance of Pearl Harbor. We got our first mail today since about June 20th. In the next three days we just took on supplies.

July 15th: We were given two bottles of beer on the fantail. We had to drink them, though, on a barge alongside (That's legal).

July 17th: 1200 I went with a liberty party to the island of Parry. We were given two cans of beer. Then I went swimming, the water was very warm, the beach was quite smooth with a coral like sand. I picked up a few pieces of coral and shells, returned about 1500 to ship.

July 19th: 1530 we were underway. Chaplain Widoff announced we are now bound for the Marianas. We will help take the island of Tinian "D" 24th.

July 22nd: 1100, Kitkun. While catapulting aircraft this morning, launched a TBM, after it left the catapult, it nosed straight upward, then went into a stall and crashed into the sea. Six seconds later the two depth charges went off, no one escaped. (Pilot, ARM, and gunner).

July 23rd: We arrived vicinity of Saipan and Tinian 1200.

July 24-25th: We sent fighter and TBMs to support ground forces on Tinian. The invasion there is proceeding with light opposition. Between the 24th and 29th, we sent planes for ground support on Tinian, we refueled during this period, we had no enemy planes come in on us during this time around Saipan and Tinian.

July 29th: We dropped anchor off Saipan on the west side. We took on ammunition and supplies. With field glasses I could see a sugar mill in ruins. The city of Garapan was bombed quite severely. We were within four miles of it, so as to enable me to see swimmers on the beach. The territory is good looking with a lot of vegetation and farm land. The United States lost over 3,000 men on Saipan.

Aug. 1st: One of our TBMs, acting as an observer, was shot down over Tinian. The plane crashed into the sea, only survivor was the aviation radioman. Therefore, observer and pilot were lost.

Aug. 2nd: Tinian was secured today, only mopping up left. At 1900 we joined two cruisers and started back for Eniwetok.

Aug. 5th: 1530 we arrived Eniwetok. Began bringing stores aboard. Continued all day. Aug. 6th: I was on working party to a navy cargo ship.

Aug.11th: We got underway at 1500, left Eniwetok, headed out with three other CVEs. We have been told we are heading for Espiritu Santo in the New Hebrides, expect to arrive 16th.

Aug. 16th: In the morning, our ASP sighted a surfaced submarine. ASP signaled it but got no return signal, the sub crashed dived, at this sign the plane dropped depth charges. The sub put its scope up, then surfaced again. It had been hit. Yes, it turned out to be a U.S. sub. But the damage had been done, and the sub barely made it back to drydock. 1200 we brought the ship to anchor, in the harbor of Espiritu Santo. 1400 we had our shellback initiation. It started in the form of a riot, but we got things quieted down and went on with it. The polliwogs got a thorough beating, of course we had a few injuries. One broken arm for sure and a lot of sprained ankles and wrists.

Aug. 17th: 0900 I went ashore to a fleet recreation center. It was a very nice place with tennis, basketball and baseball fields. Ships service and stage were in a coconut grove and surroundings were very beautiful, it was cool with plenty of sun beyond the palms. We ate coconuts there and brought some back on board. We also were given a couple cans of beer. There were some natives there selling shells, skirts, and carved things. I bought some Guam shells.

Aug. 18th: I again went to Fleet Recreation Center. This time on a working party. We cleaned up for a while, then had beer, sandwiches, etc., brought from the ship. Went swimming, explored the woods a little. (Am getting a little sick of coconuts.)

Aug. 19th: Went to Fleet landing to get stores, but really just drove around more than anything else. We went back up into the woods a little for some things. Here we saw rows and rows of native barracks stretching for miles. The woods are very beautiful and dense.

Aug. 22nd: 0900 I went to Fleet landing on power boat. I then drove a jeep until 1330. I put about fifty miles on it, taking guys around the island. The jeep is a good little car and I enjoyed driving again. Met L. A. Johnson and Dubose, so we went up to the Air Center where

Johnson has a friend, we saw a couple of movies and we talked. He brought us back in another jeep. A French ship was in Port, too.

Aug. 24th: We lifted anchor at 1200. We left with Kitkun and Gambier Bay. We headed for the Florida Island, about ten miles north and east of Guadalcanal. We expect to arrive the 26th.

Aug.25th: We anchored in Tulagi Harbor in the island of Florida at 0800. From here we can see Guadalcanal and Maltin Islands. These are good looking islands like the New Hebrides were.

Aug. 26th: The water between these islands is very calm. The sunsets and sunrises are very beautiful. The cloud formations are different than those further north. It's hotter here though, than in the New Hebrides, so the heat rash and other discomforts are starting again. 1600 we got underway again, we didn't go out very far, just wandered around until the next day.

Aug. 27th: We had flight operations. We are out on maneuvers. Returned 1600 anchored same place. A native came along side in a crude handmade canoe. He had handmade articles to trade for cloth that he wanted. Talked a few words of English.

Aug.28th: 1500 We got underway for maneuvers again, only to return.

Aug. 29th: 1430 Anchored again. We seem to be wasting time for another push.

Sept. 2nd: I went to the beach on recreation party on Florida Island. After we had our beer we hiked to the top of the hill. Passed gun emplacements, a French cometary and Jap huts that had been smashed. There were a few coconut trees around, but mostly just heavy undergrowth. Natives were selling shells and war clubs on the beach. Wanted a lot of dough for them too. They aren't so dumb.

Sept. 4th: I went to the burial of Meredith B. Johnson PhoM 1/c who drowned while swimming ashore on recreation party. They had a military funeral on Tulagi, 21-gun salute, he was buried in Cemetery

#1.

Sept. 5th: I was on a stores working party. We took MW boat and went down to another bay searching for a cargo ship. Had trouble finding it, but got a good look at the island. We covered about twenty-five miles.

Sept. 6th: I had liberty at 1300. We went to same beer spot. Wetter and I walked into the jungle exploring. We found four gun emplacements and gun shells, but they were U.S. Probably used in defending the captured guns

Sept. 8th: 0830 Underway. We left Florida Island in the Solomon's. Had an uneventful trip up to Palau, came by way of North Solomons and New Guinea. We escorted a group of twenty-two troop and cargo ships.

Sept. 12th: We crossed the equator.

Sept. 15th: "D" Day. At 0500 we were 30 miles from Palau, at day break we launched planes for ground support on island of Peleliu. We lost no planes today, just minor damage. In listening to VHF ship to plane radio, I heard our planes strafing Jap tanks and bombing buildings. There has been no air opposition since "D" Day, that has been taken care of by the big carriers this past week.

Sept. 16th: Still no enemy planes. Pilot on ASP spotted three small unidentified ships, finally identified one as Jap destroyer, what action was taken I don't know. Our planes assisted in air support of Marines on Peleliu again.

Sept. 17th: Our planes supported ground forces, (Army 81st div.), on the Island of Anguar. Repeated this on 18th.

Sept.19th: We pulled out 170 miles from island and fueled.

Sept. 20th: Back at Palau. In the evening a Jap plane came over the island. AA fire was seen from our ship, near the island, later it was said something was burning on the water. We saw no more bogey on screen.

Sept. 21st: Usual air strikes. about 1400 we left Peleliu and headed for Ulithi, an atoll west of Yap.

Sept. 23rd: We arrived Ulithi, and sent air support. Islands had few Japs on them so little air support was needed.

Sept. 25th: 1000 We anchored Ulithi atoll. At 1545 we were underway again. Nothing much here except a dozen or so atolls. Since we left the New Hebrides, the water has been like Puget Sound, at times it is completely smooth except for swells.

Sept. 27th: 2000 We crossed the equator again bound for Hollandia, New Guinea.

Sept.28th: 1000 We arrived Hombolt Harbor near the village of Hollandia in New Guinea. Quite a few ships here. Nice harbor, 6,500ft. mountains, heavy growth on land. Sept. 29th: 1600 we got underway for Manus island in the Admiralties.

Oct. 1st: Arrived Manus Island anchored 0830. This is really a good harbor, there are a lot of ships here and a lot of shore installations.

Oct. 2nd: I went ashore with Lt. Kivett, he went to intelligence office. Conly and I went to a museum they had there. Consisted of Japanese articles. Also, native goods. It was quite good.

Oct. 3rd: The guns on a TBM went off. Bullets went through hanger deck and hit two men in gallery. One AMM was severely injured by a piece of metal in his lungs. He died the next day.

Oct. 5th: I went to beach again. I forgot to mention that they drive on the left side of the road here in the Admiralties, all because of a couple of Australians.

Oct. 8th: I went ashore on liberty. We got four bottles for our trouble. There was a lot of recreation there, but I didn't feel up to it. Pittylu has a capacity of 10,000. A professional boxer was putting on fights etc. I watched this most of the two hrs. ashore. Coming back to the ship on a LCM the guys started fighting. It was very crowded and it was quite a show. When we got back aboard it started again right on the quarter deck.

Oct. 9th: We were told that our next operation will be Leyte in the Philippines. 18 CVEs are to take part. We are going to be there before "A" day, (MacArthur), to soften it up. Trouble is expected, but no one knows the answer yet.

Oct. 12th: 0500 We got underway, left the island of Manus in the Admiralties and headed for the Philippines. We have 12 CVEs, 6 cruisers, 6 battleships. total (65). Not Bad. This is a task group that will bombard from the air and sea the island of Leyte, for the final touches before the first invasion of the Philippines.

Oct. 15th: Reveille 0320-GQ0350. About the earliest yet? It is, isn't it.

Oct. 16th: We had two bogies on the radar. Probably from Mindanao on routine search. (Overcast all day). No flight operations.

Oct. 17th: We had bogies again, but they are only search planes. The weather now is very bad. Heavy sea and low viability. 51 knot wind. We are supposed to launch a strike today but because of bad weather we couldn't. At 1030 it was reported that the rangers had landed on Homonhom, a small island by Leyte. Light opposition was met.

Oct. 18th: The weather has cleared, all ships launched aircraft. The Midway lost three TBMs in the drink, none of them got more than two miles from the ship. Believe personnel were saved. Another carrier in our task unit lost a fighter over the island. The Kalinin Bay lost a TBM while preparing to bring planes aboard.

INFORMATION ABOUT THE PHILIPPINES

The Philippine Island, where upward to one million people await their liberation from Jap rule. Leyte is the eighth largest island in the Philippines, and it is 115 miles long and varies from 15-40 miles in width. Although Magellan visited the Philippines and died on a nearby island, there is no record of a white man visiting their island until 1543 when the Spanish Admiral Villalobas was received by the chief of the province.

The current occupation of Leyte by Japan began in December 1941 shortly after Pearl Harbor. The Japs have been in complete control of everything except guerrilla bands and obstinate Moros since the fall of Corregidor in April 1942, The Philippine people will be as glad to see us, as we are to get General MacArthur securely re-implanted there.

Oct. 19th: We lost a fighter this morning in drink, pilot was saved. We went to GQ at 1215, reported 11 bombers with fighter escorts heading our way from Mindanao. We saw no planes. We lost a fighter over the island. The Kalinin Bay lost a TBM while preparing to bring planes aboard. In the plan of the day today it told of our action of the 18th. One motor torpedo boat, one coastal carrier, one Sampan set on fire, about 50 trucks loaded with troops strafed and left 30 trucks burning, four gravel trucks destroyed on field repairing strip, about 30-40 Jap planes caught on ground, five Bettys, one Zero, one Lilly, destroyed; six left burning on ground. Our squadron secured one building, and one truck, and damaged two other buildings.

Oct. 20th: Smooth sea, good weather. Midway's planes shot down Jap "Sally" this morning 20 miles from us. We went to GQ at 1000, bogies in area but no enemy planes sighted. Landings were made on Leyte Island at 1000 by 4 army divisions, first cavalry met no opposition, the 24th infantry met slight opposition, and the 7th and 96th infantry met heavy opposition in the Dulag area. Our battleships pounded shore installations last night leaving little or no target for our fliers today in the northern area.

Oct. 21st: Leyte Island. The first cavalry has secured all of Tacloban airfield and at 1200, bulldozers and graders were observed working on the strip and preparing it for army planes to relieve us. Across Cancabato Bay, there is a big American flag flying from one of the provincial government buildings in the center of Tacloban city. Both the first cavalry and the 24th infantry had crossed the plains to the south of Tacloban and had reached the crest of the chain of hills which separates Tacloban valley from Leyte valley, this represents a total area of about 32 square miles and provides a safe beach-head on which all kinds of equipment has been landed to press the attack. Our squadron continued bombing of enemy positions and assisted in keeping the area clear of Jap planes.

Oct. 22nd: Pilot on ASP saw Jap Bomber 30 miles from formation. We sent planes to intercept, but enemy plane faded from our radar, and we couldn't make interception. While bringing planes on board the hook man was knocked down, and he died before morning of a fractured skull. (Bill Willson).

Oct. 23rd: Plan of Day-- "It was the sad and painful duty of the officers and men of the White Plains to commit to the deep the body of our late shipmate and comrade Bill Willson, who gave his life in a cause that he believed right and just. His memory shall remain with us as will the memory of others of our company who have joined the ranks of the illustrious dead." Leyte Island: Routine operations continued against the enemy with little opposition. Our squadron dropped their first bombs on personnel trenches on the south western coastal area of Samar Island. The Jap fleet and air force continues to be a figment of the imagination and existing only in the mind of Tokyo Rose. Our score is eight Jap planes to one of ours, and we are building them eight to their one.

Oct. 24th: 0830 we went to GQ but no planes appeared. Today our entire task unit (six-CVEs) was credited with shooting down Jap planes. The White Plains planes got shot up pretty bad, but they all returned safely. It is reported there are three Jap battleships and three cruisers with four destroyers on the other side of Leyte by Mindanao.

Oct. 25th: The most hectic day. The Battle of Leyte Gulf.

0526: At regular GQ we again had ships on radar.

0625: We secured from GQ. I leisurely loitered about waiting for the chow line to go down. I walked back into CIC from the sponson, only to learn that we heard some Japs over a short distant radio.

0655: We were 60-70 miles off Samar. ASP plane identified ships as enemy. Initial report was course130oT. Four battleships, eight cruisers, and numerous destroyers.

0659: We went to a real GQ, and I'm not kidding. The enemy was 19 miles ahead of us, but soon to be astern.

0704: A salvo of three shots just about knocked us out of the water. Some of the men on the stern of the ship were knocked down by the shock. These were the first shots fired, believed by a battleship.

These near misses knocked off all power, in CIC it was so darn quiet you could hear a pin drop. In fact, we didn't know if we were still underway or not. These first salvos twisted the fan tail, bent one drive shaft, cracked a deck plate on hanger deck. It tore a couple of holes nearly three inches in diameter through the sides. Several men were hit by shrapnel, but no one was killed. Salvos that followed also split seams forward so as to let in 36 inches of water into gasoline tanks.

0708: The power was restored by resetting the relays on main generators.

0720: The gyro was back in order again.

0731: We launched all available TBMs and FM2s. They have been shelling us all along, the WP was the closest carrier to the Japs, and so we were getting it. Everyone was making preparations for going over the side.

0733: We went into a rain squall, the firing stopped because they couldn't see us in the squall. We then gave our boilers all they could take, and when we came out of the squall, we were ahead of all the carriers, but the Japs were running us down. Shelling started again. The destroyers laid a smoke screen around us and all carriers made smoke too. We were heading back toward Samar, but few on board had any hopes of getting out of this one without swimming for it. Two cruisers broke off from the main group and also three destroyers in another group made a wide sweep, so we could only go one direction, and we did. 220o. There were no surface ships in the vicinity and only some other CVEs south of us about 20 to 30 miles, their planes assisted but that is the only outside assistance we had.

0735: The two cruisers on our port beam were close enough for our 5", so we opened up, in the following hour and a half the five-inch scored several hits with the help of our radar ranges. The admiral later complimented us on good shooting, he credited us with helping to stop the cruiser. As close as can be figured we scored from 8-20 hits on the cruiser. 0735: the admiral ordered our destroyers to make torpedo runs which they did. All the while they have been shelling us but so far, we have been lucky. The Japs were using a shell which would burst overhead and sprinkle tinfoil like particles, it was for spotting by sight or by fire control radar.

0749: The enemy has closed to 22,000 yards off our starboard beam. I walked out on catwalk and splash; a shell hit 200 yards off our beam. I could see the guns flash, and then the shells hit beside and over us. (That's not a good feeling). I watched the other carriers getting the same thing, salvo after salvo straddling the ships.

0755: Three Jap destroyers were sighted.

0800: The Jap destroyers made torpedo runs and were within 9,600 yards of us, they opened with their 5" and scored many hits on several carriers. One destroyer on our port beam was hit and sunk. The Gambier Bay was hit and began dropping back, she was pounded by two cruisers then until she sank. Other ships were calling in over TBS occasionally and reporting they were hit.

0903: The cruisers on our port side were in to 12,000 yards. Our destroyers tried to hold them off, and we were pouring our 5" into her, besides the aircraft doing what they could.

0944: The enemy appeared to be retiring, was now back to 26,000 yards. No one can understand why they can possibly be letting us get away, for everyone is more than sure that they could sink us if they would move in. I think they were afraid we had other units close at hand.

1019: We catapulted three TBMs with torpedoes. These TBMs put their fish into a battleship, other TBMs off the WP scored hits with 100 and 500 lb. bombs on battleships and cruisers. One TBM was shot down, two others are missing from our ship. Our fighters made strafing runs on the Jap ships without loss to us. When planes got low on gas and ammo they went to beach and gassed, there were no bombs ashore.

1039: The enemy has retired to 139o-39,000 yds.

1041: We recovered some of our aircraft.

1045: Six to seven Jap Zeke's with 500 lb. bombs dived on our five remaining carriers. Two missed the Midway and exploded in the sea. The 3rd one crashed on her flight deck and exploded, fire broke out, she was looking bad. She went out of control and spun crazily around and headed away from us. One Zeke dove on us and barely missed after being fired upon by our guns. It hit the water almost under the port catwalk aft. It was a terrific blast and the plane was blown to pieces. Water and parts of the plane were blown onto the flight deck. Parts of the pilot and plane were found on the bridge. It seems flesh, teeth, ears, thumbs, etc. were found all over the top side of the ship. One plane also crashed on the Kitkun Bay and others were shot down. These are the famous Jap suicide pilots and planes, they tried nothing else but just to crash on us, believe planes came off their battleships.

1058: The Midway began abandoning ship.

1105: The Midway blew up breaking her in half and blowing the bridge off. She sank within five minutes, the stern part first, then the bow. Our destroyers were ordered to stand by the Midway and pick up survivors. Therefore, we went on without any escorts.

1253: The Jap fleet was at 0540 T-60 miles from us. We could relax a little now, but still there was danger of aircraft and submarines. Sandwiches and apples were brought up to the shack, this was the first chow we had today because this started before chow this morning.

1304: We recovered more aircraft. We were into 10 miles off Samar Island, heading north.

1324: A plane from one of the other carriers went into the drink off our port bow, but we had no destroyers, so we couldn't pick him up.

1645: The Kitkun Bay asked to half-mast her flag to bury her dead

2001 - 2139: In landing aboard Lt. Maloney crashed into the barrier. The escorts reported to the admiral that they had survivors on board, so they were directed to go into Leyte Gulf. We secured from GQ after 12 hours and 44 minutes. During this period, I had two sandwiches, a couple of apples. Everyone was very tired after the long strain. I hit my sack not knowing that our radar had picked up a sub that was following us. The sub was at 3160-16,000. We had our destroyers attack sub, they dropped depth charges and say they got one sub. A second sub was reported but we didn't get it. Bogies 4-5 planes were at 27 miles, closing on us.

2310: We secured from GQ. And so, ended 16 hours of GQ today. I again hit my sack. The day almost over, and one of the most unforgettable so far in my life. GQ sounded, so out of my sack I came.

Bogies were within three miles of us, just circled around, one of the destroyers knocked one down. Taffy 1 was under air attack. She was somewhere nearby.

In summing it all up, most of the men felt darn good and happy to be alive. The Kalinin Bay received sixteen five-inch hits, two eight-inch hits and other damage I haven't learned. The Fanshaw Bay received two or three hits and a five-hundred-pound bomb hit, and other damage. The Kitkun Bay was hit by a Zeke suicide plane which killed two men and injured sixteen.

So, you can see members of the White Plains can really feel fortunate, for we received the lightest part of the whole action, but let me say it was a living hell anyway you look at it. I do think the destroyers and aircraft deserve some praise, for they really did a job.

There are many things I have forgotten, or never knew, that should go down here, but due to the confusion and lack of information this will have to do. I can't describe the things we were all thinking and the way we felt, not only at our own danger, but that of the men going down on ships around us, and our aircraft over the enemy force. Being outnumbered by superior ships and arms made everyone feel certain we were doomed, but even at the odds we faced we didn't give up hope. Like many said after it was all over; "only one great power could have pulled us through that, and He did."

REFERENCES

(1)   William B. Chase. "The Cheap Seats" in *Avenger at War* by Barrett Tillman. Charles Scribner's Sons, New York 1980.

(2)   Gerald A Thomas. Air Group 5 "Casablanca to Tokyo. A Tribute to Avenger Air Crewmen. http://www.airgroup4.com/crewmen.htm

(3)   Stephan Wilkinson. Tough Turkey: Why Grumman's TBF Avenger Was the Ultimate Torpedo Bomber. History.net. https://www.historynet.com/tough-turkey-why-grummans-tbf-avenger-was-the-ultimate-torpedo-bomber.htm

(4)   Barrett Tillman and Robert L Lawson. US Navy Dive and Torpedo Bombers of WWII. MBI Publishing Company.2001.

(5)   C.E. Fox Litt D. Threshold of the Pacific. An Account of the Social Organization, Magic, and Religion of the People of San Cristóval in the Solomon Islands. Alfred A. Knopf. 1925.

(6)   James P. Busha. Wings of War. Great Combat Tales of Allied and Axis Pilots During World War II. Lt. Thomas Rozga, USMC (RET). Devils' Darling. Pacific Island Hopping with a Warbug. Zenith Press. 2015

(7)   Col Joseph H. Alexander. Closing In: Marines in the Seizure of Iwo Jima. World War II Commemorative Series. CreateSpace Independent Publishing Platform. 2013.

(8)   James D. Horfischer. The Last Stand of the Tin Can Sailors: The Extraordinary World War II Story. Bantam Books 2004.

(9)   F. Funke, Jr. History of the USS White Plains CVE-66. 27 Sept. 43 – 8 Oct 45. 1945.

(10) Robert Jon Cox. The Battle off Samar – Taffy III at Leyte Gulf. 2010.

(11) www.bosamar.com

(12)   Battle off Samar. https://military-
       history.fandom.com/wiki/Battle_off_Samar

(13)   David Grant, Colt Denfeld, Randall Schalk. US Navy
       Shipwrecks and Submerged Naval Aircraft in Washington:
       An Overview. International Archeological Research Institute.
       Dec 1996.

(14)   Amphibious Operations Capture of Iwo Jima 16 February to
       16 March 1945. Declassified Naval History and Heritage
       Command.

(15)   Busha James P. Grasshopper Roundup. – Flight Journal

(16)   Lt Colonel Ronald J. Brown. A Brief History of the 14th
       Marines. History and Museums Division Headquarters. US
       Marine Corps. Washington DC. 1990.

(17)   Douglas E. Campbell, Ph.D. Volume II: U.S. Navy, U.S. Marine
       Corps and U.S. Coast Guard Aircraft Lost During World War
       II.- Listed by Squadron. 2011

(18)   Mark. L Evans. Naval History and Heritage Command. White
       Plains I. CVE 1943-1958

(19)   Noles James L. Jr. All Guts, No Glory for the Escort Carriers.
       Air & Space Magazine. July 2004.

(20)   Noles, James L. Twenty-Three Minutes to Eternity: The Final
       Voyage of the Escort Carrier USS Liscome Bay. University of
       Alabama Press. 2010.

(21)   Noles, James L. Mighty by Sacrifice: The Destruction of an
       American Bomber Squadron. August 29, 1944. University of
       Alabama Press. 2015.

(22)   Scearce, Phil. Finish Forty and Home. The Untold WWI Story
       of B-24s in the Pacific. Texas A&M University Press. 2012.

(23)   History of the U.S. Marine Corps Operations in WWII.
       Chapter 2 Marine Aviation in the Marianas, Carolines, and at
       Iwo Jima.

(24)   Major Carl W. Hoffman USMC. The Seizure of Tinian.
       Historical Division Headquarters, United States Marine
       Corps. 1951

(25)   Julius Brownstein. History at Random. Saved from the Sea II. A Wildcat Ditched. A Pilot Rescued – The Story in Photographs.

(26)   History of the USS White Plains 9CVE-66) 27 September 1943-8 October 1945. Declassified Authority E.O 13526 – By NDC NARA Date: Dec 31 2012.

(27)   Donald Crouse. Journal – My Life Aboard the White Plains. Unpublished 1943-1945.

(28)   Andrew J. Winnegar. Journal of time Aboard the USS White Plains with the Composite Squadron VC-4. Unpublished. 1943-1945

(29)   Russell Wood. Memoir of Battle – VC-4. Published by US Navy. 1945.

(30)   Bill Lemons. Journal of War time experiences aboard the USS White Plains and VC-4. Unpublished.

(31)   Maurice Hie. Handwritten Journal of War-time experiences. Unpublished.

(32)   Walter E. Skrzynski. Minority Plus 2: Life in the Nave; 1941-1947. A true and personal account as I remember it. Skrzynski Publishing 1994.

(33)   Mike's Research Saipan
        https://mikesresearch.com/2021/06/27/saipan-1944/

AFTERWORD AND ACKNOWLEDGMENTS

We must start by recognizing the individual and collective acts of selfless heroism and sacrifice of the young Americans who sailed and flew into battle eighty years ago to protect and preserve our nation's freedoms. They were teenagers and young men barely old enough to vote who were called upon to do something extraordinary. They did not disappoint themselves or the world. Without them, there would not be any stories or storytellers.

I want to thank the young men, Andy Winnegar, Russ Wood, Don Crounse, Maurice Hie, and Bill Lemon, for having the foresight to preserve their war-time experiences in their journals and memoirs. Andy Winnegar and Don Crounse shared their writings and memories freely with the hope that their stories could be preserved for another generation. Chris Dean shared his grandfather Bill Lemon's personal and well-written daily journal. The Hie family, Magda Lynn Vance, Fred Hie, and Chrissy Hie shared Maurice Hie's writings, photographs, and memories. Without their generosity, this work would not have been possible.

Andy Winnegar shared with me a treasure trove of old VC-4 and White Plains photographs. His son Arthur Cavazos generously scanned the photographs, which add tremendously in bringing the men and their planes back to life.

I am indebted to Royston Leonard for generously allowing me to use his colorized World War II photograph for the cover design. Royston Leonard's commitment to bringing these old photographs to life by restoring them to vivid colors is remarkable.

I am indebted to all the individuals and organizations who generously provided contemporary and historical photographs, bringing this story to life. Each is acknowledged in the image caption.

Robert Johnson's daughters, Julie Dereschuk and Nancy Johnson, generously shared photographs and memories of their parents and the many White Plains reunions Bob and Marion organized.

Finally, I would like to thank all of the readers of my previous books, "Three Coins" and "The All-American Crew," for your incredible support and encouragement. Storytellers can only exist with an audience, and I am so thankful that you, the readers and listeners, feel the connection between your lives, these stories, our past, and our present.

OTHER BOOKS
BY RUSSELL N. LOW

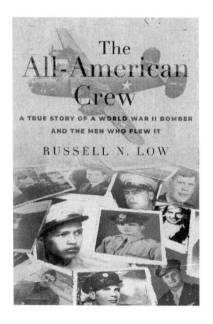
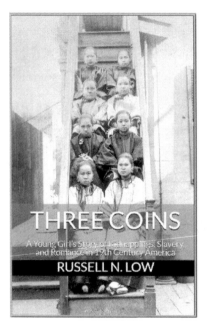

"The All-American Crew" A True Story of a World War II Bomber and the men Who Flew It.

"Three Coins" A Young Girl's Story of Kidnapping, Slavery and Romance in 19th Century America.

ABOUT THE AUTHOR

Our connections to the past are not always obvious. Yet, those connections define where we come from, who we are, and where we may be going.

Russell Low was born into a family intimately associated with the history of the American West. However, growing up in Central California, his life was more connected to hamburgers and

Figure 392 Russell N. Low. Photograph by Ken Fong.

sports than Chinese American history. His connection to the past was born out of a fascination with a treasure trove of old family photos. Many were from the early days of black and white photography. Uncovering the stories behind these photographs became a decades-long passion whose fruits became the series of Three Coins novels.

Russell used skills he had honed as a physician, researcher, and educator in the search for these stories. Applying these skills to historical research uncovered previously unknown dramas involving human trafficking, kidnappings, romance, hop farmers, laundrymen, and war heroes.

Low's storytelling takes us on a journey beginning with a nine-year-old slave girl who struggled to find freedom and romance. The three Chinese coins she threw into the water on her trip to Gum Saan in 1880 touched off a string of events that changed her life. Across decades and multiple generations, these ripples continue to change the world in ways she could never have imagined.

The "All American Crew" tells the story of Ah Ying's grandsons, Stanley and Loren, in the Pacific during WWII. The saga begins by reconnecting Stanley to his family's beginnings in America at the Presbyterian Mission Home in San Francisco. His transformation from a Chinese American boy, not yet old enough to vote or drink beer, to a B-24 Liberator nose gunner is set against the lives of the other nine American men, who are his crew members. Along the way, Stanley experiences loneliness, his first beer, his first romance, and the horrors of war. His older brother, Loren, joins the Aviation Engineers and builds the runways that the Liberators and fighters will need to win the war in the Pacific. The connections between these brothers and the events and people of WWII form the foundation of this third novel in the Three Coins series.

Avengers, Wildcats, and Crickets expands the World War II saga through the vivid memories of a man who lived through the battles in the Pacific Air War. Andy Winnegar's views of the war from a TBM Avenger torpedo bomber provide a rare personal perspective that assures unmatched accuracy.

The research and writing continue with a return to the Chinese American communities of San Francisco and Salem, Oregon, in the 1800s. There are so many more stories to explore and preserve for future generations.

Russell lives in La Jolla, California, with his wife, artist Carolyn Hesse-Low. Their family celebrates art, creativity, and exploration of things past and present. You may learn more about the author of "Three Coins," "The All-American Crew," and "Avengers, Wildcats, and Crickets," at https://russlow.com.

INDEX

Made in the USA
Columbia, SC
30 May 2022

61119412R00291